# DREADNOUGHTS
## IN CAMERA

# DREADNOUGHTS
# IN CAMERA
## BUILDING THE DREADNOUGHTS

# 1905–1920

ROGER D. THOMAS and BRIAN PATTERSON

with line drawings by

BRIAN PATTERSON

Royal Naval
MUSEUM
PUBLICATIONS

SUTTON PUBLISHING

First published in 1998 by
Sutton Publishing Limited · Phoenix Mill
Thrupp · Stroud · Gloucestershire · GL5 2BU
in association with
The Royal Naval Museum

Reprinted with corrections 1998

British Library Cataloguing in Publication Data

A catalogue record for this book is available from the British Library

ISBN 0–7509–1446–7

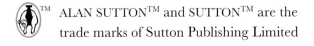
Typeset in 11/15 pt Baskerville,
Typesetting and origination by
Sutton Publishing Limited.
Printed in Great Britain by
Butler and Tanner, Frome, Somerset.

# CONTENTS

# ACKNOWLEDGEMENTS

The author's interest in the photographic images of Dreadnoughts began with the discovery of the Pescott Frost collection of photographs in Portsmouth Central Library during the early 1980s. This initially led to the exhibition in October 1985 'We Want Eight, Portsmouth and the Dreadnoughts 1905–1916'. Several years later a more ambitious exhibition was produced, entitled 'The Building of the Great Fleet, British Dreadnoughts 1905–1920'. The exhibition was supported by the University of Portsmouth, the Portsmouth Naval Base Property Trust, Portsmouth City Council, Hampshire County Council and John Brown plc. Many of the images came from the qualitative photographic records kept at the Business Record Centre, University of Glasgow. It was felt that this theme should be brought to a wider audience in the form of a book of photographs, which outlines the main phases of Dreadnought construction.

I should like to thank Dr Chris Howard Bailey and Campbell McMurray, Director of the Royal Naval Museum, for their encouragement of and support for this project and for their advice on the content of the book. I would also like to record my thanks to the librarians who have aided my search for appropriate images, in particular to Deborah Potter, Curator of Photographs at the Royal Naval Museum, to Kate Hutcheson, manager of the Business Record Centre, University of Glasgow, for her enthusiasm and interest in this project, to Michael Moss, Archivist, University of Glasgow, for his support of this project and for allowing me use of the magnificent photographs from his collection, to Allan King of the Local History and Naval Collection, Portsmouth Central Library, for his patience over the years with my incursions on Dreadnoughts, and to Emma Chaplin, collections manager, The Dock Museum, Barrow-in-Furness, for quickly responding to my inquiries and interest in the Vickers Shipbuilding and Engineering Ltd photographic slide collection. Thanks also go to Betty Owen and David Clarke for meticulously reading the text in its formative phase. I should like to express my gratitude to Brian Patterson of the Portsmouth Dockyard Historic Trust for revealing, over several years, some of his invaluable knowledge of the workings of

Portsmouth Dockyard. Thanks are due also to Sue Goodger and Michael Forder, who also compiled the index. Lastly, my thanks go to Jonathan Falconer of Sutton Publishing for his patience when I was struggling to assemble the text and images.

For photographic images, thanks are due to Vickers Shipbuilding and Engineering Ltd, Barrow-in-Furness; the Dock Museum, Barrow-in-Furness; Business Records Centre, University of Glasgow; The Royal Naval Museum Photographic Collection; The Naval History Collection, Portsmouth City Library; and Portsmouth Royal Dockyard Historic Trust.

Roger D. Thomas
1998

# INTRODUCTION:

## Photographic Images as Representational Documents

The process of building the hull of HMS *Dreadnought* at Portsmouth Dockyard (1905–6) was carefully recorded in a series of regular photographic images. In the first week, two daily photographs were taken; after this, pictures were generally taken on a weekly basis. In all there are forty-eight distinct images of *Dreadnought*'s hull. After the launch the Admiralty became reticent over granting permission for photographs to be taken of the fitting-out of *Dreadnought*, so only a few images have survived. Subsequently, a limited number of photographs were taken of the hull construction of the other eight Dreadnoughts built at Portsmouth. The photographs of Dreadnought construction in Devonport Dockyard appear to have been lost in the dockyard fires of the Second World War. The National Maritime collection has just sixty-one surviving prints, and images of fitting-out are virtually unknown. The extraordinary concentration on the first Dreadnought

partly hides the dearth of photographic material on the construction in the Royal Dockyards of later and more powerful warships. However, the Portsmouth-based photographers Silk and Cribb were able to take photographs of Dreadnought launches, with the notable exception of HMS *Royal Sovereign*, where only one image has survived.

On a comparative basis, the Royal Dockyard photographic holdings, with the exception of the launches, are unremarkable when compared with the imagery commissioned by John Brown, Clydebank. More than a thousand photographs have survived of the building of HMSs *Tiger*, *Barham*, *Repulse* and *Hood*. This is by far the largest photographic collection of this type of image in the United Kingdom. Records from the other major Dreadnought constructors are disappointing. Photographs from Sir W.G. Armstrong Whitworth and Palmers are now extremely rare. A few images can be found in contemporary naval journals.

Precisely what survives from Vickers, Barrow-in-Furness, remains something of a mystery, which will only be resolved when the surviving glass negatives are catalogued. At the moment, no images have been found of the building slip and only one of the fitting-out basin. The surviving national perspective remains highly dependent on the records of the Scottish yards, principally John Brown, Clydebank, for ship construction; and Beardmore, Dalmuir and Parkhead for workshops for machinery and armaments.

Few biographical details are known of the photographers who undertook this work. There are no local studies of the Portsmouth-based photographers Silk and Cribb, who also recorded many urban scenes in Portsmouth, so it is difficult to estimate how extensive their naval repertoire was. In these circumstances the John Brown commemorative albums are exceptional, because they contain a complete run of the different phases of Dreadnought construction and are especially significant with regard to the fitting-out phase. The photographers employed by this company tended to take pictures from three or four set positions, usually from cranes at the berth or the dockside. Their images are somewhat repetitious, although the pictures associated with HMS *Repulse* have a strong emphasis on recording the presence of shipyard workers. By way of contrast, Admiralty photographs hardly ever contain scenes of workmen. The Clydebank images also give a much better indication of the number of work gangs on a particular ship. The clarity of the detail allows the viewer to appreciate patterns and techniques of labour in much greater detail than do the narratives of contemporary books on naval architecture. However, even these fine collections have certain omissions, for there are no images of the assembly of the machinery in the boiler and engine rooms, or the interiors of turrets. Nor are there photographs of the fitting out of mess decks or officers' quarters. In the later phases of construction the ship was frequently profiled in an effort to elevate the Dreadnought's fine lines. Particularized details are sacrificed for an overall vista. These images seek to represent the omnipotence of the warship, which had both functional and aesthetic characteristics.

# ABBREVIATIONS

The following abbreviations are used in the picture credits.

| | | | |
|---|---|---|---|
| BRCUG | Business Records Centre, University of Glasgow | PRDHT | Portsmouth Royal Dockyard Historical Trust |
| DNC | Director of Naval Construction | RNM | Royal Naval Museum |
| | | VSEL | Vickers Shipbuilding and Engineering Ltd |
| PCL | Portsmouth Central Library | | |

# 1: THE DREADNOUGHT PROGRAMME

## The Programme

The laying of the first Dreadnought's keel plate on 2 October 1905 at the no. 5 building slip of Portsmouth Dockyard initiated the most concentrated programme of capital ship construction ever undertaken by the Royal Navy. When Dreadnought building ended in 1920, approximately £151 million had been spent on 35 battleships and 13 battle-cruisers. The original technical specification had been innovative – a turbine-driven battleship producing 23,000 s.h.p. for 21 knots, with a 10 × 12 inch main armament and a normal displacement of 18,120 tons. The programme ended with the successful sea trials of HMS *Hood*, a 42,600 ton battle-cruiser that achieved 32 knots at 144,000 s.h.p. and carried a heavy armament of 8 × 15 inch guns. After the First World War the Dreadnought programme lingered on in the Admiralty's 1920 drawings for a new class of 48,000 ton battle-cruisers with 9 × 16 inch guns and a class of 48,500 ton battleships with 9 × 18 inch guns. The provisional estimate for each of these ships was £7 million compared with the £1,785,68 for HMS *Dreadnought*.

Throughout the 1900s the two power standard as expressed in the numbers of British capital ships remained a political orthodoxy within Royal Naval circles, despite the reservations expressed between 1910 and 1912 by some Sea Lords about the nation's ability to sustain such high levels of naval expenditure. Some highly secret efforts were also made at the Admiralty to rethink naval strategy in 1913 in response to debates over the role of submarines and the financial anxieties of the Treasury. However, the tentative conclusions of these discussions were never released to the majority of cabinet members in the Liberal government and Dreadnoughts remained at the fore until the U-boat challenge of 1917–18.

The annual parliamentary naval vote for several years created Dreadnought classes of three ships, until 1909–10, when four Orion class battleships were ordered, a practice that continued with the subsequent King George V class in 1911, and the Iron Duke class in 1912. Between 1912 and 1913, five Queen Elizabeth class warships were laid down, followed in 1913 and 1914 by orders for five Royal Sovereigns. The private warship constructors finally built 34 battleships and battle-cruisers between February 1906 and 1920, while 17 Dreadnoughts were built in the Royal Dockyards. The Admiralty organized a system of competitive tendering from an approved list of private warship builders. Only companies that fulfilled stringent technical, organizational and management standards were listed. The Admiralty thought that management methods and the kind of supervision and control undertaken at particular shipyards directly affected the quality of work that could be expected from these firms. Initially, four companies made bids for Dreadnought contracts: Sir W.G. Armstrong Whitworth and Co. Ltd, John Brown and Co. Ltd, Fairfield Shipbuilding and Engineering Co. Ltd and Vickers Ltd. W. Beardmore and Co. Ltd and Scotts Shipbuilding and Engineering Ltd made representations to be included on the list in 1906. In all, ten firms were eventually given Dreadnought contracts: Armstrong Whitworth, which built 7 Dreadnoughts; Vickers, 6 Dreadnoughts; John Brown, 6

HMS *Valiant*, Queen Elizabeth class battleship, after the First World War, firing a broadside. (RNM Collection, 260/85(8))

Dreadnoughts; Fairfield, 4 Dreadnoughts; W. Beardmore, 3 Dreadnoughts; Palmers Shipbuilding and Iron Co. Ltd, 3 Dreadnoughts; Scotts, 2 Dreadnoughts; Cammell Laird and Co. Ltd, 1 Dreadnought; Thames Iron Works, 1 Dreadnought; and Harland and Wolff Ltd, 1 Dreadnought. Armstrong Whitworth's figures included two battleships initially contracted for foreign powers. *Rio de Janeiro* was built for the Brazilian government (1911–12) and was then transferred to the Ottoman government as *Sultan Osman I* (9 January 1914), before being taken by the British government as HMS *Agincourt*. The ship joined the Grand Fleet on 26 August 1914. HMS *Canada* was built for the Chilean government (1911–14; *Almirante Latorre*) and was purchased by the British government on 9 September 1914. Similarly, Vickers built *Reshadieh* for the Imperial Ottoman government (1912–14). The ship was then acquired for the British battle fleet as HMS *Erin* in August 1914.

## Building Costs

It has been suggested that prominent commercial firms estimated the dockyards' pricing system and labour charges and then integrated these figures with their own costings for armoured plate, armaments, turbines, auxiliary engines and boilers. They then submitted lower bids than the dockyards. However, the actual costs of Dreadnoughts remained uneven. For instance, the Devonport-built battle-cruiser *Indefatigable* (1909–11) was £220,000 cheaper than the price for *New Zealand*, built by Fairfield (1910–12). In the majority of cases, however, the private shipyards were cheaper than the Royal Dockyards. With the Bellerophon class (1906–09), Armstrong Whitworth was cheaper by £74,615, and Vickers cheaper by £123,866 with the St Vincent class (1907–10). Cheaper builds of around £35,000 were completed by W. Beardmore, Armstrong Whitworth and Thames Iron Works for the Orion class (1909–12) and, with respect to the King George V class (1911–13), lower construction costs were achieved at Scotts and Cammell Laird. Nevertheless, respective dockyard and shipyard costs for the Lion class (1909–13) were remarkably similar, and those of the Queen Elizabeth class (1912–16) mixed: *Queen Elizabeth*, Portsmouth Dockyard, £3,014,103; *Malaya*, Armstrong Whitworth, £2,945,709; *Valiant*, Fairfield, £2,537,037; *Warspite*, Devonport Dockyard, £2,524,148; and *Barham*, John Brown, £2,470,113. Costings were a complicated matter because methods of manning and squadding were different between the dockyards, which used the special category of skilled labourers, and the private yards, where plating, riveting and caulking were listed trades. It was actually quite difficult for contemporaries to produce direct comparisons between the Royal Dockyards and the private yards in terms of cost, efficiency and productivity.

The Admiralty remained rigorous over Dreadnought tendering because of the excessive profits made by some contractors, principally Fairfield, on cruiser contracts during the 1890s. It was noticed in 1902–3 that this firm had paid a 20 per cent dividend to its shareholders, which rose to

30 per cent in 1905–6. However, in the changed circumstances of the depression of 1909–10, John Brown, Clydebank, made a loss on the £312,950 contract for the cruiser HMS *Bristol*. The Admiralty usually allowed reasonable profit margins on Dreadnought contracts because of its awareness of the large capital sums invested in plant and machinery, and of the necessity for the firms on its list to remain profitable while maintaining a regular flow of capital ships.

## Rates of Construction

The building of HMS *Dreadnought* at Portsmouth Dockyard in twelve months (2 October 1905–3 October 1906) was a prestigious exercise and unrepresentative of subsequent construction work in the Royal Dockyards. Much of the material had been pre-assembled and work was well advanced in the mould loft when the keel plate was laid. The 12 inch guns and the hydraulic machinery had been ordered in January 1905, the main propelling machinery on 24 June, and the armour and principal ship castings in August. Large amounts of overtime were paid to the dockyard workers, who worked a 69 hour week and not their usual 48 hour week. Work started at 6.00 a.m. rather than the usual 7.00 a.m. and finished at 6.00 p.m. instead of 5.00 p.m. The lunch hour was reduced to 30 minutes. A six day week was also introduced. Some workers were even instructed to continue working on Christmas Day and New Year's Day. During the early construction work, 1,100 men were employed, although this was subsequently increased to 3,000. It took

just eighteen weeks from the laying of the keel plates to the launch on 10 February 1906. The ship was commissioned on 1 September. The preliminary hydraulic trials were completed on 12 and 13 September, the official steam trials were held on 1 October 1906, and the torpedo and gunnery trials were on 16 October. All trials were completed by 22 October. HMS *Dreadnought* was built two months ahead of schedule. The remarkable rapidity of the construction was intended to influence German naval observers and to exaggerate the speed of construction that could be attained in British yards.

The second Portsmouth-built Dreadnought, HMS *Bellerophon*, took 27 months to build. This was still quicker than the earlier Portsmouth battleship average of 31 months. Construction times in the private yards were longer still: 39 months for the Lord Nelson class (1905–8), Beardmore and Palmers; and 33 months for the King Edward VII class (1902–5), Fairfield, John Brown and Vickers. The later construction schedules remained similar to those of HMS *Bellerophon*. HMS *Queen Elizabeth* was built in 27 months at Portsmouth Dockyard and HMS *Warspite* in 28 months at Devonport, while HMSs *Royal Oak* and *Royal Sovereign* were completed in 27 months. This was a similar length of time to that taken by Vickers, Barrow-in-Furness, in building HMS *Revenge*, but quicker than Palmers, Jarrow, for HMS *Resolution*. Beardmore, Dalmuir, took 42 months to complete HMS *Ramillies*, but this was because of damage sustained at the launch. Private

HMS *Queen Elizabeth* in foreground with Orion-class battleships in background, *c.* 1915. (RNM Collection, 987/82)

yards could certainly achieve rapid construction times, as with *Vanguard*, Vickers, which took 22 months, and most impressively with the battle-cruisers HMS *Renown* at Fairfield, Glasgow, and HMS *Repulse* at John Brown, Clydebank, which were completed in 20 months and 19 months respectively. The final Dreadnought, HMS *Hood*, Clydebank, took 42 months to complete, although several delays were caused through changes in the ship's specification and the uncertainty over the future of the class.

## Dreadnought Designs

Although the Director of Naval Construction (DNC) at the Admiralty had the final word, the design was usually the work of a small team of naval architects, whose members were allowed some specialization. Among the more well-known naval constructors associated with the design of Dreadnoughts were J.H. Narbeth, (HMS *Dreadnought*, Invincible class, Bellerophon class), W.H. Whiting (Invincible class), W.T. Davis (Indefatigable class, Lion class), E.N. Mooney and A.M. Worthington (HMS

*Neptune*, Orion class, King George V class, Iron Duke class), E.L. Attwood (Lion class, HMS *Tiger*, Renown class, HMS *Hood*), E.N. Mooney and W.H. Gard (Queen Elizabeth class), W.H. Gard and W. Berry (Renown class) and S.V. Goodall (Glorious class, HMS *Furious*, HMS *Hood*).

The two DNCs who were strongly associated with the Dreadnought project, Philip Watts (1902–12) and Eustace d'Eyncourt (1912 onwards), had both spent many years working in private industry before taking up their Admiralty appointment. Watts had completed a shipwright apprenticeship at Portsmouth Dockyard, where he won an Admiralty scholarship to the School of Naval Architecture at South Kensington, London. He worked at Pembroke Dockyard before moving on to the Admiralty, where he was allocated to the calculating section. He had spells at Pembroke Dockyard and Chatham Dockyard before moving, in 1885, at the age of thirty-nine, to occupy the position of technical director at Armstrong Whitworth, Elswick site, a post formerly held by the then current DNC, Sir William White. On the latter's retirement through ill health, Watts was appointed DNC in 1902.

Eustace d'Eyncourt went to Charterhouse and then trained as a Naval architect at Armstrong Whitworth, where he worked in the design office under Perrett. He was sent to Greenwich Naval College as a private student by Watts, then director of Armstrong Whitworth. D'Eyncourt completed his apprenticeship in 1891 and moved to Fairfield in 1899, where he became technical director. Following Watts's appointment to DNC, Perrett invited d'Eyncourt to return to Armstrong Whitworth as chief of design. He was subsequently appointed DNC in 1912, with the support of Winston Churchill, First Lord of the Admiralty. Watts stayed on for a year in an advisory capacity, possibly because d'Eyncourt had no dockyard experience.

Ship design was the only portion of warship construction that was completely worked out at the Admiralty. The designs and working drawings for gun mountings, guns and machinery were undertaken by the main contractors. According to d'Eyncourt, a ship's brief was initially discussed at the Board of Admiralty, and the Board's decisions were then conveyed by the Controller to the DNC for him to complete a preliminary design. The DNC then worked on the ship's main features in terms of the hull, its length, breadth and draught; the hull's appropriateness to current docking facilities; the ship's armaments and propulsion, in particular the s.h.p.; and the desired speeds at varying degrees of load. A model was then run, usually at the Haslar experimental tank, to obtain more reliable figures. More detailed plans were then made of the arrangement of the ship's armour, boiler rooms and machinery space. The sketched design, showing all of the appropriate figures, the final legend and weights, was then submitted to the Admiralty Board for confirmation. Once this had been given, the full specification of the ship was worked out in relation to the hull compartments, decks, engines, boilers and auxiliary engines and the storage of fuel, ammunition, water, stores and provisions. When this work was completed, the Admiralty Board again approved the specifications and plans, and the official stamp was placed on the sheer drawings and the midships sections.

On HMS *Dreadnought* the plans initially included the sheer draught, mid sections, profile, bridge deck, flying deck and forecastle, upper deck, main deck, lower deck, platform and hold, sections fore and aft, and armour drawings. DNC Watts initially deployed a team of two assistant constructors and five draughtsmen to work on these drawings. Three more draughtsmen worked on engineering lithos, the coaling arrangements, storage and magazines, the shell rooms, the torpedo rooms, the disposition of small guns and ammunition, boat storage, the details of the masts, the control position, and the auxiliary machinery rooms and ventilation. Individual assistant constructors were also given their own briefs: Ballantyne worked on the ship's stability and metacentre, while Payne and Attwood worked on the ship's coaling, water and oil capacity. The team was steadily added to until it peaked at three assistant controllers and thirteen draughtsmen. In 1909, DNC Philip Watts informed the Admiralty Board that the specification and documents that formed the basis of a battleship contract of the Orion class hull had reached 269 pages, whereas 130 pages had been sufficient for a new battleship in 1899. These increased demands led to larger teams. A DNC letter of 15 January 1912 recorded that 24 draughtsmen were to be allocated to the Iron Duke project for a period of two years. The Queen Elizabeth class initially required 28 draughtsmen, while a further 40 were employed for 3 hours overtime each day. In all, 50 draughtsmen signed the Admiralty's security document for this class of battleship.

## The Plans

Dreadnought design plans were dispatched from the Admiralty by couriers to the dockyards and shipyards contracted to build the ships. Initially a single copy was taken, and the original plans returned to the Admiralty. The draughtsmen subsequently made duplicate copies, usually four prints. The plans that were exchanged usually included those of the lines, profile, shelter deck, flying deck, upper deck, main deck, middle deck, lower deck, platforms, hold, section forward and section aft, but copies were also made of the plans that related to the arrangement of the armour, the machinery in the engine room and the boiler room, and the location of auxiliary machinery and workshop spaces. The number of copies and the length of time for which they could be retained varied from ship to ship. For example, five sets of the Orion plans were returned from Portsmouth Dockyard to the Admiralty on 1 November 1909, but eleven further sets were then sent to Portsmouth Dockyard from Palmers, Scotts and Vickers, which had all unsuccessfully tendered for the Orion class. A major

HMS *Valiant* in the North Sea, *c.* 1918, showing war modifications of searchlight towers around the after funnel, flying off positions on 'B' and 'X' turrets and extra tops to the tripod and main mast. (RNM Collection, 127/81)

reorganization of administrative practices appears to have occurred with the King George V class, because the bulk of the copies of the plans were made at Portsmouth Dockyard and Devonport Dockyard. This practice was continued for the Iron Duke class. Although Beardmore had won the contract for HMS *Benbow* and Vickers for the *Emperor of India*, these firms were left with a minimal amount of work, which was restricted to boat storage, messing and sleeping arrangements, galleys and sky lights.

### Work in the Mould Loft

Mould lofts varied considerably in size. At John Brown, Clydebank, the room measured 376 × 53 ft, the proportions at Beardmore, Dalmuir, were 300 × 70 ft, while at Portsmouth Dockyard the mould

loft, built in 1893 and enlarged in 1908, measured 150 × 100 ft. In general the lofts had yellow pine floors, since this wood made the best scrive boards because they did not tear under the scrive knife. The planking was tongued and grooved at the edges and the screws were sunk beneath floor level. The holes were filled in with dowels. The floor was planed afresh after each ship had been layed off. The basic tools employed in the mould loft were a banjo frame for transferring curves, trammels, compasses, T-squares, measuring staffs, steel tape, quadrants, tracing paper and floor dusters. A small workshop was located nearby. This contained circular and band saws, planes and planing machines, carpenter's benches and trestle tables. A large mat was kept at the entrance to keep out dust.

While the process of recall, tracing and storage of the ship's plans was under way, the plans of the sheer draught, the decks and sections were assembled in the mould lofts of the respective yards. The loftsmen were also responsible for the selective ordering of customized plate and castings. An important aspect of the work related to 'laying off' the sheer draught, which consisted of three plans: the sheer plan, the half-breadth plan and the body plan. It was the sheer plan that showed the frame stations and bulkheads throughout a Dreadnought. It also revealed the form of the Dreadnought's hull at the centre line. The half-breadth plan showed the margin line, the water lines from stem to stern and the beam-end lines. The body plan was copied full size on the mould loft floor by means of a system of dots and chalked lines. It demonstrated the lines of each transverse frame at a given station and outlined the form of the hull at each displacement station. The full-size body plan was also the principal guide to the profile of the various frames. The frame stations and individual frames were coded, and these numbers were subsequently painted onto each frame. After the points of the lines had been drawn on the floor, a light batten secured by pins was superimposed onto the chalk profile. The lines were then cut into the scrive boards (the floor).

In the Royal Dockyards the loftsmen were shipwrights, and they were assisted by small numbers of apprentices. The work was regarded as varied and mentally stimulating – 'a gentleman's life' compared with the more exposed work on the uncovered slip. Loftsmen's work required a considerable amount of individual skill and cooperative teamwork. Although craftsmen and semi-skilled labourers had evolved an experiential knowledge of the broad processes of ship construction, this could not hide their dependency on the technical work carried out by the loftsmen.

## Models

The most well-known models were associated with the work of R.E. Froude at Haslar, where several models of the first Dreadnought's hull were used in the water tank to analyse and fine the dimensions of the ship's lines and beam. In all, seven models were made. HMS *Dreadnought*'s cover book reveals a complex correspondence between DNC Watts, assistant constructor Narbeth and R.E. Froude through February and March 1905 over displacement, filling out the ship's bow, the shape of the propellers and the location of the inward propeller shafts. Five basic hull shapes were subsequently used for ten classes of Dreadnought. The major function of the wax models that were made of Dreadnought hulls was to obtain a complete presentation of the shell plating. The frames, strakes, keelsons and side stringers were all drawn on the model, while the length of each plate and its breadth at each end were measured from the model. The measurements ordered from the model and scrive boards for plates had sufficient margins to allow for later adjustment: A. Campbell Holms (*Practical Shipbuilding* vol. 1, 1918) recorded that

7 per cent wastage on the plate was a low figure, while 11 per cent was considered to be high.

A different model from the above was that of a completed ship. There was a considerable correspondence in 1913 between the management of Armstrong Whitworth and the Admiralty over the form of the model for HMS *Malaya*. This had been requested by the Malay States, which were funding the cost of the battleship. The choice was between a $^1/_8$ inch to 1 ft model at £1,000 or an $^1/_4$ inch to 1 ft model at £1,700. The Admiralty decided on the larger scale, although the Armstrong Whitworth management insisted that this price did not include packing, insurance, freight and delivery. The model was dispatched in a glass-sided mahogany case on 25 August 1913. HMS *Malaya* was completed in February 1916. One of the largest ship models to have survived from the Dreadnought era was made of HMS *Warspite* by trainee shipwrights at Devonport Dockyard.

## Moulds

Moulds were made for the keel blocks and plates. Special moulds were manufactured for the shaft brackets, while others related to the watertight and oiltight frames, to the stem and stern castings, and to the accompanying cradle moulds for contour plates. N.J. McDermaid (*Shipyard Practice as Applied to Warship Construction*, 1911) states that two basic techniques were used for preparing armour plates: laying off, which was used for the middle portions of the hull, and mocking up, which was used for

the ends of the hull. Several moulds were made for each plate: two sections with outwinders, two planes with outsiders, and one surface mould. Individual moulds also had to be made for the rudders.

## Plate

The armoured plate used in Dreadnought construction was subject to competitive tendering from an Admiralty-approved list of companies. It was administered by the director of contracts, who laid down the specific requirements for mild steel; nickel-steel plates, which were used for the decks and protective bulkheads; high-tension steel plates, which were used for the upper deck; and armoured plate. The bulk of the armoured plate was obtained from Vickers, the River Don Works, Sheffield; Armstrong Whitworth, Elswick; Beardmore, Parkhead; John Brown, the Atlas Works, Sheffield; and Cammell Laird, the Cyclops Works, Sheffield. Individual firms often obtained the contract for several ships in the same class. Vickers had the contract for the main belt armour on HMS *Queen Elizabeth* and HMS *Warspite*. Special Admiralty inspection officers were appointed to evaluate the plate at the steel mills, as with the case of the overseer, F.E. Coast of Janson Street, Sheffield, who was instructed to inspect the armoured plate manufactured at the River Don Works for the Queen Elizabeth class. Special steel plates were also obtained for these ships from Messrs Spencer, Colville, the Steel Company, Scotland, while Hadfield Steel Ltd of the Hecla Works, Sheffield, received contracts for the conning tower roof and the armouring of the rangefinders.

After the plate had been rolled, it was sent by rail and sea to the on-site plate shops at the yards, where it had to be stacked, or bent using hydraulic bending machines. Light plate shopwork involved drilling, shearing, planing, flanging and bevelling. Much of this could be achieved using specialist machines. In 1909, Fairfield Shipyard had 20 punching and shearing machines, 7 rollers, 5 planers and 7 beam machines. In the Dreadnought era, many specialist companies manufactured shipbuilding machine tools and plate and section working tools. The journal *Jane's Fighting Ships* usually carried the advertisements of James Bennie and Sons, Glasgow; Craig and Donald, St Johnstone; Hugh Smith and Sons, Glasgow; Sir W.G. Armstrong, Whitworth and Co., Manchester; Platt and Field, Manchester;

F. Berry and Sons, Sowerby; Scriven and Co., Leeds; and Greenwood and Batley, Leeds. Admiralty orders for mild steel plates of 10 to 40 lb[1] were usually set at 4,000 to 5,000 tons; those for nickel steel plates of 20 lb, 30 lb, 40 lb and 50 lb were set at 1,000 tons, as in the case of the HMS *Orion* orders of 8 July 1909. *Orion*'s specialized 60 lb tapered plate was ordered in much smaller quantities, 200 tons being deemed sufficient, and 50 tons of nickel steel rivets were also ordered. The Admiralty kept to three or four established suppliers, as can be seen from the letter from the Director of Construction of 26 June 1912, which invited bids for special steel plates similar to those supplied to the *Iron Duke's* control director (1571–1911) from Messrs Spencer, plate numbers 391 from Beardmore, and unannealled and annealled plates similar to numbers 770 and 1812 on the 1911 list from Colville.

1. In shipbuilding, plate thicknesses are represented as pounds weight per square foot; 10 lb equals a $\frac{1}{4}$ of an inch thickness.

# 2: PREPARATORY WORK

The early manual work was concerned with the preparation of bars and frames in the heavy and light plate shops. The initial markings for the bars were obtained from the lines cut in the scrive boards. A separate frame list was also used to describe the details of each frame. A variety of bars were used on Dreadnoughts. These included angle bars, which were deployed to join plates and stiffen bulkheads and frames. They were also used with beams and carlings for the decks. Z bars were associated with beams in the platform decks. They were also used to obtain stiffening, to support bulkheads and for the framing of the ends of the hull. Channel bars were also commonly used in stiffening. T bars were restricted to masts, H and I bars were associated with watertight bulkheads, and segmental bars were used to finish the top edges of hatches, ladder ways and the coffer dams in the boiler rooms. Efforts to mechanize this preparatory work were limited. Frame angles had to be heated uniformly in furnaces and, since the shell flange stretched at the bilge when it was bent after being heated, the marking of the rivet holes were laid down to an Admiralty formula, depending on the type of work to be done. Bar and frame bending was undertaken on steel slabs, usually 12–15 yd in length and 40 yd in width. The depth was about 1 ft. The slab was perforated by large holes 1.5 inches in diameter and 6 inches apart, which took the steel plugs around which the hot frames were bent. The angle smiths used a set iron initially and fixed it into the slab using wedges and plugs. The heated frames were then taken from the furnace, fixed at one end and bent to profile to fit the set iron. The frame was hammered into shape especially on the edges if it did not fit the scrive board measurements. Once the top fitted the floor, head and bevel lines were marked on it. The shape of the frame with its marking was then drawn on the slab. The set was then reversed and the appropriate outline again drawn on the slab. The frame angle was heated up and then bent to the shape of the set using levers and iron bars to force the appropriate fit. The dogs then fixed it in position. The cooled frames were then checked against the scrive measurements. Further hammering or bending occurred if the alignment was inaccurate.

## Armaments

Heavy naval armament was dominated by two firms: Armstrong Whitworth at Elswick and Vickers at the River Don Works, Sheffield, and Barrow-in-Furness. Their rival, Coventry Ordnance, was based on three firms (John Brown, Cammell Laird and Fairfield); they did not succeed in substantively breaking into the British capital ship market before the First World War. The Liberal government elected in 1906 was particularly concerned in its early years to obtain a reduction in armament expenditure. Consequently the Admiralty had to argue in 1908 that battleship construction was needed to prevent the heavy armaments industry from coming to a standstill. It stated that the absence of orders would close down armoured plate production and the erection of gun turrets would also cease. There was some overcapacity in the industry during these years and this created serious problems for Beardmore, which had built new naval gun shops at Parkhead. Although these works were operative in 1909, the firm was only able to obtain heavy gun orders for its own ship, HMS *Ramillies*. Heavy gun barrels had to be forged, hammered, wired, bored, rifled and inspected. The lathes used in this work were among the largest of the machines utilized in heavy engineering. Specialist firms like Alfred Herbert Ltd of Coventry supplied this market. The completed gun barrels were transported by rail to the dockyards and shipyards.

## Shell Manufacture

The 12, 13.5 and 15 inch shells for the heavy guns were made at specialist firms, in particular at Hadfield Projectiles, Sheffield, which was at this time the largest shell manufacturer in the world. During the First World War, heavy shell production was greatly increased in the shell shops at Barrow-in-Furness, Elswick and Parkhead. Much of the labour force in the shell shops was diluted during the war under the terms of the 1907 Munitions Act. The machine work was generally undertaken by women operatives. Vickers had redeployed selected skilled machinists from their gun shops to the shell shops where they established the rates and charts for a premium bonus system, a method of piece-rate payment that had been recognized by the Amalgamated Society of Engineers (ASE) in the 1902 Carlisle agreement. The Vickers management promoted handymen from the shell shop to gun work in an effort to reduce wages. There was also a sustained effort to introduce more apprentices in place of handymen. These policies brought them into conflict in 1905, 1908, 1911 and 1917 with their skilled workers, who were supported by the ASE. J.T. Murphy, who worked at Vickers, Brightside, turning propeller shafts and gun barrels, came to national prominence when he wrote the pamphlet 'The workers' committee: an outline of its principles and structure' in 1917. Similar disputes occurred at Armstrong Whitworth and on the Clyde, for the workshop movement was part of a national campaign against dilution and industrial conscription.

## Marine Engineering

The most modern engine and boiler shops that had the capacity to manufacture machinery for Dreadnoughts were built at Dalmuir by Beardmore. They covered 5.5 acres and were equipped with the latest machinery, which was powered individually rather than by the older band- or shaft-driven techniques. Despite the new plant the firm was unable to obtain substantial naval contracts until 1910. The turbines used for Dreadnoughts were manufactured by Parsons, and Brown and Curtis. The battle-cruiser HMS *Tiger* (June 1912 – October 1914) was the first ship to have Brown and Curtis turbines. These were built under licence by John Brown, Clydebank. They were heavier than Parsons and were used for HMSs *Repulse, Renown, Courageous, Furious* and *Hood*. Several specialist firms, including Thos. Firth and Sons Ltd, Sheffield, obtained contracts for turbine components, while the Darlington Forge Company placed adverts in *Jane's Fighting Ships* (1916 and 1918), showing images of forged ingot steel turbine rotor drums, rotor wheels and spindles. The Admiralty awarded turbine contracts on dockyard Dreadnoughts to Scotts, Harland and Wolff, Wallsend Slipway, Hawthorn Leslie and Cammell Laird. Boiler making was dominated by two firms: Babcock and Wilcox (20 Dreadnoughts) and Yarrows (16 Dreadnoughts). Some were built under licence, as with Harland and Wolff (HMS *Neptune*) and John Brown (HMS *Barham*). Small tube boilers were adopted for HMSs *Courageous, Glorious, Furious* and *Hood*.

During the First World War, Armstrong Whitworth installed automatic machinery in its Elswick marine workshop, and increasingly introduced women workers, who undertook forms of repetitious production involving light components and the preparatory work in the electrical and turbine shops. Large numbers of women were also recruited by Beardmore, Fairfield and Portsmouth Dockyard for similar work. There were campaigns against the Munitions Act in the engineering and marine workshops in the Clyde region between 1915 and 1918 over the length of the working day – the demand was for a 40 hour week – and various forms of dilution. The shop steward committees were especially militant during 1917, although their campaigns did not spread to the Boilermakers' Society (the United Society of Boilermakers and Iron and Steel Shipbuilders; USBISS) and the Shipwrights' and Shipconstructors' Association (SSA). The Clyde Workers' Committee received support at several marine engineering works, principally Dalmuir and Parkhead, where the Independent Labour Party (ILP) socialist Kirkwood had enforced a closed shop. Other Scottish firms that had shop steward committees included the Babcock and Wilcox factory at Renfrew and Weir's factory at Cathcart, which specialized in naval hydraulic systems, condensers, circulating pumps and fuel pumps. The Barr and Stroud works at Scotstoun, which made rangefinders and naval optical equipment, also had active works committees.

The mould loft at Beardmore, Dalmuir. The room measured 300 × 70 ft. The building was erected by Sir William Arrol and Co. Ltd, Glasgow. (BRCUG)

The mould loft at John Brown, Clydebank. The room measured 376 × 53 ft. (BRCUG)

The shipyard drawing office at Beardmore, Dalmuir. Draughtsmen were recruited by examination from craftsmen of the Construction, Mechanical and Electrical Departments of the shipbuilding industry. Completed drawings were sent to the Tracing Section, which was generally staffed by women. (BRCUG)

Rolling mill, John Brown, Atlas Works, Sheffield. The plant for manufacturing armour plate was of special construction that was not adaptable to ordinary commercial work. Because of the high content of nickel and chromium used in making armour plate, exceptionally high temperatures had to be achieved in the furnaces. Ingots of 80–100 tons were used in the specially designed melting furnaces. The forging was carried out by 10,000–12,000 ton hydraulic presses. The slab was then reheated and was rolled in an exceptionally powerful mill, which was able to deal with plates of up to 15 ft in width and 50 ft in length. After the heat treatment in the furnaces, the plate was straightened under a heavy hydraulic press. A large planing machine was then used to bring it to the required thickness. (BRCUG)

Rolling armour plate, Parkhead, Glasgow. In 1904 Beardmore purchased a licence from Harvey United Steel Co., USA, to manufacture Krupps and Harvey armour plate. The profits made from the armour plate and steel production sustained Beardmore through the heavy losses of 1906–10, when the newly built naval yard at Dalmuir (completed in 1908) was unable to obtain substantial naval contracts. The annual capacity of Parkhead was 10,000 tons of armour plate, 50,000 tons of boiler and ship plate, and 60,000 tons of castings. The peak demand was in 1910, when 11,641 tons of armour plate were sold. Beardmore annually supplied *c*. 8,000 tons of armour plate to Vickers, Barrow-in-Furness, and Scotts, Greenock. Contemporary estimates in *Brassey's Naval and Shipping Annual* suggest that an annual production of 10,000 tons of armour plate involved capital costs of £1 million to £1.5 million. (BRCUG)

Bogie furnaces for carbonizing armour, John Brown, Atlas Works, Sheffield. The slab of armour plate was placed inside these special furnaces for two to three weeks, during which the carbon was adsorbed onto the face. (BRCUG)

The armour plate erection shop, Beardmore, Parkhead. Heavy overhead cranes were used to move the stacked plate. (BRCUG)

A Dreadnought's belt armour in the armour plate shop, John Brown, Clydebank. Planing machines for armour plate are at the end of the shop. (BRCUG)

Armour plate shop no. 5, Beardmore, Parkhead. (BRCUG)

Armour plate being bent by a 12,000 ton hydraulic press, Beardmore, Parkhead. (BRCUG)

*Right*: Steel ingot under a 10,000 ton hydraulic press. John Brown, Atlas Steel Works, Sheffield. (BRCUG)

*Below*: The general office and stacks of steel plate, John Brown, Clydebank. (BRCUG)

Members of the Boilermakers' Society bending frames in the plate shop at Beardmore, Dalmuir. The work was undertaken on steel slabs, which were perforated by large holes 1.5 inches in diameter and 6 inches in depth. These received the steel plugs around which the hot frames were bent. Angle ironsmiths furnaced the frames, and the platers took the frames and bent them into the appropriate

profiles. The same bending techniques were used for frames, beams and bars. This type of work was not mechanized because of the large number of variations in the profiles of the frames and beams used in the construction of Dreadnoughts. (BRCUG)

# 3: THE BUILDING SLIP

*Laying the Keel Plate and Early Framing*
On the slipway early preparatory work was the erection and alignment of building blocks on which the ship would be built. In the Royal Dockyards, five metal derricks were usually placed on either side of the hull to lift the heavier plate, which could weigh up to 8 tons, and prefabricated sections, 10 tons. In the private shipyards the capital investment in this equipment was significantly greater. In 1914 the Vickers' yard at Barrow used nine Arrol tower cranes across four berths. These had a 60 ft radius for weights of up to 10 tons and a 120 ft radius for 5 ton weights. At John Brown, Clydebank, and Fairfield, Govan, lattice masts and derrick systems were employed at the building slip. A more elaborate method was utilized by Beardmore at the naval yard, Dalmuir, where an Arrol metal gantry system had been erected over the two building berths. Additional mobile metal cranes were also used. Harland and Wolff, Belfast, had similarly installed an Arrol gantry, which was combined with hydraulic riveting, for the building of the liners RMS *Olympic* and RMS *Titanic* on slips 2 and 3, North Yard. Despite its prestigious construction contracts, this yard only received one Dreadnought order: the battle-cruiser HMS *Glorious* (1915–17).

The laying of the keel plates on the slip floor was one the earliest acts of construction. In the dockyards this was the subject of a brief naval ceremony.

'It is correct that there is no fixed ceremony, the official birth of the ship being the launch . . . when it is done at this dockyard, the ceremony (the keel plate) consists of a 20 ft keel plate being slung and landed in the position in the presence of the lady who after seeing the level applied and verifying the position of the plate with reference to the middle line and exact position fore and aft declares the plate well and truly laid.'

Admiralty memorandum to
Japanese Inquiry, 1911

'The blocks were erected forward, amidships and aft to heights given in the drawings. Midway between these a base is erected, and its lower edge sighted in with the top of the existing blocks, and a set built up to this height. From these sets of blocks a series of four or five blocks is erected and trimmed by stretching a line along the upper surface, and sighting from end to end. For the complicated stern blocks, moulds would be made on the mould loft floor, and the blocks set up to the moulds.'

N.J. McDermaid, *Shipyard Practice As Applied to Warship Construction*, 1911

The next phases were concerned with the erection of the flat and vertical keels. Work then proceeded to the construction of the double bottom with its complex network of frames, longitudinals and beams. With the Queen Elizabeth class the transverse frames were situated at 4 ft sequences, both forward and aft of the double bottom. These frames were made up from channel and Z bars. The longitudinal strength was secured by the use of stringers, which were worked intercostally with the frames. They were situated midway between the decks. The transverse frames were riveted to floor plates and secured to the keel. They were bracketed to transverse beams. On HMS *Hood* the keel box construction developed for the Royal Sovereign class was adopted. It was continued over the length of the double bottom. Z bars were used to reinforce those sections that had to bear particularly heavy weights. The framing continued amidships and commenced with the riveting together of three component parts: a frame angle, a reverse bar and a floor plate. These together formed a single unit. Frame erection was undertaken at a rapid rate. The technical details of the keel and double bottom of the first Dreadnought are outlined in clear dia-

grammatic form in J.M. Roberts' *The Battleship Dreadnought* (1992), which also contains comprehensive scale drawings of the side framing at midships, forward hull, aft hull, a profile of the outer bottom plating and the sequence of plates at the stem and stern.

## *Plating*

The craftwork that was undertaken on the building slip involved a profuse number of small gangs of workers. In the private yards the erection of the hull was organized through a series of contracts negotiated between the management and the numerous trade gangs. These gangs recruited their own labour and supervised the work to be undertaken within each gang. In the dockyards this work was organized in a quite different manner. It was largely undertaken by a stratum referred to as skilled labourers who were paid time rates. They were not classified by the Admiralty as tradesmen, despite numerous petitions requesting their recognition as riveters or caulkers. Skilled labourers were moved from job to job in the yard and were usually supervised by shipwrights. These gangs had far less control on the job than the equivalent tradesmen in private yards. In the Clyde shipyards there were separate gangs composed of both skilled tradesmen and semi-skilled men. Here the role of the shipwright was more restricted. They were responsible for liaising with the mould loft and for setting the keel blocks and the preparations for the launch. They also checked the positioning and fairing of the frames and the large castings for the stem. Plating was the province of platers, who were organized into gangs of five or six men. They were paid at a fixed rate for the completion of a row of plates. They were responsible for organizing their helpers, who were paid on a time basis. Some platers worked with the templates provided from the mould loft; others undertook the punching of holes and the bending of the plate. The plates had to be lifted by the derricks or cranes as gangs moved along the puddocks to manhandle them into position on the berth. When the work progressed to the decks, greater care had to be taken over the lifting technique. The plates were pushed into position and then bolted down. Each member of the squad knew what the other members' work was about and had undertaken this in earlier gangs. The squads acquired 'on the job' knowledge gained across working lives of all of the necessary methods required for plating on the berth. A high degree of coordination was required in this kind of work. Little daily direct supervision was given outside the individual squad, although plates were regularly inspected for the quality of the fitting by charge hands and foremen. The key representatives of the company were the foremen, who were responsible for negotiating with the gangs of platers the piece rate. They also had to maintain the smooth progress of the work so that the firm met the dates of its contract schedule.

## Riveting

Dreadnought hulls required millions of rivets, and these were put there by squads of workers. A typical riveter gang consisted of two riveters – one a left-handed striker and one a right-handed striker – a holder up and a heater, who was often a boy. The heater worked the small coke portable furnace and heated the rivets until they were white hot. He then tossed them to the holder up, who bumped them into the hole and held them there with a long hammer, known as a Dolly. In shell riveting the two hammermen were on the other side of the plate and they knocked the rivet down with alternate blows. Once the rivet was set firm and had cooled, a further sequence of blows rounded off its edge. A rivet could be hammered in in 1 minute when the squad was working flat out. This involved approximately fifteen strikes from each hitter. While several skills were required to achieve and sustain the precision and rhythm of the strikes, the riveters also had to cope with the monotony of the work, which was always exposed to the outside elements. In winter they had to cover their shirts with layers of cardigans or old jackets to keep out the wind and rain. The work was always tiring because of the required body stance. Long hours and fatigue combined to make it an arduous job. The strikers in particular preferred to work in short, intensive bursts and then to recuperate in longer recovery periods. The work was also often dangerous, with the men working high up on the puddocks on insecure deck plating. They were exposed to the hazards created by the full force of winter weather. There was a tendency for squads to keep together and to employ existing friends or relatives where possible.

A variety of rivets were required, depending on the nature of the work, the thickness of the plate and its location. Heavy hammers had to be used in keel riveting because of the length of the keel. Minor misalignments of holes were corrected by driving in tapered steel pins known as Drifts to enlarge the hole. When this was insufficient the hole was rimed by using a pneumatic power drill. Hand riveting remained predominant on Dreadnought hull construction, because hydraulic riveting machines had a limited role in the shipyards: they were usually used for the keel and beam riveting. They were not used in the Royal Dockyards for shell plating, although they were introduced at both Beardmore, Dalmuir, and John Brown, Clydebank. However, pneumatic rivet guns were widely adopted during the 1900s in both the dockyards and the shipyards. Because of the intervention of USBISS, full squads of riveters were employed whenever the guns were used, even though the work could technically have been done by an unskilled man.

Again a variety of rivets had to be used in the erection of the hull. The most common type was the pan head. Countersunk heads were utilized when a flush finish was required or in areas where structural strength and/or watertightness was required. Snap points were similar in role to hammered heads but were used in accommodation areas for an improved appearance. The countersunk rivets were used to join three thicknesses of plate. Tap rivets, which were threaded, were used to join plates to armour plate or to join plate to castings.

As with the squads of platers, the rivet gangs were organized on a different basis in the private shipyards and the Royal Dockyards. On the Tyne and Clyde, riveting gangs were paid according to how many rivets they had put in. A contract price was paid for a set figure. In theory the price reflected the speed at which the rivet could be driven down, and this in turn depended on its size. The figures were listed in a complex manner, for the price was regulated by the type of rivet being used, the location of the riveting work and whether the site was difficult and the work dangerous. The price was negotiated individually between the foreman and the gangs. Once it had been agreed, the riveters were told to get on with the job. USBISS played no role in these negotiations. Customary rates were, however, common to the particular yard and the district. Collective bargaining by USBISS officials at national and district level was primarily concerned with percentage increases or reductions to existing lists as a whole rather than the price of individual jobs. The union was also concerned over the question of apprentices, insisting on seven-year apprenticeships and a staggered entry into the trade. At the yard level the concern was with the peculiarities of the customized ship. Gangs of young riveters sometimes chased higher targets with the support of a foreman, but in general the rivet gangs knew that in any dispute other tradesmen would not do their work. Any significant undercutting would lead to various forms of social antagonism and was generally avoided. Many gangs were based on family networks or friendships. It has been suggested that 34 per cent of a commercial shipyard's supervisory labour costs was spent on riveting squads. In the Royal Dockyards the riveters were in a weaker position. The skilled labourers were not recognized as tradesmen and were not paid trade rates. The squads were frequently picked by foremen and chargehands. Dockyard riveters were paid on a time rate and did not have the scope for bargaining over the rate for rivets. They also worked a 48 hour week and had less chance of overtime work. This gave them a significantly lower wage than the riveters in the private yards. There were thus significant distinctions in manning and supervisory practices between the public and private sectors.

## Caulking

Although very good riveting gave a watertight finish, it was caulking that really achieved this. This was done by using a seam tool to make a small furrow on the edge of the plate; a setting tool was then used by the caulker to cut a groove and the displaced material constituted the shoulder that was in contact with the next plate. If the edges of the plate were far apart, strips of iron were hammered in. Caulkers used light hammers, a splitting tool and a setting-in tool. This work was undertaken by individual caulkers who were paid piece rates. The straightforward nature of the work induced employers to introduce pneumatic machines for work on the shell

and decks. The employers, especially those in the north-east, were keen to reduce wages by 50–60 per cent from hand rates for those operatives who used the power tools for caulking. USBISS showed a keen interest in these trends and negotiated an agreement in 1905 whereby the tools, principally the pneumatic hammer, were to be allocated only to the members of the society. It did, however, agree to a wage reduction of 35–40 per cent for caulkers using this equipment.

## *Employers, Workers and the Trade Unions*

Dreadnought construction involved a complex division of labour that was reflected in the sectionalized nature of the craft trade unions. There were twenty trade unions in the shipbuilding industry during the 1900s and almost 200 local transitory societies. A high degree of sectionalism existed in the yards and this fragmentation was reinforced by the spatial geography of the yards. High levels of trade union membership characterized the skilled trades in the private yards. They were able to have a considerable say on who was employed and what working practices were adopted. The Ship-constructors' and Shipwrights' Association (SSA) recruited among the loftsmen, draughtsmen and the shipwrights. It had a steady membership in the dockyards where the branches were considerably smaller than those at John Brown, Clydebank. Skilled workers kept to their own distinctive craft unions, as with the case of the pattern makers, who were usually members of the United Pattern Makers'

Society. The blacksmiths often chose to belong to regionally based trade societies, although a series of amalgamations between 1912 and 1914 created a national trade union. The draughtsmen working in the Tyne shipyards during the First World War were recruited into the Clyde-based Association of Engineering and Ship-building Draughtsmen, a small union that was still able to hold meetings of more than 350 draughtsmen on the Tyne in 1916. Riggers had their own society, while the Sailmakers' Society continued to exist in the Royal Dockyards.

The most influential and powerful trade union in the private sector was USBISS. This was a broad federation of trades and it recruited strongly among the platers, ironsmiths, riveters, caulkers and holders on. The earlier demarcation disputes of the 1890s with the SSA over the fairing of plates and the making of templates did not resurface during the 1900s, which was not a period of inter trade union rivalry. Instead, USBISS became involved in a series of conflicts with the Shipbuilding Employers' Federation (SEF). Its defence of craft practices involved limiting the adoption of mechanical riveting. The society was able to reassert unilateral action between 1911 and 1914 when it ended the practice of joint regulation with the employers. The society ensured that a squad of four was retained for riveting with no reduction in the wage rates for men using guns or machines. Wage reductions were, however, accepted for those drillers and caulkers who used pneumatic drills. Lower-paid apprentices were debarred from this work.

All of the shipyard trade unions had to recognize the enhanced power during the 1900s of the SEF, which attempted to embrace both shipbuilding and marine engineering. The federation was concentrated on the Clyde, the Tyne, the Wear and the Tees, with other major centres at Barrow, Belfast and Birkenhead. Approximately ninety firms were involved in the federation. The Clyde employers were the most hostile towards the trade unions, while north-east employers were inclined to recognize trade unions. The Tyne association had negotiated detailed agreements with drillers and platers' helpers in 1906. Comprehensive regional agreements had also been made in the north-east with USBISS. There were standing committees for each river to deal with yard issues. These committees negotiated on matters of piece rate, overtime payments and demarcation. No such agreements existed on the Clyde.

The pressure for a major redefinition of commercial and naval shipyard work relationships came from Armstrong Whitworth, Palmers, Vickers, Beardmore, Fairfield and John Brown. These firms were keen to weaken 'trade union interference', but they were not generally supported in the association by the more numerous and smaller family-based firms whose managerial and supervisory structures were less well developed. The federation's tensions with USBISS over managerial authority and labour discipline culminated in a national lock-out. On 16 August 1907 the SEF informed USBISS that the caulkers at the Walker yard of

Armstrong Whitworth had to end their strike over the employment of apprentice platers on caulking. The executive council of the society circulated its membership with a memorandum informing them that such a lock-out 'would entail a weekly expenditure which it is utterly impossible for us to meet'. The branches voted 8,341 to 2,903 for an immediate return to work. The SEF was intent on establishing a national agreement with USBISS to regulate piece rates and to make temporary decisions binding prior to discussions at local wages committees. The large naval firms also wanted to exploit the emerging slump in the shipping market to insist on wage reductions. It obtained a national agreement in March 1909 when seventeen trade unions signed an agreement that regulated general wage increases to 5 per cent. Under the terms of the agreement, no stoppages could occur before negotiations had taken place. Members of the union had to remain at work while the procedure was followed, even if the employer had changed the work conditions. USBISS had been keen to obtain notification of any proposed district changes in working practices and piecework rates and it wanted to introduce an element of neutral arbitration into the procedures. These positions were ignored by the SEF, which favoured the adoption of the Clyde practice of the discharge note, which was given to workers who struck despite the agreement on working procedures. The association also decided that the introduction of time clocks and job cards was to be a management prerogative.

Because of the 1909 agreement, USBISS fined its members at Palmers who went on strike, and in May 1910 the riveters who struck at Fairfield over the issue of a guaranteed minimum rate were forced to return to work because the SEF stated that their action was in breach of the agreement. Between 12 July and 18 August a further 14 shipyard stoppages occurred over piece rates: 5 on the Clyde and 6 on the Tyne, where Armstrong Whitworth workers struck on finding that a temporary management decision on riveting prices had led to the lowering of their wages. These disputes precipitated the enforcement of a national lock-out against USBISS between September and November 1910. When the agreement expired in March 1912, the local membership of USBISS emphatically voted for its non-renewal.

The outbreak of the First World War led to a further reassessment of shipyard working practices. On 3 November 1914 the national officials from the shipbuilding trade unions agreed that the rules governing working practices would be applied more flexibly and that such negotiations would occur at a local level. However, district officials were generally resistant to this, and USBISS and the SSA refused to allow any relaxation of trade union practices. The Admiralty became concerned over the prospect of unofficial strikes in the shipyards and was increasingly critical of the interventionist stance being adopted by the Ministry of Munitions. On 10 and 15 June 1916 the dilution commissioners reached a labour agreement with the Clyde-based committee of the SSA and USBISS. The central issues were the dilution of skilled labour through the recruitment of female labour, the demarcation of work and apprenticeships. The Admiralty remained concerned about the situation affecting warship construction and in October 1916 it was given full control in labour matters in all war shipbuilding firms on condition that it accepted the Ministry of Munitions' labour priority firms. This agreement, however, soon foundered. Subsequently a Shipyard Labour Department was set up in the Admiralty where an influential faction sought to restrain the impact of dilution and to prevent fundamental changes in existing working practices because it thought that such activities would create serious disruption to warship construction.

In this era, industrial relations in the shipyards varied from region to region. In Scotland many shipyard workers in Dalmuir, Govan and Partick became involved in the campaigns of 1915 and 1916 against local landlords because of high rent levels and evictions. Disputes also occurred at Fairfield and Beardmore over complaints that shipyard workers who refused to do dirty work were threatened with dismissal without a working certificate. After these protests, some of the terms of the Munitions Act were changed through discussions with the trade unions: the format of the leaving certificate was altered and the financial penalties that courts were allowed to impose were significantly reduced. On the Tyne and Wear the relationship between the employers and the local officials of the shipbuilding trade unions was more harmonious. In 1917 the Tyne Shipbuilders' Association stated that:

'there is no serious unrest amongst workers in the shipyards in this district as far as relations between employers and workmen are concerned . . . such unrest as does exist . . . is largely one of economics brought by the methods adopted hitherto in the lack of control of prices and unequal distribution of food.'

The trade union officials on the Tyne and Wear offered no hostile evidence to the commissioners, who in their report praised the trade unions for 'adjusting labour difficulties' and 'bringing about good relations between employers and employed on the North East coast'. The trade union district officials were prepared to support patriotic warship production, but they were also able to secure substantial pay increases for their members during the war. At Palmers, the smiths' wages rose from the prewar rate of 47s 10d to 60s 9d in October 1915, the wages of platers moved from 59s 6d to 72s 2d, and those of riveters went from 43s 3d to 50s. These improvements occurred without any fundamental changes being made to working practices.

Trade union activity in the Royal Dockyards was more muted than in the private yards because the Admiralty was opposed to directly admitting the trade unions into direct negotiations with dockyard officials or itself. Instead it insisted on the archaic practice of annual petitions. While this method of consultation appeared to be egalitarian – a dockyard worker could have his case discussed by a series of local officers, including charge hands, inspectors and foremen, then finally the Admiral Superintendent – the collective experience of the broad dockyard classes was largely negative. Nearly all significant dockyard petitions were turned down between 1905 and 1913. One of the most important issues was the dockyard men's views on the inferiority of their wages in comparison with the earnings available on the Clyde and Tyne. Dockyard men worked 48 hours a week, without overtime, compared with the 54 hours worked in several prominent yards. They said that most dockyard tradesmen were not getting the going rate for the job. The skilled labourers were also unsuccessful in their efforts to obtain trade recognition. The Admiralty justified its stance in terms of peculiar dockyard practices. In particular it referred to the advantages of men being placed on the establishment list. These men were guaranteed continuity of employment, albeit at lower rates than hired men, and also a dockyard pension when they retired at sixty-five years of age (if they lived to receive it). These pensions could not be passed on to a surviving wife. However, for several years, principally between 1905 and 1910, the establishment was closed because of the Treasury's concern over dockyard wage costs. When a hired dockyard worker reached the age of forty he was no longer considered for establishment. In some trades, such as joiners, smiths, hammermen, plumbers, there were more established men than hired, up to a 75 per cent ratio. However, in the most numerous trades the ratios were much smaller, under a third, as with the case of the skilled labourers and ship fitters. The Treasury had advised that the yearly establishment average should remain at 25 per cent, although this had fallen as low as 13 per cent by 1910 in several of the major trades. Dockyard men undoubtedly appreciated the security that establishment gave them and waged an effective campaign to increase the percentages of establishment between 1913 and 1915. Dockyard superintendents and the director of dockyards strongly approved of the establishment list as a stratagem for diluting the impact of trade unionism within the yards.

The shipwrights were traditionally the elite stratum of workers in the Royal Dockyards. They were subject to the idiosyncratic practice of the annual shoal when the senior charge hands picked their squad for the next year by rotation. This offered the opportunity to break up any established close friendships in the squads that aroused their suspicion. Familial networking could only occur if the charge hand was in agreement. Such an institution weakened the role of the shipwrights' trade union. The annual Portsmouth trades council reports of 1912 and 1913 reveal trade union affiliations from the ASE (branches 1–5), the SSA (branches A, B and C), USBISS, the Smiths and Hammermen, Copper Smiths,

Smiths and Hammermen, Copper Smiths, Iron Founders, Riggers, Sailmakers, Pattern Makers, and the Government Labourers' Union. Several shipwrights only attended 4 or 5 times out of a possible 24 meetings, a trend that was continued among the majority of USBISS delegates. Individual members, like the shipwrights Mactavish and Littlewood, and the smiths and hammermen Roberts and Beere, were active in both industrial affairs and the ILP, but dockyard workers were rarely collectively militant. The ASE merely threatened an overtime ban in 1913 and efforts to mount a joint campaign with the shipwrights failed.

A view from the head of no. 5 slipway of Portsmouth Dockyard, Monday 2 October 1905. The middle line blocks on which the *Dreadnought* will be built are being checked for straightness and declivity. The two v-shaped poles in the foreground are sheer legs which will hoist the stem casting into place. (PCL)

Portsmouth Dockyard, later on the same day. The blocks have been set up and one of the after bulkheads has been positioned. At the far end of the slip can be seen the stem casting which has been hoisted into position. (PCL)

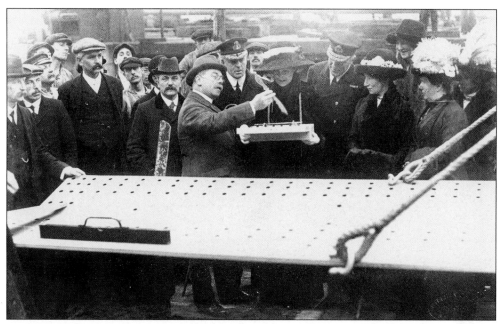

Laying the keel plate of the battleship HMS *Queen Elizabeth* at Portsmouth Dockyard, 21 October 1912. Mr J. Apsey, head of the Construction Department, presents a silver ink stand in the form of a keel plate to the Honourable Lady Hedworth-Meux, wife of the Commander-in-Chief (pictured centre). (PCL)

The battleship HMS *Queen Elizabeth* on no. 5 slip, Portsmouth Dockyard, 1913. The height of the blocks on the left of the picture would suggest that this is the after cut-up of the stern and the camera is looking into what will form the lower machinery space of 'X' 15 inch turret. Although the hull plating is well advanced the stern casting and after cut-up have yet to be erected. (PCL)

The building berth of the battle-cruiser HMS *Hood*, September 1916. The centre line blocks support the outer flat keel and frame sections, which show lightening holes in their centre. One would assume she had no single vertical keel plate but was built with two keel plates, one on each side of the frame section, forming a box. It would appear that the ground-ways, on which the vessel will be launched, are in the process of being built. The stacked timber will form props to support the structure of the ship as it is being built. (BRCUG)

The main deck of the battle-cruiser HMS *Hood*. This deck would eventually be plated with 2 inch armour, which increased to 3 inch over magazines. The peculiar round-down and slope of the deck were to assist the armour protection and were some 10 ft inside the ship. (BRCUG)

The battle-cruiser HMS *Hood*, afloat after launching. A section of 12 inch thick barbette armour is being lowered into position for 'A' turret. Armour was tongue

and grooved on its butt edges, which locked it into position. Here the groove of
the butt is clearly visible. (BRCUG)

John Brown's Shipyard, Clydebank, 14 April 1915. The outer flat keel of the battle-cruiser HMS *Repulse* is being erected. The *Repulse* was 794 ft in length and too long for the slipway, which had to be extended over the railway lines and roadway. The centre line blocks supporting the keel plate have been made into a low bridge to allow traffic to pass under the ship while it is being built. (BRCUG)

John Brown's, Clydebank, 14 April 1915. Looking forward along the starboard side of the *Repulse* as the elegant underwater shape of the battle-cruiser begins to emerge, with the erection of the lower bulkheads up to the Lower and Platform deck levels. (BRCUG)

HMS *Repulse*, 5 May 1915. Looking forward from the forward engine-room into the after boiler room before the erection of the engine-room bulkhead. The deck beams are up to Lower deck level. The deep bottom frames will either form the inner bottom tanks for storing fuel, oil and water, or become airspaces such as coffer dams that form safety barriers between tanks; the inner bottom plating is in the process of being laid. (BRCUG)

The battle-cruiser HMS *Repulse*, 6 October 1915. A view from the stern showing the after barbette. On joining the fleet, the *Repulse* and *Renown* were severely criticized for their lack of armour. During firing trials of the main armament, the hull was strained and both ships spent long periods in dockyard hands, earning them the nicknames of Refit and Repair. (BRCUG)

John Brown's, Clydebank. Looking along the inner flat keel of the *Repulse* from frame no. 44. Compressed air formed the motive power for many of the riveting, caulking and drilling machines used in the shipbuilding industry at this time. A Boyer's pneumatic drill can be seen in the middle of the picture with its air line running down the keel plate. Workmen are in the process of reaming the rivet holes before final closing of plates for riveting. (BRCUG)

The battle-cruiser HMS *Repulse* under construction at John Brown's, Clydebank, 8 July 1916. The picture belies her 90 ft beam, but shows the flare of her graceful bow; at 32.6 knots she was the fastest capital ship in the world and with her sister, *Renown*, set a new world record for construction of that size of vessel, of twenty months. (BRCUG)

John Brown's, Clydebank, September 1913. Setting up the forward frames and deck beams to the Platform deck of the battleship HMS *Barham*. (BRCUG)

John Brown's, Clydebank, 6 September 1913. A view of the stern of the *Barham*. The stern casting has been hoisted into position by the sheer legs. (BRCUG)

HMS *Barham* on the day of her launch, 31 October 1914. The teak planking that formed the backing to her side armour can be clearly seen in the armour recess on the side of the ship. (BRCUG)

*Above*: HMS *Tiger* being built at John Brown &
Co., 6 September 1913. She was the last coal-
burning British capital ship and the only battle-
cruiser to mount 6 inch guns. Plating at the fore
end is up to the weather deck and the three hawse
pipes are in position. Deck beams in way of the
two forward turrets have yet to be cut away for
the barbettes. (BRCUG)

*Left*: The battle-cruiser HMS *Tiger* at John Brown's,
Clydebank, 15 December 1913. (BRCUG)

The weather deck of HMS *Tiger*, viewed from aft, 5 December 1913. The curve of the ship's side and deck in the lower right-hand corner of the picture shows the after starboard 6 inch battery. The *Tiger* was launched on 15 December 1913. (BRCUG)

The *Dreadnought* under construction at Portsmouth Dockyard, Saturday 28 October 1905,
looking aft along the main deck. Illumination at night was provided by electric lights,

searchlights and lucal lamps. One can be seen to the left of the large hole in the deck. These were pressurized lamps that produced a large 6 ft flame similar to a blow lamp. (PCL)

# 4: LAUNCHING DREADNOUGHTS

An obvious distinction between the privately owned shipyards and the dockyards was the degree of attention given to the launch of Dreadnoughts in the Royal Dockyards. Crowds of 60,000 came to Portsmouth Dockyard on a Saturday morning to watch the launch of HMS *Iron Duke* (12 October 1912); as many as 80,000 are said to have attended the HMS *Queen Elizabeth* launch on Saturday 16 October 1913. These public spectacles expressed deep-seated and authoritative values. Each of the launches had its distinct coterie of admirals, aristocrats, politicians, naval officers, senior dockyard officials, their wives and daughters, and the massed ranks of manual workers. In matters of detail, individual launches differed from earlier and subsequent launches, although what stands out throughout these forms of naval spectacle are the powerful unifying trends: a common administrative practice and a repetition of forms, pageantry and ritual that were utilized on launch days.

A launch involved two ceremonies. The first was the naming of the ship. This was performed by a 'great lady'. In the case of HMS *Iron Duke*, this was the Duchess of Wellington, and for HMS *Queen Elizabeth* it was Lady Hedworth-Meux, the wife of the Commander-in-Chief. At a given signal the lady swung the bottle of Australian wine against the Dreadnought's bows and uttered the traditional words: 'I wish good luck to the *Iron Duke* and to all those who sail in her.' This ceremony was accompanied by a burst of spontaneous cheering. After a slight pause and on a given signal, the skilled labourers waiting beneath the ship knocked out the final block restraining her. On the launch platform the head of the construction department removed a chisel from the launch box, which was made from HMS *Victory*'s timbers, and then handed it to the lady guest who struck it with a mallet, severing the launch rope, which was situated at the bows on an oak rosette. The cutting of the rope released the half ton weights that knocked aside the last of the dog shores. The ship then began to creep along the grease-coated ground ways. As the ship's momentum increased, the crowds cheered vigorously, waving hats and handkerchiefs, while the sirens of naval ships in the harbour sounded out. The Royal Marine band always played 'Rule Britannia' as the Dreadnought steadily gathered momentum down the slip. The impact of the cacophony of sounds – the clattering restraining chains, the grinding hull and the cheering of the crowds – was magnified by the exciting visual spectacle of the Dreadnought entering the harbour waters. For many observers these were quasi-magical moments of grandeur; a time to express and articulate deeply held imperial values.

Beneath the surface spectacle a launch ceremony was the site of preplanned expectations, for the officials who arranged these ceremonial events were confident that the grand event would always function in a splendid manner. Most of the workers and their families had already seen several other launches, yet masses of people were undoubtedly thrilled and affected by the spectacle. A momentary sense of a social solidarity was achieved. Spontaneous moments reproduced memorable moments, as for instance when the dockyard workers clambered onto the slip to watch the final entry of the Dreadnought into the harbour waters. The administrators also had the seating in the south stand placed very close to the hull to enhance the ship's towering presence. The harbour setting with the moored HMS *Victory*, the lines of naval warships, plus neighbouring docks and buildings produced a scenic vista for this grand occasion. A Royal Dockyard Dreadnought launch always released powerful conformist sentiments: it was a national communion where the representatives of the national elite, the armed services and local society reaffirmed their commitment to the Royal Navy and the monarchy. These values were part of a wider frame of reference that reinforced a particular social order – an order that held particular assumptions about Englishness, Empire, great power status and the country's glorious naval traditions. Such evocations of imperial power in the 1900s were rarely exercised by the elites in a brutal and arbitrary manner; instead it was cloaked in an effective spectacle.

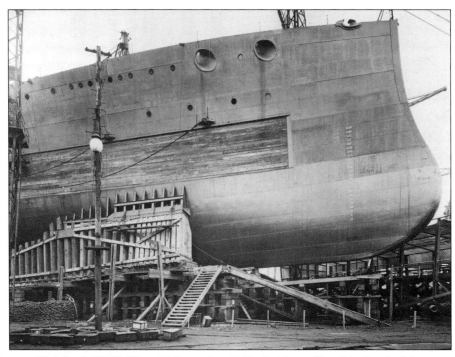

John Brown, Clydebank, HMS *Tiger*, 15 December 1913. A side profile of the head of the ways and the forward cradle. (BRCUG)

John Brown, Clydebank, HMS *Repulse*, 8 January 1916. The last of the temporary shores are removed a few hours before she takes to the water. (BRCUG)

Portsmouth Dockyard, HMS *Neptune* launch, 30 September 1909. The Duchess of Albany performed the ceremony, which was watched by Mr James Marshall, Director of the Royal Dockyards. Dockyard workers on the slipway anticipate the final convergence of ship and water, while others give three hearty cheers. A solitary Royal Marine Artillery bandsman has left the band's concert platform to get a better view of HMS *Neptune*'s baptism. This image, like several other photographs taken by Silk and Cribb, evocatively captures in a stylized manner the excitement and collective enthusiasm of launch day. (PCL)

Beardmore, Dalmuir, HMS *Ramillies*, 12 September 1916. Profile of the ship showing the Arrol gantry system. It measured 750 × 135 ft and was 150 ft high. There were four travelling cranes on each gantry side, which allowed eight squads of platers and riveters to work supported by cranes. (BRCUG)

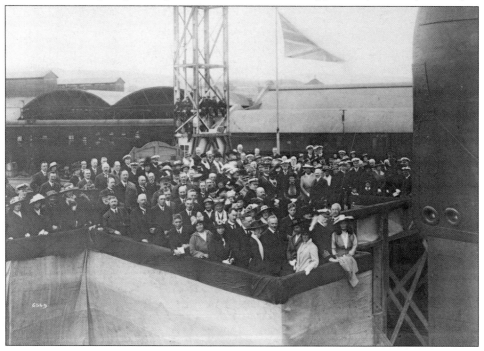

Beardmore, Dalmuir, HMS *Ramillies*, 12 September 1916. The forefoot of the battleship is on the right of the picture waiting for her baptism as spectators on the VIP stand pose for the photographer. (BRCUG)

Beardmore, Dalmuir, HMS *Ramillies*, 12 September 1916, stern view. (BRCUG)

Portsmouth Dockyard, HMS *Royal Sovereign* launch, 29 April 1915. Lady Dalmeny is instructed by the manager of the Portsmouth Dockyard Constructive Department, Mr J. Apsey, on her duties and procedure in the naming and launch ceremonies. Rear-Admiral Hedworth Meux looks on. (PCL)

John Brown, Clydebank, HMS *Hood* launch, 22 August 1918. John Brown workers watch the ship. In general the launches in the shipyards did not have any of the conspicuous pomp of the Royal Dockyard launches. The launch weight of HMS *Hood* was 21,920 tons, although this included 200 tons of buoyancy with the bilge ways. The hull structure was complete up to the forecastle except for the openings for the main machinery. There was no structure above the forecastle deck except the plating behind the armour of the conning tower erection and the aft screen bulkheads. On the starboard side of the hull, none of the side armour had been fitted apart from plates 16 and 17. The boilers were aboard but not the main machinery. (BRCUG)

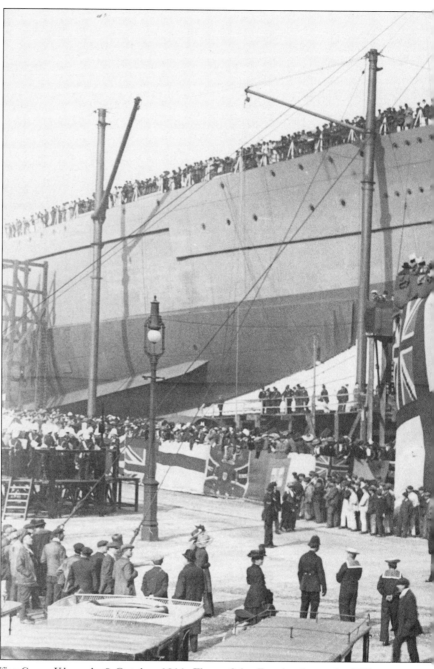

Portsmouth Dockyard, HMS *King George V* launch, 9 October 1911. Flags of the Empire drape the VIP stand, while a naval guard of honour waits to present arms to Princess Christian of Schleswig-Holstein and her entourage, who are due to arrive by carriage at the foot of the steps leading to the platform. The band of the Royal Marine Artillery is to the left. Dockyard workers gaze down from the ship's rails. The invited VIP guests were Princess Christian of Schleswig-Holstein, Princess Victoria (her daughter), Sir Arthur Moore (Commander-in-Chief), the Honourable Evelyn Moore (his sister), Alderman Sir T. Scott Foster (Mayor of Portsmouth), Rear Admiral C.J. Briggs (Controller of the Navy and Third Sea Lord), Mrs Briggs, Rear Admiral Herbert King Hall (Director of Naval Mobilization), Lady Margaret

King Hall, Rear Admiral Troubridge (Private Secretary to the First Lord), Mrs Troubridge, Maj.-Gen.
William Nicholls (Deputy Adjutant General of the Royal Marines), Mr F.W. Black (Director of Naval
Contracts), Mrs Black, Sir J.B. Marshall (Director of Dockyards and Dockyard Labour), Lady Marshall,
Engineer Commander J.W. Horn (Engineer Assistant to the Director of Dockyards), John Apsey
(Manager of the Construction Department, Portsmouth Dockyard), J.S. Sanders (Manager of the
Engineering Department, Portsmouth Dockyard), Mr M.J. Maguinness (Constructor) and various
managing directors from Sir W.G. Armstrong Whitworth and Co. Ltd, W. Beardmore and Co., Harland
and Wolff, Palmers Shipyard and Iron Works, Scotts, the Thames Iron Works and Vickers Ltd. (PCL)

Portsmouth Dockyard, HMS *King George V* launch, 9 October 1911. Shipwrights knock out the shores of the building blocks at the after end of the ship a few days before the launch. (PCL)

Portsmouth Dockyard, HMS *King George V* launch, 9 October 1911. The ship is moored 200 yd from no. 5 slip as the crowd wanders over the ways and disperses. The panoramic image has been taken from the VIP platform and seeks to convey a visual context for the concluding moments of launch day. (PCL)

Portsmouth Dockyard, launch of HMS *Queen Elizabeth*, 16 October 1913. A large assembled crowd in the south enclosure awaits the ceremonies. The launch ceremony was performed by Lady Hedworth-Meux, the wife of the Commander-in-Chief. (PCL)

Portsmouth Dockyard, HMS *Queen Elizabeth* launch, 16 October 1913. Dockyard workers emerge from the assembled crowd and climb on the slip to watch the ship enter the harbour waters. (PCL)

Portsmouth Dockyard, launch of HMS *Dreadnought*, 10 February 1906. The northern section of

the crowd stands patiently awaiting the arrival of King Edward VII. (PCL)

Portsmouth Dockyard, HMS *Dreadnought* launch, 10 February 1906. An impressive image that lends support to the articles in the local newspapers, which suggested that crowds of 60,000 people and more attended these Dreadnought launches. (PCL)

Portsmouth Dockyard, HMS *Dreadnought* launch, 10 February 1906. As the crowd disperses, several curious workmen explore the ways and one young boy hails the cameraman. (PCL)

Portsmouth Dockyard, building slip no. 5, HMS *Bellerophon*, 27 July 1907, setting the cradle on to the *Bellerophon*. Some 500 dockyard shipwrights hammer in long wooden wedges, which were placed between the bilge ways and the poppet boards for the entire length of the Dreadnought. The hammering was commenced from the stern at low tide, while the strikes were coordinated to the chimes of a bell. 'Setting up' involved transferring the dead weight of the ship's hull from the building blocks to the cradles, which would carry the ship into the harbour waters. (PCL)

Portsmouth Dockyard, HMS *Bellerophon* launch, 27 July 1907. Dockyard workers standing on the front of the lower platform give three hearty cheers for the ship. (PCL)

Portsmouth Dockyard, HMS *Iron Duke* launch, 12 October 1912. The Duchess of Wellington uses the traditional wooden mallet and chisel to cut the rope, which will release the ship's suspended weights. (PCL)

Portsmouth Dockyard, HMS *Iron Duke* launch. An awed response from the platform as VIPs watch the *Iron Duke* descend the ways. Those in attendance on the VIP platform included the Duchess of Wellington, the Duke of Wellington, Admiral Sir Hedworth-Meux (Commander-in-Chief), Lady Hedworth-Meux, Sir J. Forcey (Director of Dockyard Stores), Rear Admiral H.L. Heath (Admiral Superintendent of Portsmouth Dockyard), Vice Admiral Sir H.B. Jackson (Head of the War College), Sir John Scott (Lord Mayor of Portsmouth), Mrs Scott (Lady Mayoress), Admiral Charles Beresford MP, Bertram Falle MP, Mrs Falle, Mr Winston Churchill MP (First Lord of the Admiralty), Mrs Churchill, Sir William Nicholas (Adjutant General of the Royal Marines), Sir James Marshall (Director of Dockyards), Lady Marshall, Mr F.W. Black (Director of Naval Contracts), Captain E.S. Alexander-Sinclair (Paymaster-in-Chief), Commander A. Bromley, Lieutenant M. Boissier, Rear Admiral Wishart (Engineer), Colonel M. Oldfield, Colonel L.J. Pease, Mr G. Hammond-Etherton (Clerk to Portsmouth), and heads of dockyard departments Mr J. Apsey, Mr W. Renny and Mr Drummer. (PCL)

Portsmouth Dockyard, HMS *Iron Duke* launch. The local photographer has managed to frame the ship's profile. (PCL)

Portsmouth Dockyard, HMS *Iron Duke* launch, 12 October 1912. Dockyard workmen collect the floating slum, which greased the slipway, from the harbour waters after the launch. This scene was frequently reproduced on local postcards. (PCL)

# 5: FITTING-OUT:
## Superstructure, Propulsion and Armaments

Vickers, Armstrong Whitworth, Beardmore and John Brown supplied the main machinery for their own Dreadnoughts. However, the Admiralty insisted that other firms competed among each other for work after the main contractor had been decided. At Portsmouth Dockyard the HMS *Queen Elizabeth* machinery contract was given to the Wallsend Slipway and Engineering Company. The main machinery involved were twenty-four Babcock and Wilcox boilers and their accompanying fittings: the stop valves, steam pipes, main feed valves, water gauges, air cocks, test cocks, pressure gauge cocks, circulating valves and emptying valves. The Parsons turbines were made at the Wallsend Slipway Engineering Company under licence. The auxiliary machinery purchased for HMS *Queen Elizabeth* included feed pumps, air pumps, condensers, circulating water pumps, lubrication pumps, turning engines, steering gear (Napier Brothers), evaporators, distillers (G.J. Weir, Cathcart), capstan engines, electric light

engines and generators. The refrigeration and ice-making machinery was manufactured by the Liverpool Refrigeration Company. The Admiralty imposed rigid schedules that itemized the powers of the overseers in terms of their appointment and their powers with regard to inspecting and rejecting work, plus requesting drawings and sketches of parts. In the dockyards the gun mountings and heavy armament were supplied by Armstrong Whitworth or Vickers, whose workers supervised their installation. Dockyard engine fitters petitioned the Admiralty in 1913 and 1914 for permission to undertake this work, but their request was denied.

The range of work tasks required in fitting-out was more varied and complex than that associated with the erection of the hull. Decks were subdivided into cabins, messes, storage rooms, magazines and workshops; miles of electric cabling had to be laid; and ladderways and lifts installed. On such large ships the effectiveness of the ventilation system was essential – it was achieved by the use of electrical fans and a comprehensive network of ventilation trunking. The main deck of the Queen Elizabeth class had fourteen sets of $12\frac{1}{2}$ inch fans with electric heaters and motors along with eight sets of $7\frac{1}{2}$ inch fans with heaters. Large vent-trunking was also employed to bring cool air to the boiler rooms, while the magazine rooms were cooled by refrigeration machinery. The upper and main deck plans of the designated flagships, HMS *Iron Duke* and HMS *Queen Elizabeth*, itemize the extensive number of areas that were required for a ship's company of 2,000 men. In some cases the furnishings were lavish, most obviously in the admiral's quarters. His suite of rooms contained bookcases, tables, a rolltop writing desk, settees, book racks, cupboards, large sideboards, a silver cabinet, wardrobes and chests of drawers. The chief stokers' and naval artificers' messes, by way of contrast, were much more simple and consisted of a table and lockers, while the sailors' and stokers' messes had ditty box lockers. A variety of equipment had to be brought on board. Some pieces related to the ship's galleys and involved boilers, sinks, dressers and racks. The sick bay in the forward section of the main deck had to be built, and tables, stools, lockers, wash basins, baths, lavatories and urinal troughs had to be installed. On the lower decks, storage rooms had to be built for paint, canvas, cordage, bunting, food and ammunition.

Dockyard workers employed on fitting-out worked a different regime from those employed on the erection of the hull. In June 1911 an agreement was concluded between the dockyard shipwrights and the Admiralty over a 51 hour week. On the day shift there was a 1 hour break per day. From Monday to Thursday the hours were 7.00 a.m. to 12.00 p.m. and 1.00 to 5.00 p.m. Those of Friday and Saturday were 7.00 a.m. to 12.00 p.m. and 1.00 to 6.00 p.m. Sunday morning was worked between 7.00 a.m. and 12.00 p.m. On night shifts, which were worked when needed on five consecutive nights, two 45 minute breaks were allowed between 10.00 and 10.45 p.m., and between 2.30 and 3.15 a.m. The shift lasted from 6.00 p.m. to 7.00 a.m., and the rate of pay was time and a quarter for all hours. A Dreadnought became a complex and, at times, confused workplace. Work sites ranged through the freshwater tanks, the oil fuel compartments and the feedtanks of the double bottom, to the boiler and engine rooms, the magazines, the steering compartments and the watertight compartments of the hold, upwards through the lower deck, to the platform deck, to the middle and main decks, the upper deck and the forecastle deck. Superstructure work involved the erection of the funnels, conning tower, masts and compass platform. On the lower decks, ship fitters and engine fitters had to master the intricacies of boiler and turbine design, even if they were supervised by the contractor's employees. Rigid demarcations existed, because the work undertaken by the electricians and engine fitters in the Royal Dockyards could not be undertaken by skilled labourers. Engine fitters in their 1913 and 1914 petitions had sought the Admiralty's permission to work on boiler room gratings, handrails, ladders and the hydraulic systems. These requests were all denied. Between 1912 and 1914, the skilled labourers had also requested increased payments for their own riveting work with high-tension rivets, which were used for deck plates and bulkheads, but this request was again denied by the Admiralty.

The distinct work gangs required to work in dispersed locations meant there was little of the homogeneity associated with the collective work in hull erection. An indication of the varied nature of this work can be understood with reference to the men working at the lower levels of the conning tower of HMS *Queen Elizabeth*. Different gangs of men had to build hatches, five ladderways and four skylights, fit out the navigation officer's cabin, the officers' WCs, the rooms for the officers' oilskins, and install the ventilator shafts to the engine room. The ship's conning tower required the installation of sounding machines, semaphore machines, searchlight controllers, Evershed transmitters, Vickers range clocks, the revolution telegraph, the engine telegraph, the steering wheel and various communication tubes. The tower was protected by 15 inch armour plate made by Armstrong Whitworth, Elswick, while the control tower armour was made at Beardmore and the plate for the roof of the rangefinder came from the Hecla Works, Sheffield. The 15 inch gun Barr and Stroud rangefinder was sited in the control tower, which was mounted on top of the conning tower. This kind of fitting required complex scheduling from the

foremen in order to achieve an effective rotation of the gangs. Inspection and supervision were vital matters in terms of achieving the qualitative build required by an Admiralty contract. Planning of the work routines for platers and riveters, ship and engine fitters, carpenters and painters required prompt regulation. Management delegated most of this supervision to charge hands, inspectors and foremen, whose responsibility it was to visit the men on the job.

## Dock Inspections

These followed standard procedures in the private shipyards and the Royal Dockyards. Admiralty letters of 7 August 1915 informed the Wallsend Slipway Company that HMS *Queen Elizabeth* was to be ready for steam trials in December 1915. The letter detailed that the turrets and guns had to be placed onboard, the turbines had to be lined up with the shaftings and complete connections were to be established with all of the turbines. Water tests were to be conducted on the main steam pipes, the feed section lines, the condensers and oil feed pipes. Dockyard officials were instructed to provide the additional auxiliary boilers that were required when the hydraulic machinery was tested. The final dockyard inspections occurred on 25 January 1915. They involved the ship's engines, for, although the hydraulic system was tested, it could only be finally assessed at the gunnery trials. The boilers were inspected and steam was raised in each boiler, but they were not tried at full power because the ship remained moored. Particular care was taken over measuring the expansion of the turbine blades and their freedom of movement. The engine room ventilation was checked and the closed exhaust fittings tested. The electrical machinery and wiring, including the refrigeration and electrical motors, were inspected and passed. Tests were carried out on the ship's electrical bells, telephones and hoists. The rigging, magazines and bilges were inspected. A longer sequence of inspections had been carried out earlier (1 December 1914–5 January 1915), when the bulk-heads and double bottom had been inspected. Surveys were made of the inner and outer surfaces of the plates, from the waterline to the double bottom, and then from the waterline to the topside. The wing components were the most difficult to reach. These surveys also included the cooking galley, the ammunition hoists, the boat hoists and the derricks. The inspections revealed that a considerable amount of work remained to be completed in the engine room, where there was incomplete lagging of the oil pipes in boiler room 1, while the starboard drainpipes to the heating had not been completed, nor were the exhaust pipes finished. New scheduling was agreed. Additional work was also undertaken on the coffer dam built in the engine rooms.

# Superstructure

John Brown, Clydebank, 9 March 1915, HMS *Barham*. The machinery housing to 'X' barbette being lifted onboard. (BRCUG)

John Brown, Clydebank, 9 March 1915, HMS *Barham*. 'X' barbette being lowered into position. (BRCUG)

John Brown, Clydebank, 17 May 1915, HMS *Barham*. A 15 inch gun barrel for 'X' turret being lifted into position; each barrel weighed 98 tons. The gun barrel is suspended from a 150 ton tower crane. (BRCUG)

John Brown, Clydebank, 7 June 1915, HMS *Barham*. The rollers and gearing of 'B' turret are exposed. (BRCUG)

John Brown, Clydebank, 8 July 1915. Profile of HMS *Barham*. Between 1914 and 1918, John Brown built the battleship HMS *Barham*, the battle-cruiser HMS *Repulse*, 2 light cruisers (*Canterbury* and *Ceres*), a sea plane carrier, 35 destroyers and 3 'E' class submarines. (BRCUG)

John Brown, Clydebank, 5 April 1916, HMS *Repulse*. The imposing tripod mast and fore funnel have been completed. (BRCUG)

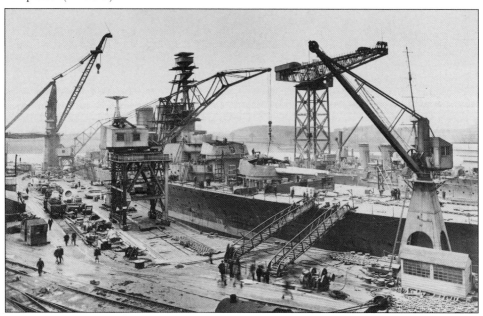

John Brown, Clydebank, 21 April 1916, HMS *Repulse*. Five distinct types of crane are being deployed at the fitting-out basin. The second 15 inch gun for 'A' turret has been placed onboard prior to the completion of the turret roofs. (BRCUG)

John Brown, Clydebank, 18 May 1916, HMS *Repulse*. A 15 inch gun barrel for the 'Y' turret being lowered into position. The 150 ton Arrol hammerhead crane profile dominates the yard skyline. (BRCUG)

John Brown, Clydebank, 8 August 1916, HMS *Repulse*. Impressive view of the forward 15 inch Mark I guns. For the first time in British battle-cruisers there were two directors, one on the foremast and the other in the armoured hood on the conning tower roof. (BRCUG)

John Brown, Clydebank, 15 July 1916, HMS *Repulse*. Profile of the fitting-out basin. The Arrol electric derrick cranes clustering around the building slip dominate the skyline. They were originally purchased for the building of the Cunard liner *Lusitania* in 1906. 'A' and 'B' turrets have been completed. (BRCUG)

John Brown, Clydebank, 13 August 1916, HMS *Repulse* raising steam. The ship's main armament was praised by contemporary naval commentators, although the triple 4 inch Mark I gun mountings were subsequently criticized for being difficult to operate. (BRCUG)

John Brown, Clydebank, 4 August 1914, HMS *Tiger*. The three equally spaced funnels gave the *Tiger* a grace that pleased the eye of all who saw her. In 1917 the searchlight platforms gave way to searchlight towers, fitted around the third funnel. The tripod foremast, with its high topmast and armament director at the foretop, has yet to be fully built. (BRCUG)

The forward 13.5 inch guns of HMS *Conqueror*. A gang of dockyard workers examine the plating on the roof of 'A' turret. (PCL)

John Brown, Clydebank, 2 December 1919, HMS *Hood*. Steam is being raised in the forward boilers. The 15 inch guns have been fitted in 'A' and 'B' turrets but remain exposed to the elements. The general offices are visible in the centre of the image. The unusual stature of the large conning tower and the observation tower is dramatically realized in this photograph. The base of the conning tower extended down to the main deck. Its main structure consisted of two shells with 11 and 9 inch armour in the upper sections. The two shells were linked by a narrow passage. The conning tower armour weighed 600 tons and the whole structure 900 tons. (BRCUG)

John Brown, Clydebank, HMS *Hood*, 8 March 1920. The morning shift leaves the ship. (BRCUG)

# Propulsion

Vickers, Barrow-in-Furness, the turbine shop. Two types of naval turbine were used in Dreadnought battleships and battle-cruisers. Parsons developed reaction turbines, while John Brown, Clydebank, undertook a joint development with the US firm Curtis to produce impulse turbines. Parsons direct-drive turbines were fitted to British Dreadnoughts between 1906 and 1914 (HMS *Dreadnought*, Invincible class, Bellerophon class, St Vincent class, Indefatigable class, Colossus class, HMS *Neptune*, Orion class, Lion class, King George V class, Iron Duke class, HMS *Erin* and HMS *Agincourt*). HMS *Canada* had a mixture of Brown-Curtis and Parsons turbines (1911–14). Brown and Curtis direct-drive turbines were fitted to HMS *Tiger* (1912–14), while in the Queen Elizabeth class (1912–16) Brown and Curtis turbines were used on HMS *Barham* and HMS *Valiant* and Parsons turbines for HMS *Queen Elizabeth*, HMS *Warspite* and HMS *Malaya*. The Renown class (1915–16) had Brown and Curtis turbines, the Royal Sovereign Class (1913–16) had Parsons turbines, the Glorious class (1915–17) had Parsons turbines and HMS *Furious* (1915–17) and HMS *Hood* (1916–20) had Brown and Curtis turbines. (VSEL)

Vickers, Barrow-in-Furness, turbines for the battleship HMS *Vanguard*. The upper cast-iron cylinder weighed approximately 36 tons, a cast turbine rotor drum weighed 22 tons, a ribbed rotor drum 17 tons, a rotor wheel 26 tons and a steel tube for the spindle 70 tons. (VSEL)

Vickers, Barrow-in-Furness, turbines for the battle-cruiser HMS *Lion*.

In reaction turbines, steam passes through a continuous ring of fixed blades, and is directed by them upon the first ring of moving blades. This changes the direction of flow, after which the steam comes into contact with the second ring of fixed blades, where the direction of flow is again changed. The steam then enters the second set of moving blades, and in like manner passes through succeeding stages, at each stage the diameter of the rings is increased. The steam, therefore, had more space as it goes through the turbine, and the whole expansion takes place as it passes through the blades . . . Reaction turbines rotate at slower speeds than do impulse turbines.

A.E. Ingham, *Machine Construction and Drawing*, Book II, 1914.

Parsons reaction turbines had small radial clearances and with the early turbines the blade tips were susceptible to damage from distortion of the rotor, particularly when being 'warmed up' before operation. Brazed segmental blades with side locking pieces were adopted to overcome this problem. (VSEL)

Vickers, Barrow-in-Furness, two sets of low-pressure turbines for HMS *Lion*. These produced 70,000 s.h.p. Each set consisted of HP and LP ahead turbines and HP and LP astern turbines. The HP had a cruising stage at the forward end for working at low power. The steam passed over this stage by means of a special bypass when the turbines ran at higher power. The photograph reveals the aft ends of the low-pressure turbines, showing the bed plate connections and the system of stays in the exhaust branch. It also shows the turning gear and its electrical motor. (PCL)

Vickers, Barrow-in-Furness, foundry. (VSEL)

John Brown, Clydebank, turbine erecting shop. The firm acquired a licence for the construction of Parsons turbines in 1903 and received a licence from Curtis in 1908 to undertake joint development work on naval turbines. Curtis-Brown impulse turbines were different from Parsons turbines in having a single cylinder: the complete range of expansion from boiler steam to condenser pressure was carried out in the one turbine. (BRCUG)

John Brown, Clydebank, brass finishing shop. Brass was used for underwater fittings. (BRCUG)

John Brown, Clydebank, central boiler shop. The Yarrow boiler was described in the *Stoker's Manual* of 1912:

> The steam drum runs the whole length of the boiler above the centre of the fire-grate and extends beyond it at the front and back; at each side of the fire-grate there is a water drum. The bottom plate of the steam drum is connected to the top plate of the water drum on each side of the boiler by the generating tubes which are straight, except that rows nearest the fire are bent slightly to it. At the front of the drum outside the boiler casing are two large downcomer tubes connecting the steam drums with the water drums. The feed water is led into the outer sides of the bottom drums, which have a space opposite the top rows of tubes furthest away from the fire baffled off from the rest of the drum. The internal feed pipes are in the space so partitioned off. The whole of the boiler, except the ends of the drums which project, is surrounded by a casing, which is brick-lined and lagged as necessary. The furnace doors, grate-fires, and ash pans are arranged as usual. The gases from the fire are burned in the space above it, mixing with air admitted through a tube in the back casing, and they pass through the tubes on either side reaching the division of the uptake.

(BRCUG)

John Brown, Clydebank, large machine shop, the engine works. (BRCUG)

John Brown, Clydebank, machine shop. (BRCUG)

Parsons, turbine shop. This shop was built by Sir William Arrol and Co., Dalmarnock Iron Works, Glasgow. (BRCUG)

Wallsend Slipway Company, boiler shop. The Babcock and Wilcox boiler was described in the *Stoker's Manual* of 1912:

In this boiler the tubes forming the vertical heating surface are attached to forged steel boxes or headers placed vertically in the boilers. A pair of headers with its connecting tubes form an element. The front headers carry doors through which the tubes, which are placed in zig-zag rows, may be either cleaned or renewed when necessary. The rows of tubes just above the fire and connecting the bottoms of the headers are of larger diameter than the others; these tubes are placed one above the other in the headers, the smaller ones above are placed in pairs side by side. The vertical rows of tubes are staggered to make sure that the gas passes over all tubes, and the headers are similarly bent. Each tube communicates directly with the front and back header, and when elements are in position in the boiler the tubes lie at an angle of 15 degrees with the horizontal. Each front header is connected at the bottom with the feed collector which is a square tube running across the boiler above the furnace doors and at the top with the bottom of the steam collector. Each back header is connected at the top with the steam space of the steam collector by two large tubes. The ends of the steam collector communicate with the downcomers which lead into mud drums, and the water from these returns to the feed collector before going again to the tubes. In this boiler there is a definite water level which is maintained in the steam collector, and each tube is connected to the headers of its element. The headers are placed side by side, forming an airtight wall front and back, between which the flames from the furnaces are directed by baffles over the whole of the tube surface.

(BRCUG)

Beardmore, Dalmuir, cast steel shaft brackets, weight 97 tons. The stern frames, rudders and stem for Dreadnoughts had to be cast individually. (BRCUG)

Beardmore, Dalmuir, patternmakers' shop. It was here that exact wooden replicas were made of equipment that needed to be cast. The patterns were then passed to the foundry where their shapes were replicated in sand moulds ready for casting. (BRCUG)

John Brown, Atlas Works, Sheffield, forging shop. (BRCUG)

John Brown, Atlas Works, Sheffield. After forging, propeller shafts were machined to their required size on long lathes similar to those in the above picture. Thos. Firth and Sons Ltd built the four shafts for HMS *Queen Elizabeth*. Each shaft was 67 ft in length and 17 inches in diameter. (BRCUG)

# Armaments

Beardmore, Parkhead, gun factory, a forged tube for 12 inch gun, weight 67 tons. The forging process often took four weeks because the plant was used only intermittently. (BRCUG)

*Left*: Beardmore, Parkhead, a jacket for a 12 inch gun under a 4,000 ton hydraulic press. The first stage in making a heavy gun was to run the molten metal from the 60 ton furnaces into an octagonal mould. After the ingot had cooled it was placed in a boring mill, where a hole was trepanned through it. The trepanned ingot was reheated until it glowed. It was then put under hydraulic pressure, which squeezed and forged the metal to the desired dimensions. To keep the profile of the bored hole, a hollow mandrel was inserted into the tube. Streams of cold water were passed through the mandrel to cool it as it came into contact with the red-hot gun tube. (BRCUG)

*Below*: Beardmore, Parkhead, gun factory lathes. When the forging process had been completed the jacket was planed and smoothed by machine tools. A tube forging, which weighed approximately 47 tons for a 12 inch gun, was rough turned on a lathe with a bed of 90–108 ft. Lathes were driven by 40–50 hp independent electric motors and served by 100 ton cranes. These lathes could also be used for large propeller shafts. (BRCUG)

Beardmore, Parkhead, gun factory, hardening (tempering) the tube in oil for a 12 inch gun. The oil bath was sunk vertically into the ground for about 90 ft. It was filled with 126 tons of oil. Above it was the 130 ton Goliath crane, which had a clear lift of 100 ft above the ground. The tube was reheated in the gas-fired furnace. The temperatures were then checked by pyrometers. After this the tube was lifted by the crane and steadily lowered into the oil bath until it was completely immersed. (BRCUG)

Beardmore, Parkhead, gun factory. When the tube was removed from the oil bath, pieces were cut from the ends and examined to make sure that the forging had been satisfactory. (BRCUG)

Beardmore, Parkhead, gun shop. Unlike continental guns, which were hooped, British heavy naval guns were wire wound. The gun's jacket was enveloped in an outer casing of rectangular section steel wire. This was achieved by placing the jacket onto a lathe-type machine, which spun the wire from a large reel of wire on a nearby machine in an endless spiral from one end of the jacket to the other. A contemporary paper presented at the British Association of Science by Mr Douglas Vickers and Lt Dawson RN of the Vickers company stated that 130 miles of wire were wound round the jacket of a 12 inch gun. This increased to 170 miles for a 15 inch gun. The reel carrying the wire was fitted with special gear that maintained a steady tension throughout the winding operation. The tension was varied according to the number of layers. On a 12 inch gun there were approximately ten layers of wound wire. After the tube had been wired it was returned to a lathe, which skimmed off any irregularities in the wire until the exterior of the jacket was symmetrical. (BRCUG)

Beardmore, Parkhead, gun shop, 'one week's output'. Heavy naval guns were more than 60 ft in length and weighed more than 100 tons. They usually took a year to complete. The lengthy routines involved in the making of guns and the accompanying turrets imposed a rigid timetable on Dreadnought construction. (BRCUG)

Beardmore, Parkhead, boring machine for heavy guns. (PCL)

*Left*: Sir W.G. Armstrong Whitworth and Co. Ltd, Elswick, applying a pressure of 10,000 tons to the tube of a 12 inch gun. Approximately 500 tons of ingots were required to make each forging. Cranes of 200 ton lifting capacity were situated on each side of the hydraulic press and were fitted with special turning gear for revolving the billet while it was being forged under the press. (PCL)

*Below*: Sir W.G. Armstrong Whitworth and Co. Ltd, Elswick. After the jacketed wire-wound tube had been further hardened, it was returned to the lathe, the operator of which gave the gun a smooth external finish. The wire casing was then measured and an outer casing prepared. This casing was bored at a slightly smaller diameter than the external diameter of the wired tube. The external tube was then heated up and placed over the inner tube. As it cooled, the two tubes became homogenous. The final process was to give the inner surface of the barrel its distinct rifling. (PCL)

Sir W.G. Armstrong Whitworth and Co. Ltd, Elswick, turret erection shop. The shop had to have powerful overhead cranes to cope with the heavy weights involved. Brick pits of about 50 ft in depth were made below floor level. The diameter at the bottom was 15 ft, while the diameter at the top was 40 ft with stairways, electric power and light distribution. The gun turrets were erected in the pits, this involved constructing the plate and angle housing for the guns. This weighed approximately 230 tons and was made of steel plates and bars. Within these were built the training, elevating, hoisting and loading gears, gun wash-out plant, sighting and firing apparatus, electrical and auxiliary pumping machinery, flash-proof doors and interlocking safety devices. Supported on the plate, in addition to the working chamber and trunk, was the main and auxiliary machinery, which weighed about 300 tons. The turntable containing the guns, the machinery and the armoured shield were erected complete in the shop. The turrets usually took between eighteen months and two years to build, although the separate testing of new models could take a further four to six months. If the turret was passed as satisfactory it was then dismantled and taken to the appropriate dockyard or shipyard. (PCL)

Sir W.G. Armstrong Whitworth and Co. Ltd, Elswick. Putting the 13.5 inch guns and turrets onboard HMS *Monarch*. The first lift was put onboard at 2.00 p.m. on 22 July 1911 and the last was completed on 26 July 1911. The total weight of the material handled in four days was 2,800 tons, and the whole operation involved 250 lifts. These were made by a 150 ton crane built in the Elswick Engine Works. (PCL)

The Barr and Stroud factory, Scotstoun, fitting shop for naval rangefinders. (BRCUG)

Vickers, River Don Works, Sheffield, south gun shop. (BRCUG)

Vickers, River Don Works, Sheffield, inspection shop. Final dimensional check before issuing for proof firing. (BRCUG)

Vickers, Barrow-in-Furness, gun erecting shop, 13.5 inch Mark II gun for the battle-cruiser HMS *Princess Royal*. (VSEL)

Vickers, Barrow-in-Furness, gun erecting shop, 15 in gun for the battleship HMS *Revenge*. (VSEL)

Vickers, Barrow-in-Furness, gun mounting department. (PCL)

5211. 19·Nov·'15
BAY N°6.

Vickers, Barrow-in-Furness, 19 November 1915, no. 6 bay in the shell shop. (VSEL)

# 6: COMMISSIONING, SEA AND GUNNERY TRIALS

No photographs have survived of the commissioning of the Dreadnoughts in the Royal Dockyards, but the John Brown photographic collection does record this with respect to HMS *Barham*, commissioned on 19 August 1915, and HMS *Repulse*, commissioned on 8 August 1916.

*'Admiralty Instructions for the Barham's Trials, issued on 30 July 1916, John Brown, Clydebank.*

Monday 9th August, 'X' and 'Y' turret crews to join ship.

Tuesday and Wednesday August 10th and 11th, Gunnery equipment trials and hydraulic tests for 'A', 'B', 'X' and 'Y' turrets.

Wednesday 18th August, 10.30 Captain Superintendent's inspection.

Thursday 19th August, All crew to join ship.

Tuesday 24th August, 6 inch ammunition, 40 rounds per gun, to be brought aboard; gunnery equipment and hydraulic tests for 'A' and 'B' turrets.

Wednesday 25th August, gunnery tests for 6 inch guns and further tests in 'A' and 'B' turrets.

Thursday 26th, noon, ship to proceed down river, past survey ship, preliminary trial, return to Tail Bank, then torpedo trials, ship to embark 1,000 tons of oil.

Friday August 27th, HMS *Barham* to steam at 4 hours full power for trials, to carry out 6 inch gun trials, to return to Greenock, to carry out steaming trials, proceed to instructed destination.'

The sea trials usually began with an assessment of the main and auxiliary machinery and the closed exhaust system. Tests were then made running the ship at full power for an hour. There were then analyses of fuel consumption and a 24 hour test, with 12 hours at half power and 12 hours at three-quarters power. A further 4 hour test was made with the ship running at full power. Observations and measurements were made of the ship's water consumption, water feeds and condensers. The bilge pumps were tested. Further engine trials included stopping, starting, reversing and deep load trials. The performance of the auxiliary machinery was carefully monitored. This involved pumping the engines with hydraulic steam and testing the electrical generators, the electrical compressors, the steering gear, the capstans, the refrigerating and ice-making machinery and the electrical generators. The emergency valves in the main steam-pipes were also rigorously tested, as were the feed pipes and the boiler feed valves. Compressed air tests were undertaken and the distilled water of the hydraulic system was examined. There were then further tests for anchorage, and turning trials were undertaken. Those of HMS *Agincourt* were carried out in the North Sea on 22 June 1914. There were full-power and lower-power circle tests. The ship advanced 642 yd while the tests were undertaken at a speed of 20.7 knots. The responsibility for taking the records during the trials lay with the fleet officers and their naval staff. Gangs of dockyard and shipyard workers remained onboard and assisted with the recording of temperatures, the tally of fuel consumption and the recording of water measurements. The Dreadnought was then put through its speed trials. HMS *Repulse*'s trials were carried out on 23 August 1916 using the measured mile on the island of Arran. Ten runs were made, commencing at 125 rpm for the inner shafts, and ending at 269 rpm outer port shaft, 271 rpm for the starboard outer shaft, 253 rpm for the inner port shaft and 281 rpm for the inner starboard shaft. The timed mile speed was recorded at 32.14 knots, which was delivered at 119,250 s.h.p.

The final Dreadnought trials were for the ship's armaments. HMS *Canada*'s were completed on 6 and 7 September 1915 for

'A' and 'B' turrets and 13 September for the 'X' and 'Y' turrets. The report began by stating that, although the guns and machinery were complete as regards loading arrangements, they were not complete in many important details. Schedules outlining in detail the necessary corrective work were handed over to the senior management of W.G. Armstrong and Whitworth Ltd. The gunnery trials for HMS *Queen Elizabeth* were carried out on the equipment on 20, 21, 22, 23, 25 and 29 September 1915. The final report from Capt. Fowler of the naval gunnery school, HMS *Excellent*, contained many critical qualifications.

'It is desired to point out that the tests of Gunnery Equipment of the ship have been seriously hampered by an apparent lack of appreciation of the necessity for the tests on the part of the turret machinery contractors. It was immediately evident in commencing the tests that the representatives of messrs W.G. Armstrong and Whitworth Limited were disposed to adopt the attitude that the preliminary hydraulic trials having already been carried out by Admiralty officers, the testing of equipment by HMS *Excellent* was of no importance. The attitudes reflected in the foremen in charge of the turrets, was the cause of frequent delays, such as pressure not being on the different machines, the ammunition cages not being in adjustment etc., which could have been avoided had a better organization existed for dealing with the defects and necessary adjustments made from the day to day programme of the trials. The result of this lack of organization on the part of the representatives of the hydraulic machinery contractor has been very protracted trials.'

The subsequent report was fifty-five pages in length – the longest of Dreadnought gunnery reports. Its contents were as follows:

I. General remarks on gun trials
II. Programme of firing and remarks
III. Blast
IV. a. General remarks on gunnery equipment
b. Remote and special fittings under trial
c. Criticism of the 15 inch Mark I mounting
V. Its effect for other ships

In the gun houses of 'A' and 'B' turrets the voice pipes were found to be incomplete and there was no branch for transfers to the director and trainer. The voice pipe from the cabinet to the working chamber was incomplete and there should have been a further branch to the officer of quarters. The front guard for the gun layer was found not to be in place, while the front breech lever fouled the floor plates at elevation. The breech cut-off gear required adjustment and the blast excluders were not properly fitted. In the working chamber the interlocking gear between the main hoist and the shell and cordite doors required adjusting. In the shell rooms and magazines the spring on the stop lever was useless as it was fitted too close to the

fulcrum, and the stop on the after ends of the rails for the outer and centre runners was badly fitted for preventing the projectiles from running into the bulkhead. Twenty-three faults were itemized for the shell rooms and magazines, and a further nineteen items were outlined for the working chamber. When 'Y' turret was tested it was found that the left cage was adjusted slightly too low, which made it very difficult to load heavy shells into the cage. The automatic teller did not work and it was hard to assess if the tail did not acknowledge that it was 'not ready' when the top of the hoist was reached. The auxiliary cordite cage right door was bent, which meant that the door did not close, the locking gear at the top of the doors was found to be very difficult to work, while the safety lever when the cage was closed did not prevent the cage from being raised. In 'X' turret the engine ran more smoothly to the right than to the left. The left engine became very hot on the rear end bearing and stopped. In general, erection was not good, with regard to both lubrication and bearing. With regard to the criticism of the 15 inch Mark I gun, the report noted that there was a lack of opportunity for continuous loading. The greatest number of rounds loaded was merely seven wooden projectiles and drill cartridges; none of the remaining heavy guns did more than four consecutive loads. A figure of seventy consecutive loads was recommended for an effective assessment. The Gunnery Captain concluded that it was difficult to form any estimate of the effectiveness of the equipment in these conditions.

However, the report's final observation was that many of the difficulties could be remedied easily for future ships because the faults did not result from faulty design. For example, in the gun house the stiffness of the levers on the gun cages was caused by the presence of dirt and the absence of effective lubrication. Most of the faults related to incorrect fitting and adjustment. Some flaws did remain, as with the steps on the back of the gun loading cage, which received heavy blows every time a projectile was rammed into the gun-loading cage in the working chamber, despite the buffer. These gunnery reports varied from ship to ship for, while the HMS *Queen Elizabeth* report amounted to fifty-five pages, the report for the sister ship HMS *Warspite*, whose gunnery trials were completed on 12, 13 and 15 August 1915, was only twenty-two pages. The reason for this was that HMS *Queen Elizabeth*, as a prototype, had the first 15 inch guns, which obviously had to be thoroughly tested.

John Brown, Clydebank, HMS *Barham*, 25 August 1915, one of the Queen
Elizabeth class battleships. These were the first 15 inch gun battleships, the

first oil-fired battleships and the first to steam over 24 knots. They are considered to be the finest product of the Dreadnought period. (BRCUG)

John Brown, Clydebank, HMS *Barham*, 25 August 1915, ship's commissioning. The 6 inch casemates under 'Y' turret were never fitted. Only the *Queen Elizabeth* was completed with the after 6 inch guns, which were removed later. To compensate, a singular 6 inch gun in an open gun-house was mounted each side amidships in all of the class.

John Brown, Clydebank, HMS *Repulse*, 12 August 1916, ship's commissioning. (BRCUG)

*Overleaf: top:* Profile of HMS *Hood* at speed, undated. Torpedo trials were carried out on 23 February and 3 March 1920. Steam and gunnery trials occurred throughout March. With a displacement of 42,200 tons with 1,200 tons of oil on board, HMS *Hood* recorded 151,280 s.h.p. and achieved 32.07 knots at 207 rpm. With a displacement of 44,600 tons, 150,220 s.h.p. was recorded for a mean speed of 31.9 knots at 204 rpm. On completion of the trials, careful examinations of the hull were carried out in Rosyth Dockyard. (BRCUG). *Bottom:* HMS *Repulse*, 23 August 1916, measured mile trial. The *Admiralty Steam Manual* of 1910 listed the following trials: Preliminary Trial, Contractors' Trials, Commissioning Trial, Turning Trials, Special Measured Mile Trial. The ship left Clydebank and arrived at the Tail of the Bank, Firth of Clyde, at 3.00 p.m. (BRCUG)

Arran Course Trials:

Displacement: 28,202 tons
Draught: 26 ft 2 inch forward, 27 ft 7 inch aft
Diameter of propellers: 13 ft 6 inch

Mean rpm: 273.5
Mean s.h.p.: 116,992
Speed: 31.31 knots

HMS *Hood* leaving Clydebank, 9 July 1920. John Brown had received permission from the Admiralty to let the almost complete battle-cruiser leave the fitting-out basin to allow the firm to complete various merchant vessels. Some preliminary trials occurred in the Firth of Clyde while the ship was en route for Rosyth Dockyard. On this trip the

ship encountered a force 8 wind from the west, which soon showed that HMS *Hood* was a wet ship. This was partly caused by the additional armour added to the ship during the course of its construction. It was estimated that deep load for HMS *Hood* was 46,680 tons, some 2.7 per cent heavier than the original selected design. (BRCUG)

Fitting-out basin, Vickers, Barrow-in-Furness, HMS *Princess Royal* and the Japanese battle-cruiser *Kongo*. (VSEL)

Portsmouth Dockyard, HMS *Dreadnought* entering 15 dock; HMS *Bellerophon* can be seen fitting-out on

the left of the picture. (PCL)

# 7: EPILOGUE

*To imagine a battle between two great modern iron-clad ships, you must not think of . . . two men in armour striking at each other with heavy swords. It is more like a battle between two egg shells striking each other with hammers.*

Winston Churchill, First Lord of the Admiralty, House of Commons, 1912

The complex issues of naval policy and doctrine associated with the Dreadnought programme and its strategic assumptions have occupied naval historians and students of policy to a remarkable extent, and their deliberations have yielded a formidable historiography, which is still unfolding.

Always controversial, the debate got into its stride in the modern period with the work of Arthur Marder, whose magisterial writing on the subject is contained in the volumes entitled *From the Dreadnought to Scapa Flow: the Royal Navy in the Fisher Era* (London, Oxford Unversity Press, 1961–1970, vol. 1) and *The Road to War, 1904–1915*. The latter is particularly relevant to the above discussion. More recently, Jon Sumida, in his *Defence of Naval Supremacy: Finance, Technology and British Naval Policy, 1889–1913* (London, Unwin Hyman, 1989), has drawn attention to the problems of fire control in the Dreadnoughts, which did not adopt the superior Pollen system until after the Battle of Jutland. Sumida has also set out the case for reassessing several of Marder's assumptions concerning Fisher's services as First Sea Lord, in particular his attitude towards ship design and naval strategy. The extent to which naval affairs impinged on British politics and their part in the events that led to the First World War has been admirably covered by Paul Kennedy in *The Rise of Anglo-German Antagonism, 1860–1914* (London, Allen and Unwin, 1980) and R.J. Morris *The Scaremongers: the Advocacy of War and Re-armament* (London, Routledge, Kegan and Paul, 1984). With regard to Dreadnought design and technical specifications, R.A. Burt, John Roberts and Ross Watton have undertaken thorough appraisals of the technological and operational histories of the early Dreadnoughts and later Super-Dreadnoughts. Their books, listed below, also contain selections of photographs of completed Dreadnoughts, both battleships and battle-cruisers, and Roberts' books contain outstanding sectional ship drawings.

While Hugh Lyon, in his paper on 'The Admiralty and private industry' (in *Technical Change and British Naval Policy*, ed. Brian Ranft, London), looks at the often fraught relationship between the Admiralty and private industry, including the shipbuilders and the armament manufacturers, Hugh B. Peebles, in the early chapters of his *Warshipbuilding on the Clyde: Naval Orders and the Prosperity of the Clyde Shipbuilding Industry, 1889–1939* (Edinburgh, John Donald, 1989), shows the significant part played by the Scottish shipbuilders in the Dreadnought years and looks at the impact on the industry of fluctuating demand for warships. Finally, in a new challenging work by Andrew Gordon, *The Rules of the Game: Jutland and British Naval Command* (London, John Murray, 1996), the encounter between Jellicoe's Grand Fleet and the German High Seas Fleet of Admiral Scheer is put under a particularly sharp and searching scrutiny.

Who won and lost the action remained for a long time in dispute. Admiral Scheer, relieved to have got away with the loss of one Dreadnought and the sacrifice of some 2,500 men, claimed a victory, at least in numerical terms, over the Grand Fleet, which lost three Dreadnoughts and some 6,000 men. In material terms, Scheer sunk 115,000 tons against the loss of some 60,000 tons, yet scholarship inclines to the view that Jellicoe's actions won the day for Britain, in effect successfully deterring the Germans from making any further, large fleet sorties and securing the position of the Royal Navy in the North Sea as the dominant sea power. The extraordinarily complicated progress of the battle, as Andrew Gordon demonstrated, conceals a more interesting subplot, embracing strategic confusion, tactical errors and operational misjudgements that, added to muddled objectives and clashes of personality, have helped to keep the Jutland controversy bubbling away.

This book has sought to demonstrate, chiefly by visual means, something of the scale of the effort that went into constructing the British Dreadnought battlefleet. The financial expenditure, the hard work and long hours of overtime, by a highly skilled and determined shipbuilding labour force in both the Royal Dockyards and in the commercial shipyards, and the huge quantities of materials consumed have all been touched on, although we have not examined the, at times frenzied, political debate that characterized the period and the sacrifice of other political aims – in the fields of education, social warfare, housing reform – to the Naval vote. The Dreadnought programme had worked up the expectations of the public to an almost impossible degree, and it is fairly clear that the British embarked on the Naval war in 1914 expecting to win it simply by fighting another Trafalgar. Hence the sense of disappointment that swept the country in the aftermath of Jutland: so much had been promised; so little, it seemed, had been delivered. Of course, the Royal Navy did indeed help to win the war, but it was by the unseen, and to some extent unsung, blockade of Germany, and by the defeat of the U-boat in the North Atlantic, that victory was in due time to be achieved. For after Jutland the Germans turned to the submarine in their quest for maritime superiority.

Thus, while the nation's pride, the mighty Grand Fleet, lay fretting at anchor in Scapa Flow, seething with disappointment at its failure to achieve a decisive result in the sole encounter with the High Seas Fleet, it was the relatively enfeebled portion of the Royal Navy dedicated to anti-submarine warfare, neglected in the push for Dreadnought supremacy, that had to carry the fight to the enemy. Battleships, battle-cruisers and the large armoured cruisers on which naval construction had concentrated, were ineffective against the new enemy. The rules of the game had changed and things would never be quite the same again.

# ALPHABETICAL LIST OF DREADNOUGHTS

Agincourt
Ajax
Audacious
Australia

Barham
Bellerophon
Benbow

Canada
Centurion
Colossus
Collingwood
Conqueror
Courageous

Dreadnought

Emperor of India
Erin

Furious

Glorious

Hercules
Hood

Iron Duke
Indefatigable
Indomitable
Inflexible
Invincible

King George V

Lion

Malaya
Marlborough
Monarch

Neptune
New Zealand

Orion

Princess Royal

Queen Elizabeth
Queen Mary

Ramillies
Renown
Repulse
Resolution
Revenge
Royal Oak
Royal Sovereign

St Vincent
Superb

Temeraire
Thunderer
Tiger

Valiant
Vanguard

Warspite

# APPENDIX

[All details of ships are as on completion from the builders.]

## BRITISH BATTLESHIPS

### DREADNOUGHT (Battleship, 1905 Programme)

| Ship | Built at | Laid down | Launched | Completed |
|---|---|---|---|---|
| *Dreadnought* | Portsmouth | 02/10/05 | 10/02/06 | Dec. 1906 |
| **Dimensions** | 527'×82'×26.5' | | | |
| **Displacement** | 17,900 tons | 21,845 tons deep load | | |
| **Armament** | 10×12" 27×12 pdr | 18" torpedo tubes | | |
| **Protection** | Belt 11"–8"–6"–4" Bulkheads 8" Barbettes 11"–4" Turrets 11" Control Tower 11" | | | |
| **Machinery** | Parsons turbines 23,000 hp 21 knots 4 screws 18 Babcock & Wilcox boilers | | | |
| **Fuel** | 2,900 tons coal 1,120 tons oil | | | |
| **Radius** | 6,620 at 10 knots 4,910 at 18 knots | | | |
| **Complement** | 773 | | | |
| **Fate** | Sold March 1921, broken up at Inverkeithing 1923. | | | |

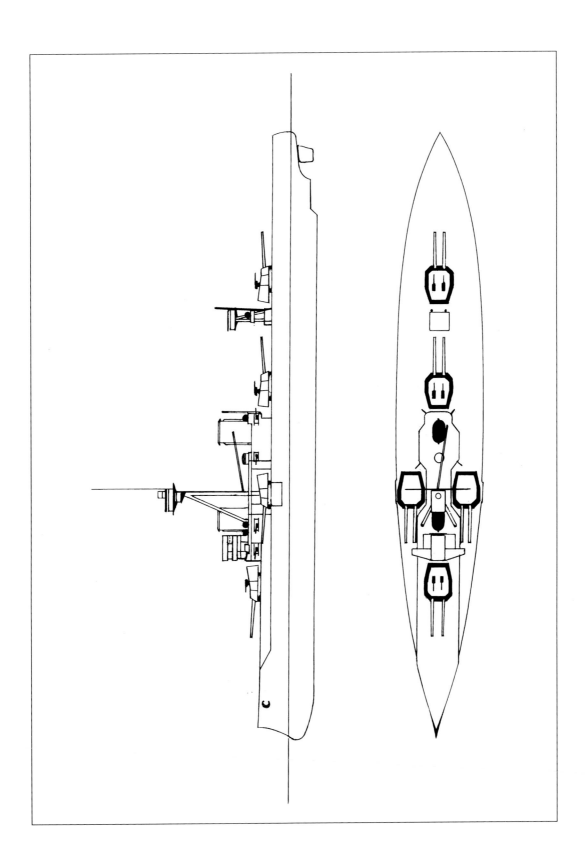

**INVINCIBLE Class (Battlecruiser, 1905 Programme)**

| Ship | Built at | Laid down | Launched | Completed |
|------|----------|-----------|----------|-----------|
| *Invincible* | Elswick | 02/04/06 | 13/04/07 | 20/03/08 |
| *Inflexible* | John Brown & Co. | 05/02/06 | 26/06/07 | 20/10/08 |
| *Indomitable* | Fairfield | 01/03/06 | 16/03/07 | 25/06/08 |

| | |
|---|---|
| **Dimensions** | 567'×78.5'×25.5' |
| **Displacement** | 17,400 tons    20,130 tons deep load |
| **Armament** | 8×12"    16×4"    5×18" torpedo tubes submerged |
| **Protection** | Belt 6"–4"   Bulkheads 7"–6"   Barbettes 7"–2"   Turrets 7"   Conning Tower 10"–6" |
| **Machinery** | Parsons turbines 41,000 hp   25 knots   4 screws   31 Babcock or Yarrow boilers |
| **Fuel** | 3,084 tons coal    725 tons oil |
| **Radius** | 3,000 at 25 knots |
| **Complement** | 784 |
| **Fate** | *Invincible*   Suffered a magazine explosion after being hit on 'Q' turret at the Battle of Jutland, broke in two halves and sank with the loss of 1,026 men, 31 May 1916. |
| | *Inflexible*   Sold 1922 and broken up in Germany. |
| | *Indomitable*   Sold December 1922 and broken up at Dover. |

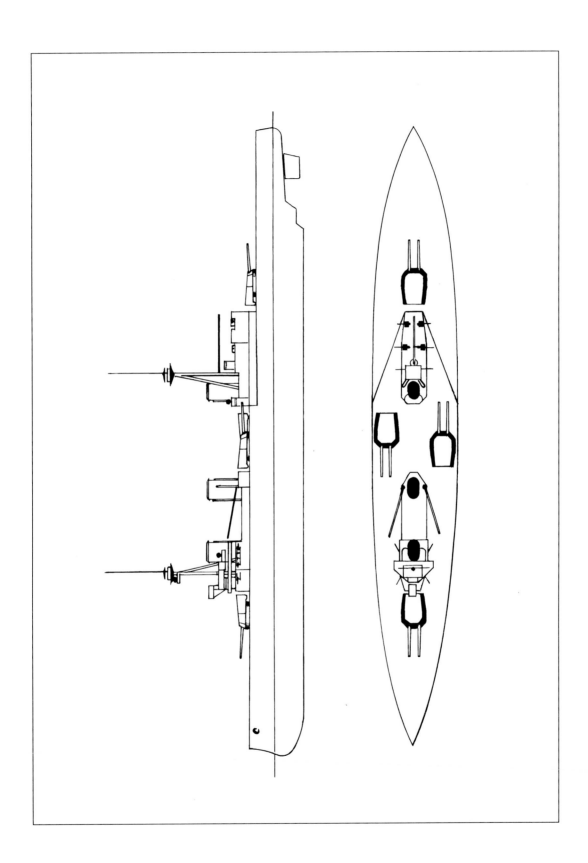

**BELLEROPHON Class (Battleship, 1906 Programme)**

| Ship | Built at | Laid down | Launched | Completed |
|---|---|---|---|---|
| *Bellerophon* | Portsmouth | 03/12/06 | 27/07/07 | Feb. 1909 |
| *Superb* | Elswick | 06/02/07 | 07/11/07 | May 1909 |
| *Temeraire* | Devonport | 01/01/07 | 24/08/07 | May 1909 |

**Dimensions** 526'×82.5'×27.2'

**Displacement** 18,600    22,100 deep load

**Armament** 10×12"    16×4"    4×3 pdr    5×18" torpedo tubes

**Protection** Belt 10"–5"    Bulkheads 8"    Barbettes 9"–5"    Turrets 11"    Conning Tower 11"

**Machinery** Parsons turbines 23,000 hp    20.75 knots    18 boilers    4 screws

**Fuel** 2,648 tons coal    842 tons oil

**Radius** 5,720 at 10 knots    4,250 at 18.3 knots

**Complement** 733

**Fate**
*Bellerophon*    Sold 8 November 1921 and broken up in Germany.
*Superb*    Sold 12 December 1922 and broken up at Dover.
*Temeraire*    Sold 7 December 1921 and broken up at Dover.

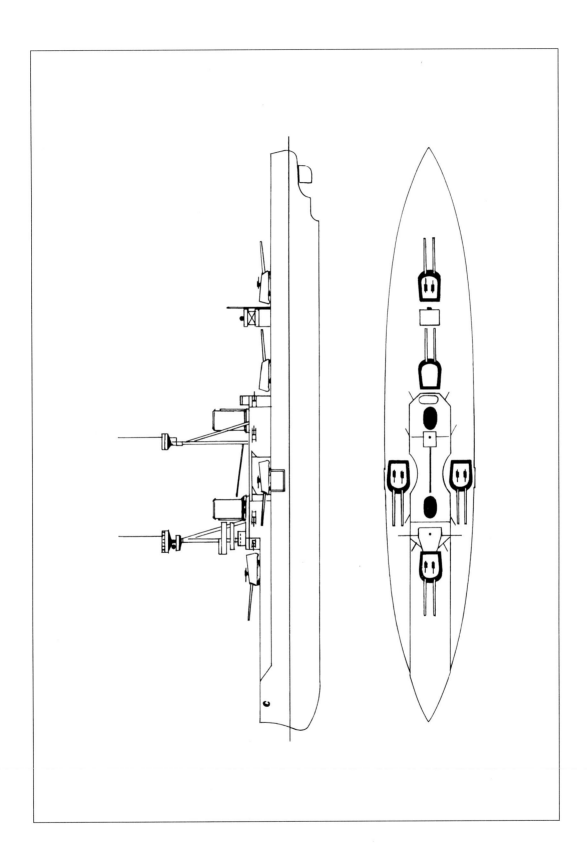

**ST VINCENT Class (Battleship, 1907 Programme)**

| Ship | Built at | Laid down | launched | Completed |
|---|---|---|---|---|
| *St Vincent* | Portsmouth | 30/12/07 | 10/09/08 | May 1909 |
| *Collingwood* | Devonport | 03/02/08 | 07/11/08 | Apr. 1910 |
| *Vanguard* | Vickers | 02/04/08 | 22/02/09 | Feb. 1910 |

**Dimensions**  536'×84'×25.25'

**Displacement**  19,250 tons  23,030 deep load

**Armament**  10×12"  20×4"  4×3 pdr  5×18" torpedo tubes

**Protection**  Belt 10"–7"  Bulkheads 8"–4"  Barbettes 9"–5"  Turrets 11"  Conning Tower 11"–8"

**Machinery**  Parsons turbines 24,500 hp  21 knots  4 screws

**Fuel**  2,800 tons coal  940 tons oil

**Radius**  6,900 at 10 knots  4,250 at 18.7 knots

**Complement**  758

**Fate**
*St Vincent*  Discarded under the Washington Treaty 1 December 1921 and broken up at Dover.
*Collingwood*  Discarded under the Washington Treaty 12 December 1922 and broken up at Newport.
*Vanguard*  Destroyed by internal explosion at Scapa Flow 9 July 1917, 804 men perished.

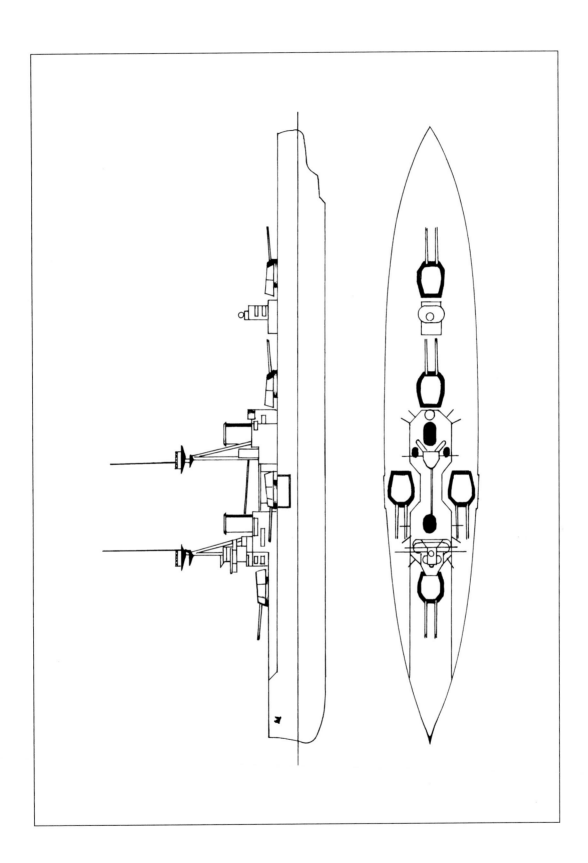

## NEPTUNE (Battleship, 1908 Programme)

| Ship | Built at | Laid down | Launched | Completed |
|---|---|---|---|---|
| *Neptune* | Portsmouth | 19/01/09 | 30/09/09 | Jan. 11 |
| **Dimensions** | 546'×85'×24' | | | |
| **Displacement** | 19,680 tons | 22,720 deep load | | |
| **Armament** | 10×12"    16×4" | 4×3 pdr | 2×18" beam & 1×18" stern torpedo tubes | |
| **Protection** | Belt 10"–7"   Bulkheads 8"–4" | Barbettes 9"–5"   Turrets 11" | Conning Tower 11" | |
| **Machinery** | Parsons turbines 25,000 hp | 21 knots   4 screws | Yarrow boilers | |
| **Fuel** | 2,710 tons coal | 790 tons oil | | |
| **Radius** | 6,330 at 10 knots | 3,820 at 18.5 knots | | |
| **Complement** | 759 | | | |
| **Fate** | Discarded under the Washington Treaty 1 September 1922 and broken up at Blyth. | | | |

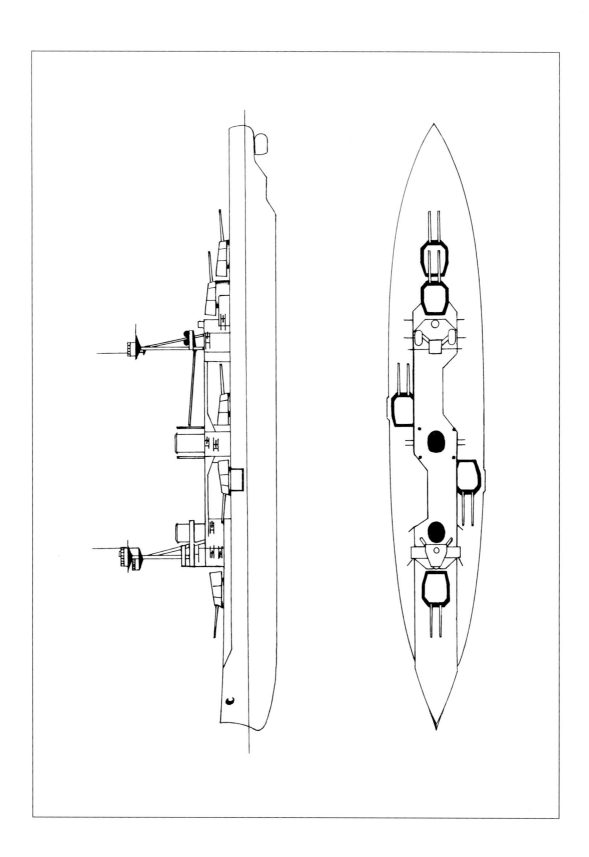

## INDEFATIGABLE Class (Battlecruiser, 1908 Programme)

| Ship | Built at | Laid down | Launched | Completed |
|---|---|---|---|---|
| *Indefatigable* | Devonport | 25/02/09 | 28/10/09 | Feb. 1911 |
| *Australia* | John Brown & Co | 23/06/10 | 25/10/11 | Jun. 1913 |
| *New Zealand* | Fairfield | 20/06/10 | 01/07/11 | Nov. 1912 |

**Dimensions** 590'×80'×24.75'

**Displacement** 18,800 tons 22,080 deep load

**Armament** 8×12" 16×4" 4×3 pdr 2×18" torpedo tubes

**Protection** Belt 6"—5" Bulkheads 4" Barbettes 7"—4" Turrets 7" Conning Tower 10"

**Machinery** 44,000 hp 25 knots 4 screws 31 Babcock & Wilcox boilers

**Fuel** 3,170 tons coal 840 tons oil

**Radius** 6,330 at 10 knots 2,290 at 23.5 knots

**Complement** 800

**Fate**

*Indefatigable* Destroyed by magazine explosion during gun duel with *Von der Tann*, Jutland, 31 May 1915, 1605 hrs, 1,017 men lost.

*Australia* Discarded under the Washington Treaty and sunk off Sydney harbour, 1924.

*New Zealand* Discarded under the Washington Treaty and broken up in Germany, 1922.

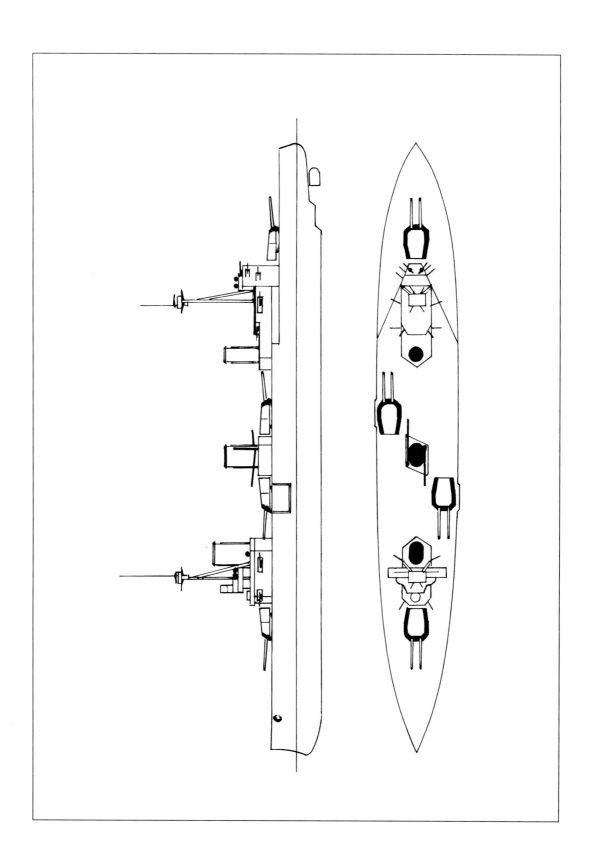

# COLOSSUS Class (Battleship, 1909 Programme)

| Ship | Built at | Laid down | Launched | Completed |
|---|---|---|---|---|
| *Colossus* | Scotts | 08/07/09 | 09/04/10 | Jul. 1911 |
| *Hercules* | Palmers | 30/07/09 | 10/05/10 | Aug. 1911 |

| | |
|---|---|
| **Dimensions** | 546'×85'×25.25' |
| **Displacement** | 20,000 tons | 23,050 tons deep load |
| **Armament** | 10×12" | 16×4" | 4×3 pdr | 2×21" beam & 1×18" stern torpedo tubes |
| **Protection** | Belt 11"–8"–7" | Bulkheads 10"–8"–5"–4" | Barbettes 11" down to 4" | Turrets 11" | Conning Tower 11" |
| **Machinery** | Parsons turbines 25,000 hp | 21 knots | 4 screws | 18 Yarrow or Babcock boilers |
| **Fuel** | 2,900 tons coal | 800 tons oil |
| **Radius** | 6,680 at 10 knots | 4,050 at 18.5 knots |
| **Complement** | 755 |
| **Fate** | *Colossus* | Discarded under the Washington Treaty and broken up at Alloa, 1922. |
| | *Hercules* | Discarded under the Washington Treaty 8 November 1921 and broken up at Kiel. |

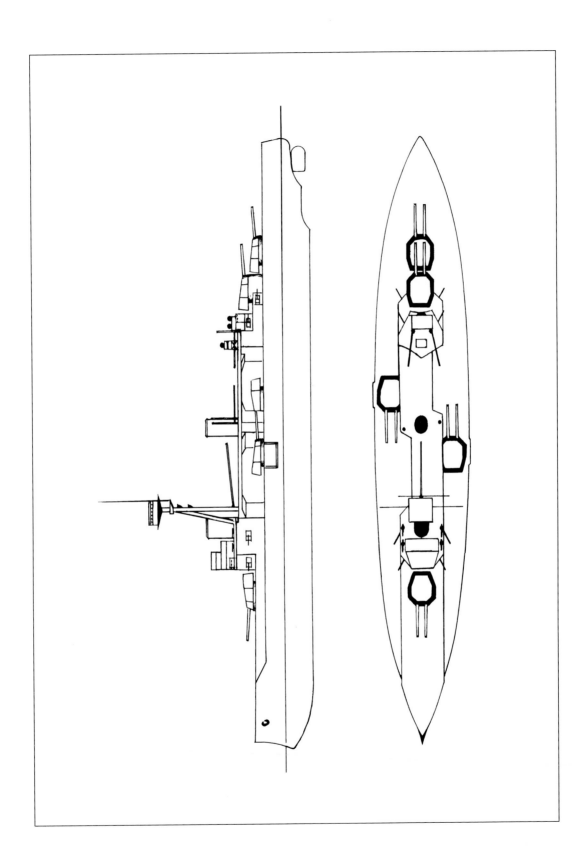

**ORION Class (Battleship, 1909 Programme)**

| Ship | Built at | Laid down | Launched | Completed |
|---|---|---|---|---|
| *Orion* | Portsmouth | 29/11/09 | 20/08/10 | Jan. 1912 |
| *Monarch* | Armstrong | 01/04/10 | 30/03/11 | Mar. 1912 |
| *Conqueror* | Beardsmore | 05/04/10 | 01/05/11 | Nov. 1912 |
| *Thunderer* | Thames Iron Works | 13/04/10 | 01/02/11 | June 1912 |

**Dimensions** 581'×88.5'×24.9'

**Displacement** 22,500 tons   25,870 tons deep load

**Armament** 10×13.5"   16×4"   4×3 pdr   2×21" beam & 1×18" stern torpedo tubes

**Protection** Belt 12"–9"–8"   Bulkheads 10"–8"–3"   Barbettes 10"–7"–6"   Turrets 11"   Conning Tower 11"

**Machinery** Turbines 27,000 hp   21 knots   4 screws   18 Babcock & Yarrow boilers

**Fuel** 3,300 tons coal   800 tons oil

**Radius** 6,730 at 10 knots   4,110 at 19 knots

**Complement** 752

**Fate**

*Orion* — Discarded under the Washington Treaty 19 December 1922 and broken up at Upnor.

*Monarch* — Sunk as fleet target by *Revenge* off Scilly Islands, 20 January 1925.

*Conqueror* — Discarded under the Washington Treaty 19 December 1922 and broken up at Upnor.

*Thunderer* — Sold 10 December 1926, ran aground en route to Blyth for breaking up, 1927.

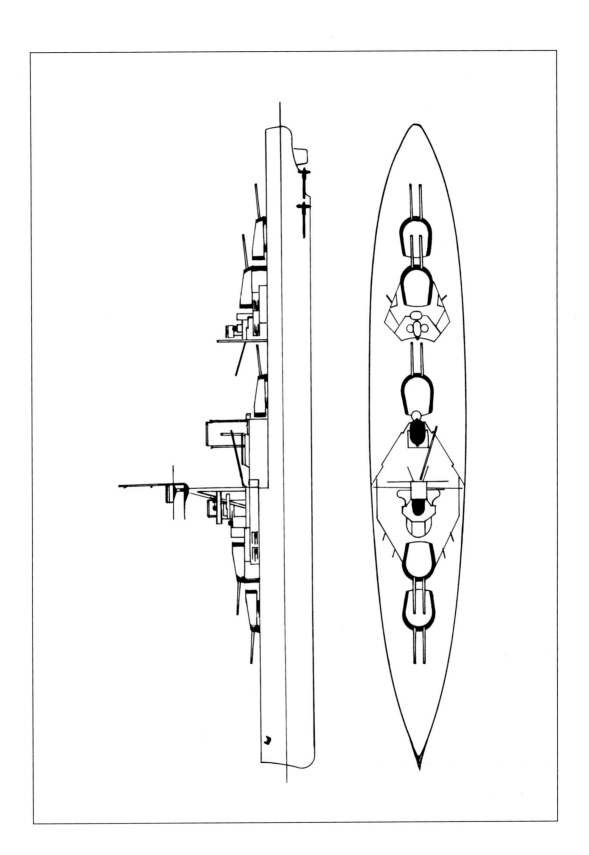

**LION Class (Battlecruiser, 1909–10 Programme)**

| Ship | Built at | Laid down | Launched | Completed |
|---|---|---|---|---|
| *Lion* | Devonport | 29/11/09 | 06/08/10 | May 1912 |
| *Princess Royal* | Vickers | 02/05/10 | 29/04/11 | Nov. 1912 |
| *Queen Mary* | Palmers | 06/03/11 | 20/03/12 | Sep. 1912 |

**Dimensions** 700'×88.5'×26.4'

**Displacement** 26,270 tons    29,680 tons deep load

**Armament** 8×13.5"   16×4"   4×3 pdr   2×21" torpedo tubes

**Protection** Belt 9"–6"–4"   Bulkheads 4"   Barbettes 9"–6"–4"–3"   Turrets 9"   Conning Tower 10"

**Machinery** Parsons s.h.p. 70,000   27 knots   4 screws   42 Yarrow boilers

**Fuel** 3,500 tons coal   1,135 tons oil

**Radius** 5,610 at 10 knots   2,420 at 23.9 knots

**Complement** 997

**Fate**
*Lion*   Discarded under the Washington Treaty; sold January 1924 and broken up at Jarrow.
*Princess Royal*   Discarded under the Washington Treaty 1922, sold and broken up at Rosyth 1926.
*Queen Mary*   Destroyed by magazine explosion after direct hits from German battlecruisers, 31 May 1916, 1626 hrs, 1,266 men perished.

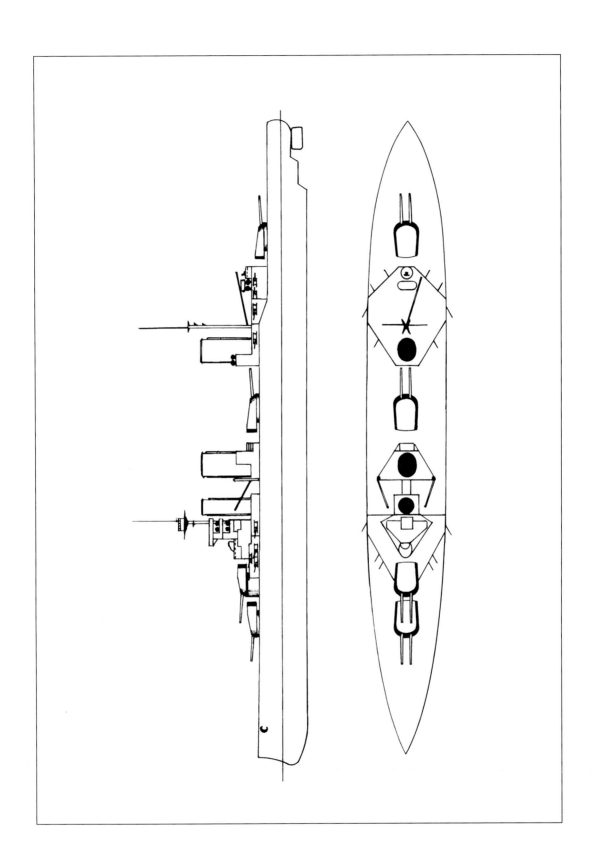

**KING GEORGE V Class (Battleship, 1910 Programme)**

| Ship | Built at | Laid down | Launched | Completed |
|------|----------|-----------|----------|-----------|
| *King George V* | Portsmouth | 16/01/11 | 09/10/11 | Nov. 1912 |
| *Ajax* | Scotts | 27/02/11 | 21/03/12 | Mar. 1912 |
| *Audacious* | Lairds | 23/03/11 | 14/09/12 | Oct. 1912 |
| *Centurion* | Devonport | 16/01/11 | 18/11/11 | May 1913 |

**Dimensions** 597.5'×89'×26.6'

**Displacement** 23,000 tons 25,700 deep load

**Armament** 10×13.5" 16×4" 4×3 pdr 3×21" torpedo tubes

**Protection** Belt 12"–9"–8" Bulkheads 10"–6"–4" Barbettes 10" Turrets 11" Conning Tower 11"

**Machinery** Parsons turbines 31,000 hp 21.7 knots 4 screws

**Fuel** 3,150 tons coal 800 tons oil

**Radius** 4,060 at 18.15 knots

**Complement** 782

**Fate**
*King George V* Sold December 1926 and broken up at Rosyth.
*Ajax* Sold November 1926 and broken up at Rosyth.
*Audacious* Sunk by mine near Lough Swilly, 27 October 1914.
*Centurion* Sunk as block ship after Normandy landing, 9 June 1944.

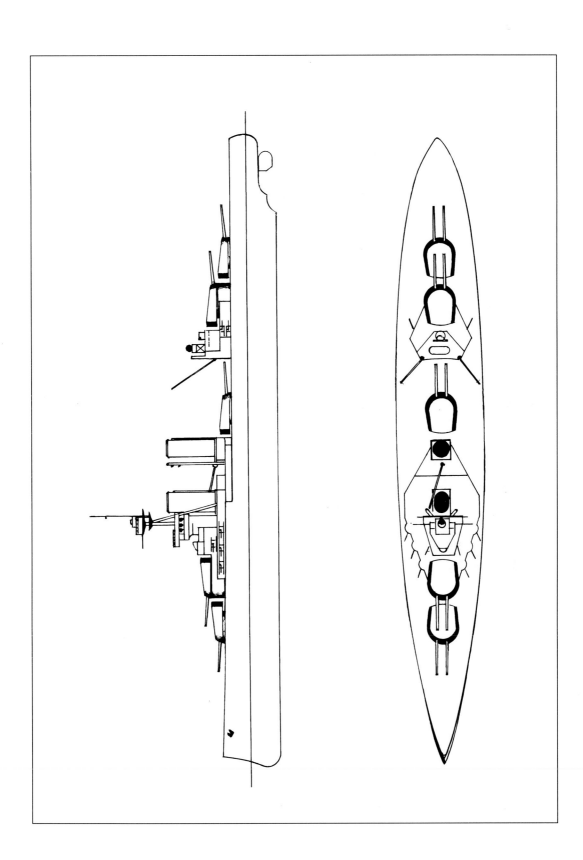

**IRON DUKE Class (Battleship, 1911 Programme)**

| Ship | Built at | Laid down | Launched | Completed |
|---|---|---|---|---|
| *Iron Duke* | Portsmouth | 12/01/12 | 12/10/12 | Mar. 1914 |
| *Marlborough* | Devonport | 25/01/12 | 24/10/12 | June 1914 |
| *Benbow* | Beardmore | 30/05/12 | 12/11/13 | Oct. 1914 |
| *Emperor of India* | Vickers | 31/05/12 | 27/11/13 | Nov. 1914 |

**Dimensions** 622.75'×90'×27.4'

**Displacement** 25,000 tons    30,380 tons deep load

**Armament** 10×13.5"    12×6"    2×3"    4×3 pdr    4 × 21" torpedo tubes

**Protection** Belt 12"–9"–8"–6"–4"    Bulkheads 8"–6"–4"    Barbettes 10"–3"    Turrets 11"    Conning Tower 11"

**Machinery** Parsons turbines s.h.p. 29,000    21.25 knots    4 screws    18 boilers

**Fuel** 3,250 tons coal    1,600 tons oil

**Radius** 4,840 at 19 knots    7,780 at 20.4 knots

**Complement** 995

**Fate**

*Iron Duke* Reduced under the terms of the Washington Treaty. Sold for breaking up at Faslane 2 March 1946.

*Marlborough* Reduced under the terms of the Washington Treaty. Sold for breaking up at Rosyth 27 June 1932.

*Benbow* Reduced under the terms of the Washington Treaty. Sold for breaking up at Rosyth, January 1931.

*Emperor of India* Reduced under the terms of the Washington Treaty. Sunk as target off Owers Bank, 1 July 1931, raised and broken up at Rosyth, December 1931.

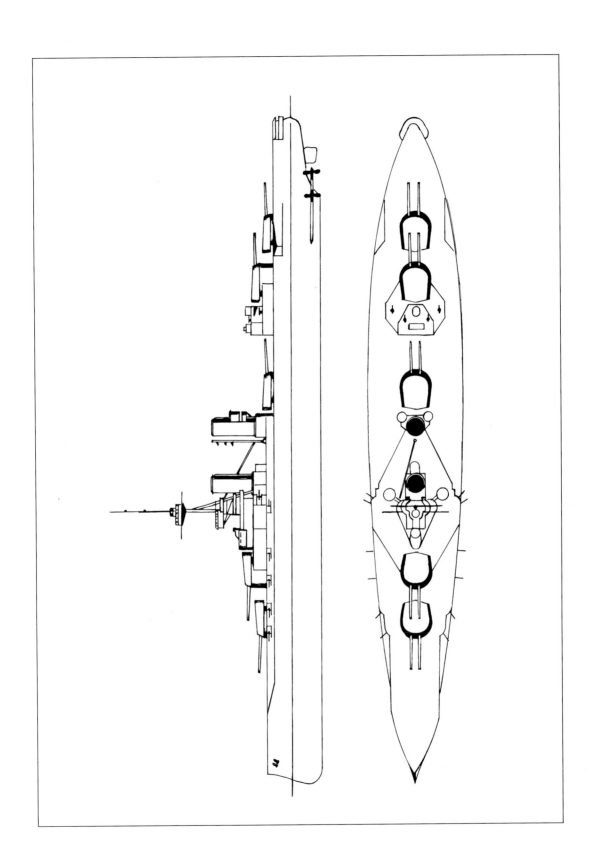

**TIGER (Battlecruiser, 1911 Programme)**

| Ship | Built at | Laid down | Launched | Completed |
|---|---|---|---|---|
| *Tiger* | Browns & Co | 20/06/12 | 15/12/13 | Oct. 1914 |

**Dimensions** 704'×90.5'×28.4'

**Displacement** 28,430 tons   35,160 tons deep load

**Armament** 8×13.5"   12×6"   4×3 pdr   4×21" torpedo tubes

**Protection** Belt 9"–6"–5"–4"–3"   Bulkheads 4"–2"   Barbettes 9"–8"–4"   Turrets 9"   Conning Tower 10"–3"

**Machinery** Brown-Curtis Turbines s.h.p. 108,000   29 knots   4 screws   39 Babcock & Wilcox boilers

**Fuel** 3,480 tons coal   450 tons oil

**Radius** 5,700 at 12 knots

**Complement** 1,121

**Fate** *Tiger* Sold February 1932 and broken up at Inverkeithing.

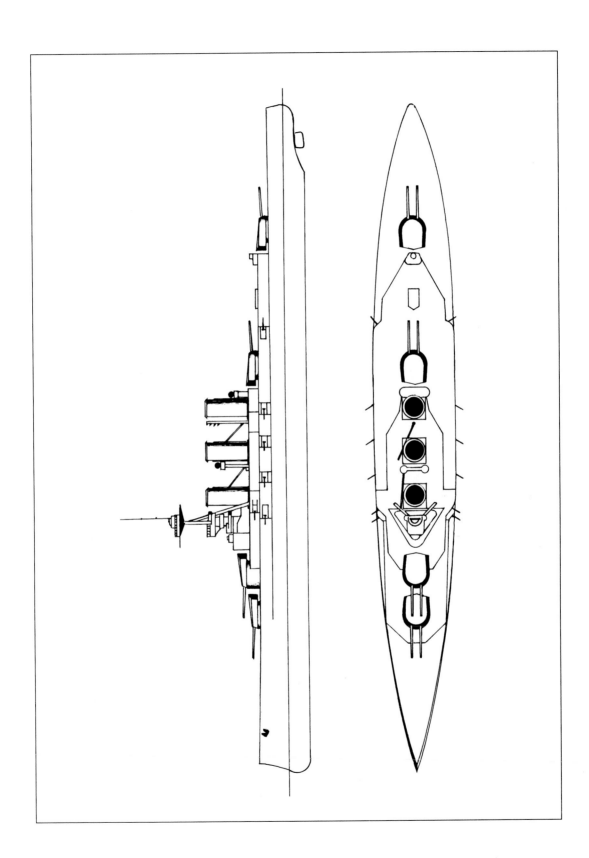

**QUEEN ELIZABETH Class (Battleship, 1912 Programme)**

| Ship | Built at | Laid down | Launched | Completed |
|---|---|---|---|---|
| *Queen Elizabeth* | Portsmouth | 21/10/12 | 16/10/13 | Jan. 1915 |
| *Barham* | John Brown & Co. | 24/02/13 | 31/10/14 | Oct. 1915 |
| *Malaya* | Armstrongs | 20/10/13 | 18/03/15 | Feb. 1916 |
| *Valiant* | Fairfield | 31/01/13 | 04/11/14 | Feb. 1916 |
| *Warspite* | Devonport | 31/10/12 | 26/11/13 | Mar. 1916 |

**Dimensions** 654.75'×90.5'×29.6'

**Displacement** 27,500 tons   33,000 tons deep load

**Armament** 8×15"   14×6"   2×3"   4×3 pdr   4×21" torpedo tubes

**Protection** Belt 13"–6"   Bulkheads 6"–4"   Barbettes 10"–4"   Turrets 13"   Conning Tower 11"

**Machinery** Turbines 75,000 hp   24 knots   4 screws   24 boilers

**Fuel** 100 tons coal   3,400 tons oil

**Radius** 6,540 at 10 knots

**Complement** 951

**Fate**

*Queen Elizabeth* Sold June 1948 and broken up at Dalmuir & Troon.

*Barham* 25 November 1941 when on patrol between Crete and Cyrenaica she was struck by three torpedoes from U-331, capsized and blew up with the loss of 862 men.

*Malaya* Sold April 1948 and broken up at Faslane.

*Valiant* Sold March 1948 and broken up at Cairnryan & Troon.

*Warspite* Ran aground at Prussia Cove, Cornwall, while under tow to the shipbreakers, 23 April 1947, broken on site.

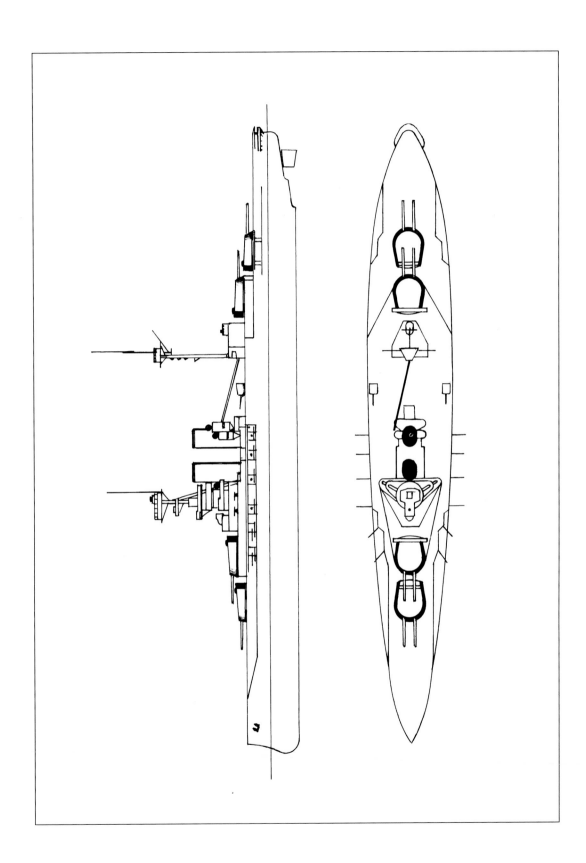

## ROYAL SOVEREIGN Class (Battleship, 1913 Programme)

| Ship | Built at | Laid Down | Launched | Completed |
|---|---|---|---|---|
| *Ramillies* | Beardmore | 12/11/13 | 12/09/16 | Sep. 1917 |
| *Resolution* | Palmers | 29/12/13 | 14/01/15 | Dec. 1916 |
| *Revenge* | Vickers | 22/12/13 | 29/05/15 | Mar. 1916 |
| *Royal Oak* | Devonport | 15/01/14 | 17/11/14 | May 1916 |
| *Royal Sovereign* | Portsmouth | 15/01/14 | 29/11/15 | May 1916 |

**Dimensions** 624.25'×88.5'×28.6'

**Displacement** 27,500 tons 31,200 tons deep load

**Armament** 8×15" 14×6" 2×3" 4×3 pdr 4×21" torpedo tubes

**Protection** Belt 13"–6"–4" Bulkheads 6"–4" Barbettes 10"–9"–7"–6"–4" Turrets 13" Conning Tower 11"

**Machinery** Parsons s.h.p. 40,000 23 knots 4 screws 18 Babcock & Wilcox or Yarrow boilers

**Fuel** 140 tons coal 3,400 tons oil

**Radius** 6,800 at 10 knots

**Complement** 997

**Fate**

*Ramillies* Sold April 1948 and broken up at Cairnryan.
*Resolution* Sold May 1948 and broken up at Faslane.
*Revenge* Sold March 1949 and broken up at Inverkeithing.
*Royal Oak* Struck by four torpedoes from U-47 in Scapa flow, capsized and sank within ten minutes with the loss of 833 men, 14 October 1939.
*Royal Sovereign* Sold April 1949 and broken up at Inverkeithing.

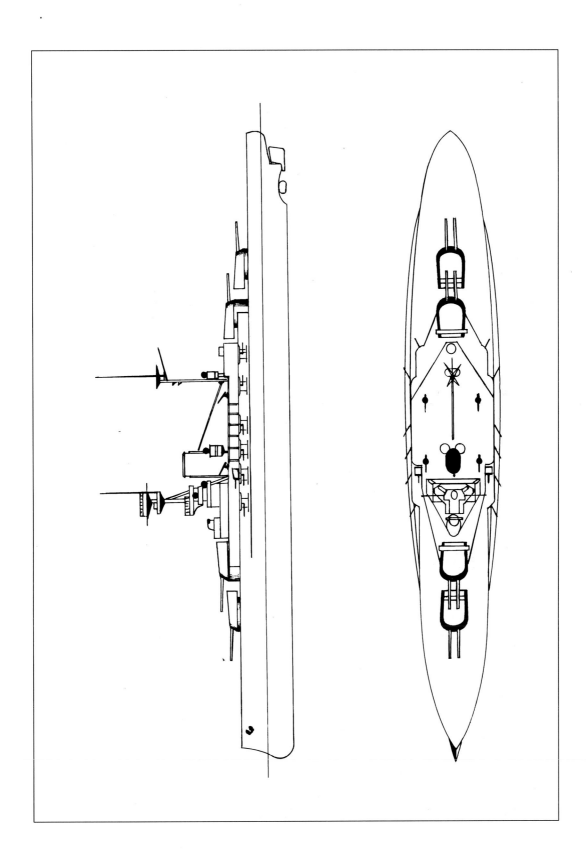

**ERIN (Battleship, War Purchase)**

| Ship | Built at | Laid down | Launched | Completed |
| --- | --- | --- | --- | --- |
| *Erin* | Vickers | 01/08/11 | 03/09/13 | Aug. 1914 |

**Dimensions** 559.5'×91.6'×28.8'

**Displacement** 23,000 tons    25,250 tons deep load

**Armament** 10×13.5"    16×6"    6×6 pdr    4×12" torpedo tubes

**Protection** Belt 12"–9"–8"–6"–4"    Bulkheads 8"–5"–4"    Barbettes 10"–9"–5"–3"    Turrets 11"    Conning Tower 12"–4"

**Machinery** Parsons made by Vickers s.h.p. 26,500    21 knots    4 screws    15 Babcock & Wilcox boilers

**Fuel** 2,120 tons coal    710 tons oil

**Radius** 5,300 at 10 knots

**Complement** 1.070

**Fate** *Erin*    Originally built for Turkey and launched as *Reshadieh*, seized by the British government August 1914 and re-named *Erin*. Discarded under the Washington Treaty 1921. Sold and broken up at Queenborough, December 1922.

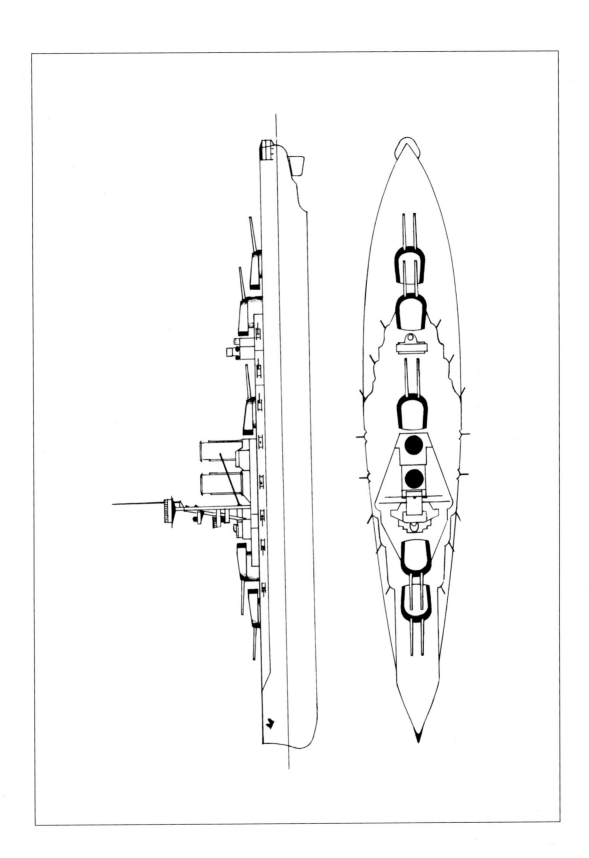

**AGINCOURT (Battleship, War Purchase)**

| Ship | Built at | Laid down | Launched | Completed |
|------|----------|-----------|----------|-----------|
| *Agincourt* | Elswick | 14/09/11 | 22/01/13 | Aug. 1914 |
| **Dimensions** | 671.5'×89'×27' | | | |
| **Displacement** | 27,500 tons | 30,250 tons deep load | | |
| **Armament** | 14×12"    20×6" | 10×3"    3×21" torpedo tubes | | |
| **Protection** | Belt 9"–6"–4"  Bulkheads 6"–3"  Barbettes 9"–3"  Turrets 12"  Conning Tower 12" | | | |
| **Machinery** | Parsons s.h.p. 34,000  22 knots  4 screws  22 Babcock & Wilcock boilers | | | |
| **Fuel** | 3,200 tons coal | 620 tons oil | | |
| **Radius** | 4,000 at 10 knots | | | |
| **Complement** | 1,115 | | | |
| **Fate** | *Agincourt* | Originally laid down as *Rio de Janeiro* for Brazil. Sold to Turkey 9 January 1914, re-named *Sultan Osman I*. Seized by British government 2 August 1914 and re-named *Agincourt*. Discarded under the terms of the Washington Treaty 1921 and broken up at Rosyth. | | |

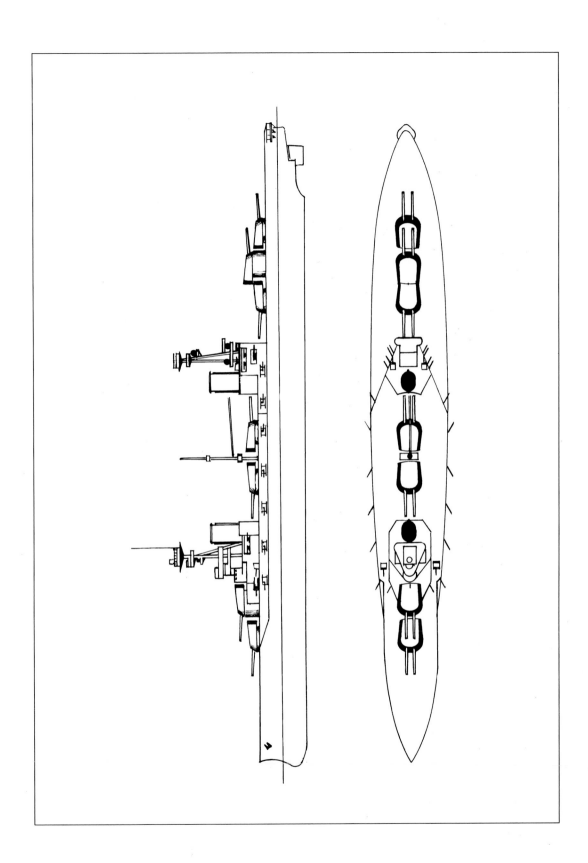

**CANADA (Battleship, War Purchase)**

| Ship | Built at | Laid down | Launched | Completed |
|---|---|---|---|---|
| *Canada* | Elswick | 27/11/11 | 27/11/13 | Sep. 1915 |
| **Dimensions** | 661'×92'×29' | | | |
| **Displacement** | 28,600 tons | 32,120 tons deep load | | |
| **Armament** | 10×14"  16×6"  2×3"  4×3 pdr  4×21" torpedo tubes | | | |
| **Protection** | Belt 9"–4"  Bulkheads 4.5"–3"  Barbettes 10"–4"  Turrets 10"  Conning Tower 11"–6" | | | |
| **Machinery** | Brown-Curtis (HP) and Parsons (LP) turbines s.h.p. 37,000  22.5 knots  4 screws  21 Yarrow boilers | | | |
| **Fuel** | 3,300 tons coal  520 tons oil | | | |
| **Radius** | 4,400 at 10 knots | | | |
| **Complement** | 1,167 | | | |
| **Fate** | *Canada* | One of two battleships built for Chile. Launched as *Almirante Latorre*. 9 September 1914 purchased by British government and re-named *Canada*. 1 August 1920 returned to Chile as *Almirante Latorre*. Discarded 1958 and broken up in Yokohama 1959. Sister ship *Almirante Cochrane* purchased by British government in 1917 for conversion to aircraft carrier and re-named *Eagle*. Torpedoed and sunk on Malta convoy ('Operation Pedestal'), 11 August 1942. | | |

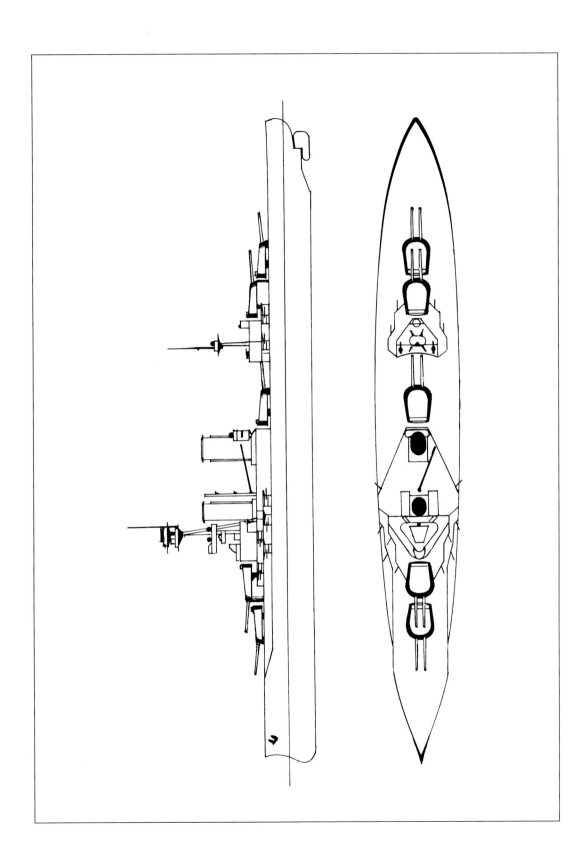

**RENOWN Class (Battlecruiser, Emergency War Programme)**

| Ship | Built at | Laid down | Launched | Completed |
|---|---|---|---|---|
| *Renown* | Fairfield & Co. | 25/01/15 | 04/03/16 | 20/09/16 |
| *Repulse* | John Brown & Co. | 25/01/15 | 08/01/16 | 18/08/16 |

| | |
|---|---|
| **Dimensions** | 794'×90'×25.7' |
| **Displacement** | 26,500 tons   32,727 tons deep load |
| **Armament** | 6×15"   17×4"   2×3"   4×3 pdr   2×21" torpedo tubes |
| **Protection** | Belt 6"–4"–3"–1.5"   Bulkheads 4"–3"   Barbettes 7"–5"–4"   Turrets 11"–7"   Conning Tower 10" |
| **Machinery** | Brown & Curtis turbines s.h.p. 112,000   32.6 knots   4 screws   42 Babcock & Wilcox boilers |
| **Fuel** | 4,243 tons oil |
| **Radius** | 4,200 at 10 knots |
| **Complement** | 967 |
| **Fate** | *Renown*   Sold and broken up at Faslane, 19 March 1948. |
| | *Repulse*   Bombed and torpedoed by Japanese aircraft off the east coast of Malaya, 10 December 1941; sank with the loss of 327 men. |

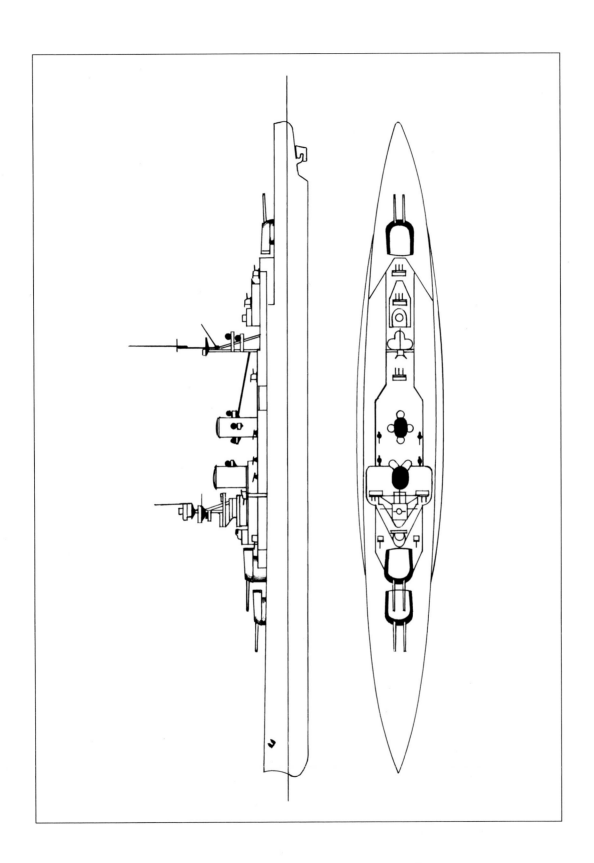

# COURAGEOUS, GLORIOUS & FURIOUS (Emergency War Programme)

| Ship | Built at | Laid down | Launched | Completed |
|---|---|---|---|---|
| *Courageous* | Elswick | 28/03/15 | 05/02/16 | Jan. 1917 |
| *Glorious* | Harland & Wolf | 01/05/15 | 20/04/16 | Jan. 1917 |
| *Furious* | Elswick | 08/06/15 | 15/08/16 | Jul. 1917 |

**Dimensions**
*Furious* 786'×81'×23.4'
786.5'×88'×19.75'

**Displacement**
18,600 tons
*Furious* 19,513 tons    22,690 tons deep load
22,890 tons deep load

**Armament** 4×15"    2×3"
*Furious* 2×18" designed    11×5.5"    2×3"    4×3 pdr    2×21" torpedo tubes
1×18" completed    6×21" torpedo tubes

**Protection** Belt 3"–2"    Bulkheads 3"–2"    Barbettes 7"–4"–3"    Turrets 13"–11"–7"–4.5"

**Machinery** Parsons geared turbines s.h.p. 90,000    31.32 knots    4 screws    18 Yarrow small tube boilers
*Furious* Brown & Curtis geared turbines s.h.p. 94,000    31.5 knots    4 screws    18 Yarrow small tube boilers

**Fuel** 3,160 tons oil

**Radius** 3,200 at 19 knots

**Complement** 880

**Fate**
*Courageous* Converted to aircraft carrier 1924-8. Torpedoed and sunk by U-29 22 September 1939, 515 men lost.
*Glorious* Converted to aircraft carrier 1924–30. Sunk by German battlecruisers *Scharnhorst* and *Gneisenau* off Norway, 8 June 1940; over 800 men lost.
*Furious* Converted to aircraft carrier 1921–5. Sold and broken up at Troon, January 1948.

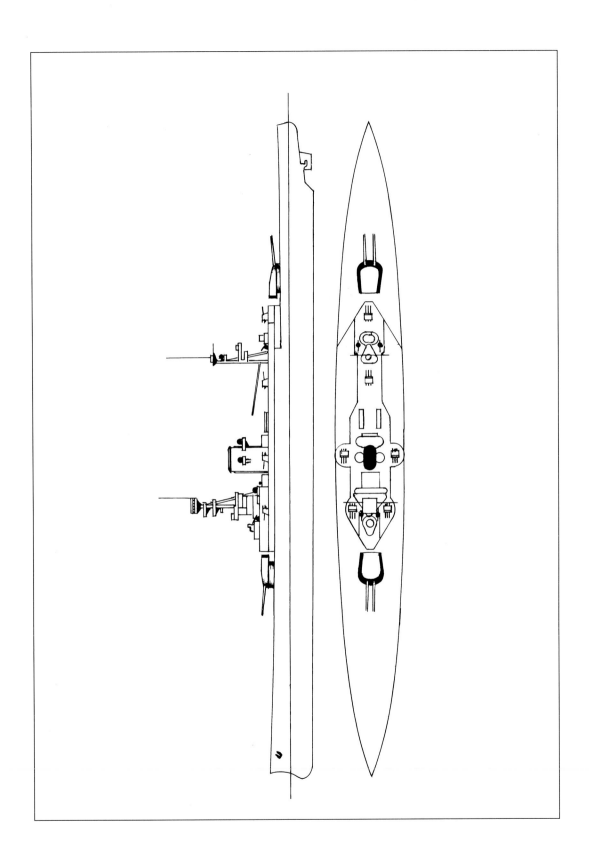

## HOOD Class (Battlecruiser, Emergency War Programme)

| Ship | Built at | Laid down | Launched | Completed |
| --- | --- | --- | --- | --- |
| *Hood* | Clydebank | 01/09/16 | 22/08/18 | Mar. 1920 |
| *Anson* | Armstrongs | 09/11/16 | | |
| *Howe* | Cammell Laird | 16/10/16 | | |
| *Rodney* | Fairfield | 09/10/16 | | |

**Dimensions** 860'×104'×28.5'

**Displacement** 41,200 tons    45,200 tons deep load

**Armament** 8×15"    12×5.5"    4×4"    4×3 pdr    6×12" torpedo tubes

**Protection** Belt 12"–7"–5"  Bulkheads 5"–4"  Barbettes 12"–6"–5"  Turrets 15"–11"–5"  Conning Tower 11"–9"

**Machinery** Brown-Curtis geared turbines s.h.p. 144,000  32 knots  4 screws  24 Yarrow small tube boilers

**Fuel** 4,000 tons oil

**Radius** 6,300 at 12 knots

**Complement** 1,477

**Fate**

*Hood* — Sunk by magazine explosion during gun action with *Bismarck* and *Prinz Eugen* in the Denmark Strait, 24 May 1941, 1,338 men perished.

*Anson* — Construction halted 9 March 1917. Contract cancelled 17 March 1919.

*Howe* — Construction halted 9 March 1917. Contract cancelled 17 March 1919.

*Rodney* — Construction halted 9 March 1917. Contract cancelled 17 March 1919.

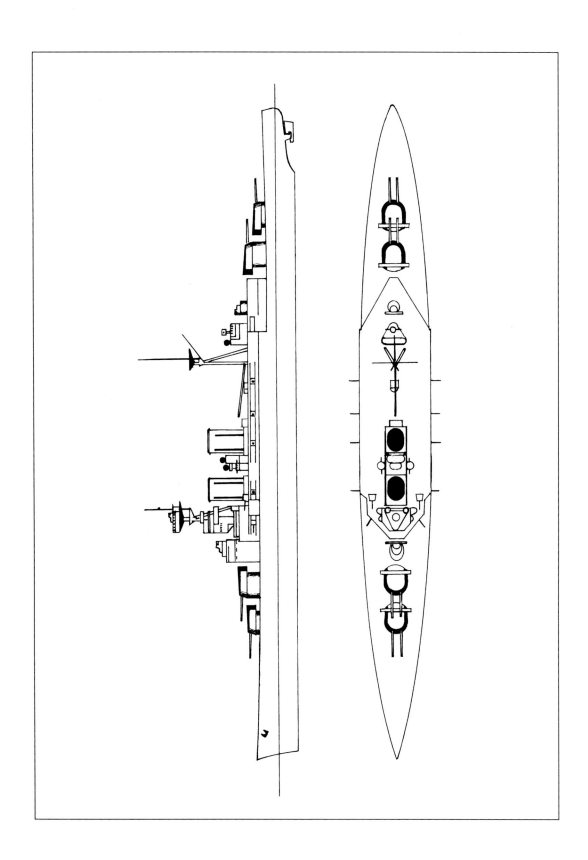

# BIBLIOGRAPHY

Attwood, E.L. *War-Ships*, Longmans, Green and Co., London, 1912.

Brown, D.K. *A Century of Naval Construction*, Conway Maritime Press, London, 1983.

Burt, R.A., and Trotter, W.P. *Battleships of the Grand Fleet: A Pictorial Review of the Royal Navy's Capital Ships in World War One*, Arms and Armour Press, London, 1982.

Burt, R.A. *British Battleships of World War One*, Arms and Armour Press, London, 1986.

Campbell-Holmes, A. *Practical Shipbuilding*, 2 vols, Longmans, Green and Co., London, 1st edition 1904, 2nd edition 1908, new impressions 1914, 1916, 1917, 1918.

Gordon, A. *The Rules of the Game: Jutland and the British Naval Command*, John Murray, London, 1996.

Hume, J.R. and Moss M.S. *Beardmore: The History of a Scottish Industrial Giant*, Heinemann, London, 1975.

Kennedy, P. *The Rise of Anglo-German Antagonism, 1860–1914*, Allen and Unwin, London, 1980.

Lorenz, E.H. *Economic Decline in Britain: The Shipbuilding Industry 1890–1970*, Oxford University Press, 1991.

Mackay, R.F. *Fisher of Kilverstone*, Clarendon Press, Oxford, 1973.

Marder, A. *From Dreadnought to Scapa Flow: The Royal Navy in the Fisher Era, 1904–1914*, Oxford University Press, 1964.

McDermaid, N.J. *Shipyard Practice as Applied to Warship Constructions*, Longmans, Green and Co., London, 1911.

Morris, A.J. *The Scaremongers: The Advocacy of War and Re-armament, 1896–1914*, Routledge, Kegan and Paul, London, 1984.

Moss, M., and Russell, I. *Range and Vision: The First Hundred Years of Barr and Stroud*, Mainstream Press, 1994.

Parkes, Oscar. *British Battleships*, Seeley, London, 1957.

Peebles, H.B. *Warshipbuilding on the Clyde: Naval Orders and the Prosperity of the Clyde Shipbuilding Industry, 1889–1939*, John Donald, Edinburgh, 1990.

Ranft, B. *Technical Change and British Naval Policy*, London, 1995.

Reid, A. 'The Division of Labour in the British Shipbuilding Industry 1880–1920', PhD thesis, Cambridge University, 1980.

Roberts, J. *The Battle-cruiser Hood*, Conway Maritime Press, London, 1983.

—— *The Battleship Dreadnought*, Conway Maritime Press, London, 1992.

Sumida, T. *In Defence of Naval Supremacy: Finance, Technology and British Naval Policy, 1880–1914*, Hymans, London, 1989.

Thearle, S.P. *The Modern Practice of Shipbuilding in Iron and Steel*, 2 vols, Collins, London, 1910.

Trebilcock, C. *The Vickers Brothers: Armaments and Enterprise 1854–1914*, Europa Publications, London, 1977.

Warren, K. *Armstrongs of Elswick*, Macmillan, London, 1990.

Watton, R. *The Battleship Warspite*, Conway Maritime Press, London, 1988.

# DREADNOUGHT
# BIBLIOGRAPHY

## Ship's Covers

The National Maritime Museum, The Old Brass Foundry, Woolwich Arsenal.
Dreadnought ships' covers: Dreadnought, Orion Class, King George V Class, Iron Duke Class, Queen Elizabeth Class, Royal Sovereign Class, HMS *Agincourt*, HMS *Erin*.

## Dreadnought Ship's Plans

HMS *Orion*, HMS *Iron Duke*, HMS *Queen Elizabeth*, HMS *Tiger*, HMS *Royal Sovereign*, HMS *Hood*.

## Visual Bibliography

The Business Record Centre, 3 Thurso Street, University of Glasgow, Glasgow G11 6PE.
John Brown, Clydebank, Collections:
HMAS *Australia* UCS1/116/5.
HMS *Inflexible* UCS1/116/213.

HMS *Tiger* UCS1/116/10 and UCS1/116/11 (98 images).
HMS *Barham* UCS1/116/12, UCS1/116/13, UCS1/116/14, UCS1/116/15, UCS1/116/16 (253 images).
HMS *Repulse* UCS1/116/17, UCS1/116/18, UCS1/116/19, UCS1/116/20, UCS1/116/21, UCS1/116/22 (344 images).
HMS *Hood* UCS1/116/24, UCS1/116/25, UCS1/116/26, UCS1/116/27, UCS1/116/28, UCS1/116/29, UCS1/116/30 (412 images).
Illustrated brochure, John Brown, Clydebank Shipyard and Engineering Works, *c*. 1910, UCS1/115/17.
Illustrated Brochure, John Brown and Co., *c*. 1919, UCS1/115/26.
Beardmore, Parkhead and Dalmuir albums:
UGD100/1/11/1, UGD100/1/11/2, UGD100/1/11/4, UGD100/1/11/7.

# INDEX

Ship names are in italic script. All names are HM Ships unless otherwise stated. Illustration captions and the Appendix are included in the index.

# the**anti-ageing**plan

**FOR**

**Harriet, my mother, for her love, support and constant inspiration.**
**A powerful role model who has always embraced life's changes**
**pragmatically and with great creativity. She's damned stylish, too!**

**Jane Garton for her help and advice –**
**and for not losing her temper with me too often.**

THIS IS A CARLTON BOOK

Text and design copyright © Carlton Books Limited 1997

First published as *Forever Young* in 1997.
This edition published by
Carlton Books Limited 2004
20 Mortimer Street
London W1T 3JW

ISBN 1 84442 827 3

**Project Editors:** Jane Laing, Liz Wheeler
**Art Direction:** Zoë Maggs
**Design:** Mary Ryan
**Special Photography:** Sue Atkinson
**Picture Research:** Rachel Leach
**Production:** Sarah Schuman

Printed and bound in Dubai

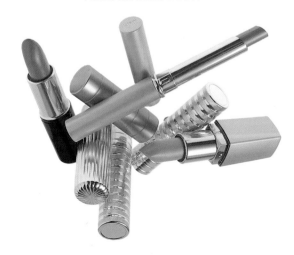

# the**anti-ageing**plan

## Your complete guide to the secrets of staying young

### Vicci Bentley

CARLTON
BOOKS

# Contents

# The psychology of ageing

## LOOKING GREAT AND FEELING BEAUTIFUL WHATEVER YOUR AGE

**According to US sociologist Nancy Friday healthy good looks is "not so much about eternal youth as about extended life". Keeping yourself realistically fit and healthy is an investment that is also an expression of self-honouring – actively giving yourself what you deserve, rather than what you need to survive. If during your early years, you spend time nurturing and supporting others – partners, children – your middle years onward present the opportunity for a growing self-realization and awareness. Many women reach the peak of their sexual confidence in later years.**

### BELIEVING IN THE *Diversity of beauty*
The US sociologist, Wendy Chapkis, author of *Beauty Secrets,* says: "In reality, the female body is a constantly changing landscape. From the budding breasts of adolescence, through the rounded belly of pregnancy and generous curves of maturity, to the smooth chest of mastectomy and deep creases of old age, our bodies weather and reshape. To call beauty only the still life of unchanging 'perfection' is no praise for creatures so lively and diverse as womankind."

Wendy Chapkis feels strongly about the pressures put upon today's woman to maintain the "perfect" face and body. She cites Jane Fonda, "the acknowledged queen of physically fit mid-life beauty", who revealed a few years ago her years battling with compulsive eating and bulimia nervosa. "In her attempt to maintain a perpetually thin and youthful beauty, Fonda was faced with the choice of starving to death (stay pretty, die young) or control (not showing the effects of eating, of ageing)," summarizes Chapkis. This "live but don't change" ethos is at the root of fear of ageing and the self-loathing it may engender.

The real key to looking and feeling great is believing that beauty is attainable whatever your age and that youthful looks is not all there is to feeling beautiful. Anti-ageing creams can't turn back the clock or embalm your features out of time, and make-up is notoriously unreliable at painting a girlish face. However, cosmetics can act as a comfortable buffer against environmental damage, which hastens skin ageing, and boost your confidence by offsetting some of the more visible signs of growing older. The more confidence you have in your appearance, the more confidence you are likely to have in yourself, and the more enjoyment you are likely to be able to get from life.

### POSITIVE *Role models*
Psychologists agree that role models play a powerful role in endorsing women's idea of beauty. In *The Power of Beauty,* Nancy Friday states: "To believe that women's beauty is neither limited to youth nor to the roles that traditional women lived requires models who are the living, breathing proof."

The fashion business is not without its 30- and 40-plus role models. Wife, mother and self-styled "thinking woman's" designer Donna Karan chooses 30-something actress Demi Moore as her mature muse. Jean Paul Gaultier once more made a catwalk celebrity of white-haired Anna Pawloski, a vintage Jean Patou model. In the beauty world, Lauren Hutton was 47 and Melanie

66 The older we get, the more we shed meaningless things and negative pre-occupations. We are becoming the women we have wanted to be. 99

**MARIANNE WILLIAMSON,**
**A Woman's Worth**

Griffith 37 when Revlon signed them up; and Isabella Rossellini was the 42-year-old face of Lancôme before joining the board of directors at Lancaster cosmetics. Forty-six-year-old Dayle Haddon smiles from Estée Lauder adverts and in her mid-50s, Catherine Deneuve is deservedly an Yves St Laurent beauty icon.

What distinguishes these mature role models from the young ones is elegance and poise and a look that exudes wisdom and confidence. Their image has a serenity that transcends confrontation. Of course, with good photography and a little help in the re-touching department, they look pretty damn good. But their real and undeniable

attraction comes from the feeling they project that they're happy with the way they look. They have relaxed and accepted themselves as they are now; they are confident.

### Maintaining a *Positive attitude*

British psychologist Gayle Lindenfield, author of *Positive Woman,* proposes that the crucial differentiating factors between people who foster despondency about age and those who inspire a sense of enrichment, are self-esteem and general attitude to life. "If these are positive", she says, "we are much more likely to cope efficiently and courageously with any physical difficulty or limitation that may be placed upon us." It's estimated by some experts that up to 90 per cent of age-related diseases are not inevitable but in fact largely attributable to poor levels of nutrition and exercise.

Marianne Williamson, in her best-selling *A Woman's Worth*, describes it most eloquently: "We're young, we're old, we're neither, we're both. Every age bears a beautiful gift, it's own brand of joy and loneliness and grief. Let's become more beautiful with age. Above all, let's not be ashamed of age. Youth is not a great prize, and age a sad afterthought. If anything, youth is the bud and age is when we blossom. The older we get, the more we shed meaningless things and negative pre-occupations. We are becoming the women we have wanted to be."

This book is filled with practical advice on how to make the most of your appearance whatever your age and how to maintain a healthy body and mind through exercise, nutrition, stress-reducing techniques and effective use of complementary medicines. I hope it will enable you to feel great about yourself so that you can become the woman you always wanted to be.

**20s, 40s, 60s:** Every decade brings its own reward, from the fresh-faced vigour of your early 20s to the self-acceptance of your 60s and beyond.

# Prime times

## CELEBRATING THE CHANGES WITH A GAMEPLAN FOR EACH DECADE

### YOUR 30S

During this decade, you notice the first signs of ageing. In your 30s bone structure becomes more defined as skin loses plumpness when collagen and elastin fibres begin to weaken and production slows. Spots and adult acne are triggered by stress, pregnancy, contraceptive and fertility drugs. Crow's feet, smile and frown lines begin to show. Use a mild foaming cleanser and oil-free UV-screening moisturizer with antioxidant ingredients together with a lightweight eye cream to help protect against further skin damage. Use AHAs to loosen debris and dead cells from pores and a gentle exfoliating scrub twice a week. Do facial exercises to keep skin toned. Use light-reflective, oil-free foundation; dust blusher on cheek apples and brow bones; apply light-reflective highlights on mid-lids and browbones. Experiment with eye make-up, blending to create soft, smudgy shapes, but steer clear of hard colours and harsh, black lines. Outline lips carefully or prime with "lipfix" formula to prevent feathering at the edges. Try vegetable "wash in, wash out" colour to cover a less than 10 per cent sprinkling of grey hair. Use mild, frequent use shampoo and a lightweight, oil-free conditioner.

• Aerobics, such as step or cardiogym, boost cardiovascular activity, keep muscles toned and maintain stamina. Yoga helps to dissolve stress.

• Take B-complex if you're on the Pill. Vitamin C aids collagen production and iron absorption. Start calcium supplementation and make sure you get enough EFAs.

Here now, at the age of wisdom,
it is time to take life in hand and bend
it, shape it, make it what we will.  **NANCY FRIDAY,**
**The Power of Beauty**

## YOUR 40S

Genetic factors that determine the way you age begin to kick in. Accumulated sun damage heightens a deepening frown, smile and crow's feet. Eye bags, loss of tone around the jaw line, rings around the neck and a general loss of firmness all begin to show. Oil glands become enlarged and the T-zone pores start to dilate. Your oily centre panel may become more apparent. Exfoliation is pivotal in your routine. Use AHA-based day and night moisturizers and apply serums directly to troublespots. Look for firming eye creams and consider compresses to relieve shadows and puffiness. Face masks may become great brightening allies. Mild foams are still the best cleansers; use astringent toners on the centre panel only.

Opt for medium-cover, demi-matt foundations with light-reflecting pigments. Concentrate powder to the centre panel. Dust blusher over cheeks, brow bones, on the brow near the hair line and along the jaw line. Eye make-up should be neutral, low-key shadow and simple definition along the lash lines – strictly no hard lines. Choose moist-finish lipsticks in warm beige, rosewood and coral tones. Try restyling your hair from long to short. Use mousses to build volume and practice "scrunching" hair dry to work a natural-looking texture into your style. Use a mild "frequent use" or moisturizing shampoo. A leave-in conditioner cares for tinted hair.

• Opt for exercise that maintains stamina and flexibility – a combination of aerobic exercise and yoga is ideal. Exercise with weights helps maintain bone density and helps tone and spot-reduce trouble zones.

• Calcium supplementation is now important for bone maintenance. EFAs are important to enhance absorption. Magnesium helps ease depression. Antioxidant vitamins A, C and E are useful in helping to prevent age-related problems such as heart disease and cancer.

## YOUR 50S

There are now very tangible signs of ageing. Skin begins to sag and thin as collagen and elastin production slow dramatically and firmness diminishes. First age spots may appear, as melanin bundles clump and produce uneven pigmentation. Hormonal fluctuations throughout the menopause can trigger acne flare-up but for the most part, skin becomes dehydrated, emphasizing lines and surface coarseness. However, research suggests that HRT minimizes collagen breakdown after the menopause and stimulates production of hyaluronic acid, skin's own moisture-retaining connective tissue lubricant.

For day time use moisturizing, firming creams with elastin boosters, sunscreens and antioxidant ingredients. Overnight, AHA-based creams resurface the skin and help moisture ingredients to penetrate. Serums are helpful in precision-treating more marked lines and wrinkles. Gentle foaming cleansers are still acceptable as they increase circulation and exfoliation. If skin feels tight after cleansing change to a milk cleanser, then rinse or flannel off. Moisturize neck and hands liberally and frequently. In the salon, choose rejuvenating, firming or deep moisturizing facials.

Use a creamy, light-reflective foundation and a warm tawny-pink, or soft coral blush. A pale beige, demi-sheen eye shadow opens up hooded eyes; the barest trace of brown powder shadow under lower lashes defines them. Opt for brown mascara and outline thinning lips with a neutral pencil, building slightly over the natural contour before filling in with a natural lip-tone lipstick. Gentle acid demi-perms gently body-build thinning hair to look fuller by lifting it up from the scalp. Mousses also volumize hair but may prove "scurfy" if your scalp is very dry. Overcome this by moisturizing hair and scalp with a no-rinse daily conditioning cream, whether after mild-shampooing or between washes. Spray-on glossing serums polish grey hair to an attractive, light-catching sheen.

• Opt for low-impact exercise, such as swimming and T'ai Chi, which tones muscles and improves co-ordination. Yoga maintains flexibility and encourages relaxation. Power walking and dancing maintain cardiovascular activity. Gentle weight training maintains bone density.

• Take B-complex supplements if you're taking HRT. Antioxidants A, C, and E may help protect against cancer, heart disease, cataracts and arthritis. Vitamin C also contributes to collagen production and general skin fitness, and vitamin E also improves skin's ability to retain moisture. EFAs help relieve hot flushes, vaginal dryness and night sweats, and protect heart against risk of cholesterol.

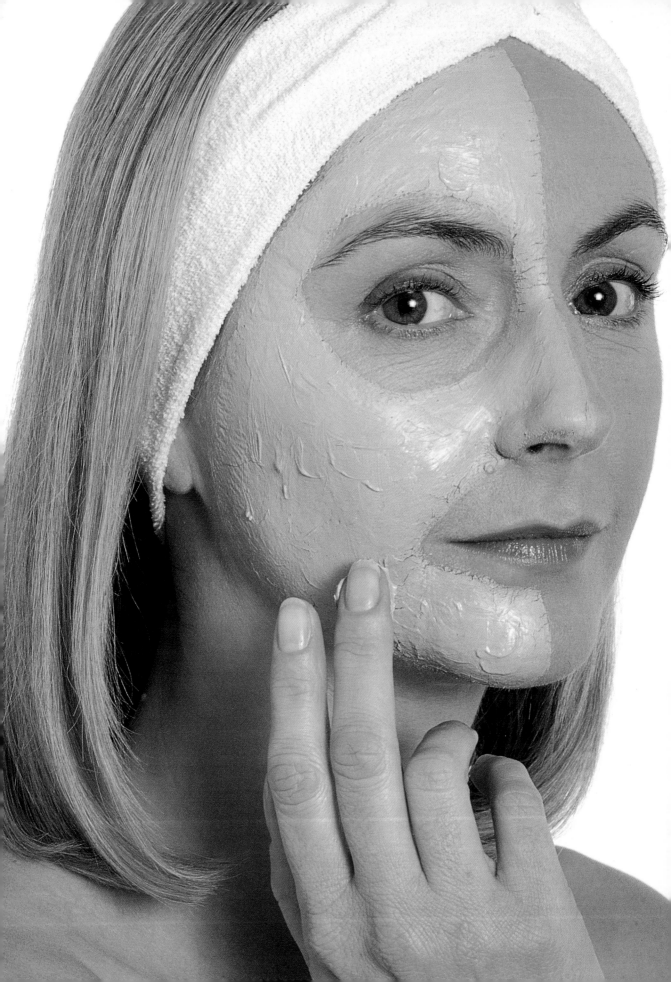

# CHAPTER 1

# Skin care

Skin is often considered the most accurate barometer of your general wellbeing and your age. Whereas young skin is resilient enough to withstand wear and tear, more mature complexions are quick to register fluctuations in health, diet, exercise and sleep patterns. Skin's function goes far beyond the aesthetic wrapping. Not only does it play a key role in facilitating internal body processes, skin protects you from external aggression – an important factor in its own ageing process.

# The structure of the skin

## UNDERSTANDING YOUR PROTECTIVE WRAPPING

**Think of skin as a three-layer sandwich. The outer horny layer, or stratum corneum, is composed of flat skeletons of cells made up of keratin protein. These overlap like scales and are glued together with lipids – the skin's natural oils. Although this layer is technically dead, its protective "armour plating" is vital to skin health. Its horny, water-resistant structure forms a barrier against moisture loss from within the skin, while repelling potentially hazardous external elements. A cocktail of friendly flora gives it anti-bacterial properties that help withstand infection. This outer layer is sealed by a membrane that lies between it and the living cells of the next layer down – the epidermis.**

The epidermis has two functions. It supplies the stratum corneum with cells while attracting and preserving moisture to keep the skin soft and plump. From the bottom, or basal line, of the epidermis, cells bud off, divide and migrate toward the surface, progressively maturing, ageing and flattening until they become the dead scales of the stratum corneum. In healthy skin, this cell-turnover process takes around 28 days. There are two growth spurts daily: one in the early morning and a milder phase in the early afternoon, when levels of the life-giving hormone cortisol are lowest and body repairs take place. New cells arriving at the surface of the outer layer push off old skeleton cells, so the stratum corneum is constantly renewing itself. Both the stratum corneum and the epidermis are referred to as the skin's upper layers. This vital layer of the skin is relatively narrow, the deepest of the skin's layers is the the next layer down, the dermis.

### BENEATH THE *Upper layers*

Directly below the basal line of the epidermis is the dermis – the skin's lowest layer. Here, parallel bundles of collagen and elastin form the supportive structure at the skin's foundation. These proteins are also responsible for the skin's firmness, plumpness and elasticity. Also running through the dermis is a network of nerves and an extremely rich system of blood vessels or capillaries. These supply cells with essential nutrients and give the skin its rosy glow. The strength and proximity to the surface of these capillaries determines how prone the skin will be to "broken veins" as it ages.

Hair follicles are rooted in the dermis where they are served by nerves and blood vessels. Further up toward the basal line of the epidermis, sebaceous glands supply each hair with lubricant oil (see Chapter 4 for more detailed information on hair). This oil, or sebum, works its way up the hair follicle and spills out on to the skin's surface. Composed of more than 40 acids and alcohols, sebum creates a protective film known as the skin's acid mantle, which assists in the horny layer's barrier function against moisture loss and infection. To maintain its anti-bacterial, antiseptic status, the acid mantle must remain at between pH (acid balance) 4 and 6. Alkaline detergents and some cleansers disrupt this balance, leaving the skin vulnerable to dryness and possibly infection. Hyperactive sebum secretion poses problems of its own (see p.29 for advice on oily skin).

Sweat glands (which help regulate body temperature and fluid levels, and eliminate fluid waste) originate in the dermis and end in outlets, or ducts, on the skin's surface. Sweat is one of the body's major means of temperature control: as the temperature rises more sweat is excreted to the the skin, then as the sweat droplets evaporate this has a cooling effect at the skin's surface. The other components of sweat, such as minerals, waste products and hormones, vary around the body. Sweat excreted from the underarm and groin areas are heavily laced with hormones, which give sweat (particularly after contact with the skin bacteria inhabiting these areas!) its own, distinctive, natural aroma.

The dermis is also involved in another means of temperature regulation. When the body overheats, the fine capillaries near the surface of the skin dilate, increasing the blood supply. This has the effect of cooling the blood near the external surfaces of the

**S**TRATUM CORNEUM  **E**PIDERMIS  **H**AIR FOLLICLE  **D**ERMIS

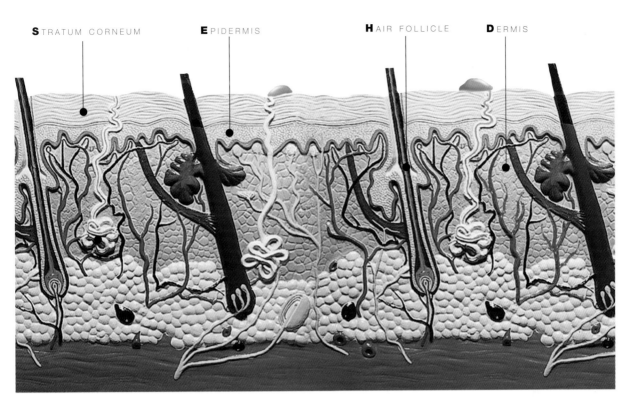

body. When the external temperature becomes significantly cooler, the capillaries contract, drawing blood away from the cool surface of the skin and into the body's warmer core. Hence that pale face when you are uncomfortably cold, and the red face when you have been working out in the gym – it just shows your body's systems are working efficiently!

Beneath the dermis lies a layer of subcutaneous fat threaded through with veins and arteries. This insulating layer preserves warmth and provides the body with fuel in "lean" times. It is more generously distributed in women and can harbour cellulite (see p.64).

## SENSE AND *Sensitivity*

The dermis is packed with microscopic sensors responsible for touch – which is a combination of light pressure, heavy pressure, heat, cold and pain. There are different kinds of sensor, each responsible for a different sensation, and located at different depths.

## WHAT HAPPENS WHEN *Skin ages?*

Like the rest of our body tissue, skin gradually loses its youthful appearance and efficiency with age. By the time you've reached your early to mid thirties, the outward signs are already becoming established.

- **Changes in the dermis reflect on the surface.** Production of collagen and elastin slows down, so the skin becomes thinner, losing its plumpness, firmness and elasticity. As the structure of the collagen bundles become uneven, the skin's foundation begins to crumble. Surface signs are deeper lines, wrinkles and a sagging skin texture.

- **A more sluggish circulation results in a paler complexion.** Less efficiently nourished cells also become sluggish. Turnover can become as much as 50 per cent slower, meaning that dead cells hang around on the surface longer.

- **A build up of redundant cells on the surface means an inefficient barrier function.** In addition, hormonal fluctuations lead to a reduction in sebum production, so the skin's surface becomes rougher, dryer and less able to prevent moisture loss from below.

- **Chronic moisture loss means cells risk dehydration and skin loses its plumpness even further.** Dry skin also risks sensitivity. Harsh environmental conditions heighten these risks and increase skin damage.

- **Efficient skin care can't actively slow down this natural ageing process but it can significantly help limit damage and improve skin appearance.**

## SKIN CANCER CHECK

Melanomas and other cancers can be cured if caught early. Check face and body regularly for changes in the appearance of moles, or new patches of pigmentation. Look for moles or growths with uneven colour or edges; moles that are increasing in size or changing shape; moles that are over 1 cm in diameter; moles that are inflamed, discharging, bleeding or scabbing; moles that are itching or numb. Watch too for sores that won't heal. If two or more symptoms occur, check immediately with your doctor or dermatologist.

# Protecting the skin

## THE SENSE OF SKIN DEFENCE

**Skin is our first line of defence from external hazards. Battle scars sustained in the process may be inevitable, yet with foresight the damage can be limited.**

### EVERYDAY *Environmental hazards*

It is irrefutable that environmental factors undermine skin integrity. In our offices and homes, the arid atmosphere generated by air-conditioning and central heating leaches moisture from the skin, encouraging a dry, taut and potentially sensitive surface. Outside, further threats await. Cold winds dehydrate and stress the skin, especially by contrast – going straight from a warm room into icy air gives skin scant time to adjust its temperature and circulation setting. Atmospheric pollution creates a further risk by triggering the action of free radicals – destructive molecules within the skin itself.

**SUN DAMAGE:** These twins were both aged 71 when photographed for research. One (left) was a sun lover; the other (above) was a sun hater. The damage is clear to see.

Free radicals are opportunist, super-oxygenated molecules that cruise the bloodstream ready to pick on weak and ailing cells. As members of the body's "clean-up" squad they play a key role in natural tissue breakdown. But they are also highly excitable. Smoking, traffic fumes and sunlight all trigger free radical activity.

Free radicals oxidize skin lipids both between cells and on their surface. To neutralize the damage, skin chemicals are released, notably the anti-inflammatory interleukin-II. In the skin's blanket attempt to neutralize toxic activity, cells themselves become casualties. Antioxidant ingredients in skin creams help counteract environmental damage (see p.20), but the best way to avoid excessive skin cell destruction is to minimize your skin's exposure to pollution and sunlight.

### SUNLIGHT – *A glaring danger*

Skin colour depends on a natural brownish pigment called melanin. Melanin is produced by cells called melanocytes, situated at intervals between cells in the dermis. All skins – from Scandanavian pale to Ethiopian mahogony – contain the same quota of melanocytes, but the melanocyte cells of some skins are more efficient producers of melanin than others.

The function of melanin is to act as a natural sunscreen that absorbs and filters ultraviolet rays so they cannot reach and damage the dermis. Sunlight stimulates the melanocytes to produce melanin to stave off UV radiation. Consequently, people who originate from nearest the equator have the most efficient melanocytes, while those of Northern European origin have the most inefficient, and are therefore at greatest risk from sun damage. Freckles indicate unevenly distributed melanin and poor protection against ultraviolet damage.

### IS IT WORTH *Getting a tan?*

Whereas moderate sunlight enables the skin to synthesize vitamin D, excessive sun is the single greatest threat to skin health. Dermatologists estimate that 80 per cent of lines, wrinkles, sagging and coarsening are directly caused by ultraviolet light. Countless comparisons between the weatherbeaten faces of octogenarians and their smoother, seldom exposed body zones show how a lifetime under the sun leaves its mark.

Sunlight ages the skin and creates a potential cancer risk. It used to be thought that only the "burning" ultraviolet-B rays posed a threat. Now it is known that whereas 95 per cent of these short-wave rays are absorbed by the epidermis, 80 per cent of so-called "tanning" ultraviolet-A rays penetrate down to the dermis. Here, they undermine the skin's structure by distorting DNA and RNA at the cell's nucleus and distorting collagen and elastin arrangements. This damage is both cumulative and largely irreversible. Distorted cells reproduce inefficient mutations, resulting in an increase in the number of lines and wrinkles, a decrease in firmness and elasticity, and an epidermis that no longer retains moisture as it should.

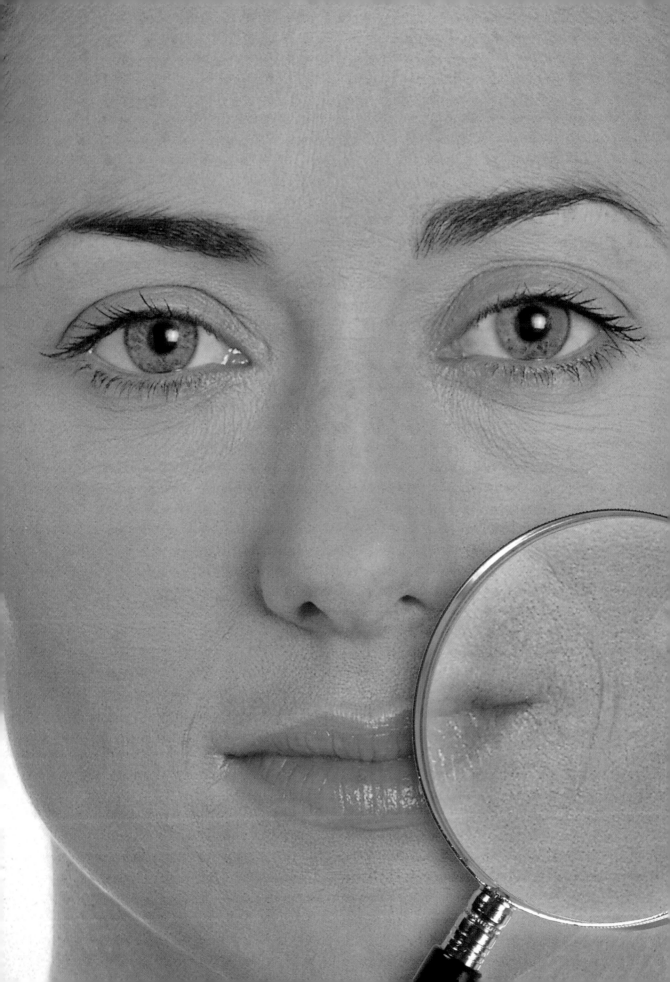

# Anti-ageing creams

## CAN THEY HOLD BACK THE CLOCK AND REPAIR THE LINES?

**Anti-ageing creams belong to skincare's most contentious and emotive sector. Each year, more and more "wonder" formulas flood the market, claiming to solve skin's million dollar mystery – how to cure lines and wrinkles. Many formulas borrow theories and active ingredients from mainstream medicine, which lends them a scientific image. But anti-ageing creams are still cosmetics – not drugs, and despite high-tech formulas, the real keys to skin defence remain surprisingly simple.**

### THE IMPORTANCE OF *Moisture*

Skin needs moisture – that's the bottom line. A water quota of no less than a healthy 60 per cent gives skin its smooth, plump, translucent quality, bathes cells with nutrients and keeps them soft and functional. A moisturizer's most basic job is to supplement the skin's Natural Moisture Factor (NMF) (a cocktail of moisture-attracting humectants and preservatives), help preserve fluid in the skin's upper layers and prevent losses which hasten ageing. As environmental factors such as sunlight, central heating, wind, cold and pollution all encourage moisture loss, state-of-the-art creams are designed to buffer external aggression by reinforcing the skin's own barrier mechanisms.

In young, healthy skin natural oils and friendly flora preserve the slightly acidic mantle that keeps the barrier function of the horny outer layer intact. Overlapping dead skin cells form a scaly, water-resistant seal against dehydration. As skin ages, however, natural oil production drops and the skin surface becomes drier and less moisture-retentive. Surface scales roughen and gaps appear in

**LAB TEST:** The key to ageless beauty may be less than skin deep. Latest skin cream formulas are strictly superficial to stay inside cosmetic law.

the barrier, through which moisture can escape. As cell turnover also slows with ageing, it takes longer for replacement cells to reach the surface and repair breaches. A malfunctioning surface barrier leaves cells in the skin's lower layers vulnerable to damage. So, creams that help to reinforce the stratum corneum seem like the obvious answer. For, if the horny layer is doing its job, the deeper skin layers – where ageing begins – are more able to look after themselves.

### MARKETING *Science*

From a manufacturer's point of view, this theory is a marketing godsend for it is illegal for a cosmetic to claim penetration as far as the dermis – the skin's bottom layer with direct access to the bloodstream. Only drugs are allowed to do that. Any cream that claims to cause physiological changes in the skin's foundations is making a drug-related claim and, strictly speaking, is no longer a cosmetic. Nevertheless, throughout the 80s, major cosmetics companies ran the gauntlet with the US Food and Drug Administration (FDA) by making skindeep claims. Liposomes – microscopic carrier molecules that carry active ingredients deep into the skin – were designed specifically to aim for the dermis.

A concerned FDA responded by stating that if claims could be substantiated, creams involving liposomes were of drug status and could be sold only in licensed pharmacies. Threatened with the inevitable pairing down of profit margins that selling their wares in restricted outlets would lead to, manufacturers prudently backpedalled. Liposomes, they said, delivered skin-saving goods to the skin's surface only – well short of contention.

But the age of the cosmeceutical – the cosmetic with a pharmaceutical action – had well and truly dawned. Although stringent advertising rules screen out broad hints that creams can influence the dermis, there's nothing to stop enthusiastic editorial in glossy magazines passing on the precious word of mouth that seals a cream's success.

## CREAMS CONTAINING
### *Alpha-hydroxy acids (AHAs)*

Creams containing AHAs, also known as fruit acids, bridge the gap between cosmetics and cosmeceuticals. More commonly used AHAs include citric acid, which is derived from citrus fruits; tartaric acid from grapes; malic acid from apples; and mandlic acid from cucumbers. Glycolic acid, which is derived from sugar cane, is one of the most widely used in creams because its small molecules penetrate further than other AHAs.

Creams containing AHAs exfoliate the skin by loosening the glue-like bonds that hold together the dead cells on the surface of the outer horny layer. Consistent exfoliation boosts slow cell turnover and helps other skin-care ingredients to penetrate below the surface. AHAs are also said to reduce the appearance of lines and pigment patches and boost the skin's hyaluronic acid (moisture) quota. There is evidence that they also improve sun-tolerance up to an equivalent of SPF 25. Trials at the University of California, Los Angeles, indicate they may even encourage collagen production.

High concentrations of AHAs may cause sensitive skin reactions. Newest cream formulas hover around a "safe" 4 per cent of the total mass. However, at a recent conference, dermatologists stated that the acidity level of the AHA used was the crucial factor. Glycolic acid, for example, with a pH (acid value) of 3.5 – close to the skin's own – is better tolerated. Even at higher percentages, AHAs work well for mature, 35-plus skin. They also help to unclog

**AGE DEFENCE:** These creams and serums are all formulated to refine, firm and moisturize the skin.

pores and regulate oily, acne-prone skin. Results are rewardingly rapid.

## CREAMS CONTAINING
### *Vitamins*

Vitamins A, C and E are all antioxidants. They mop up free radicals and convert them into harmless compounds which can then be eliminated from the skin. When applied in the form of a cream, they protect against environmental damage and UV rays. They have a neutralizing effect on free radicals that is the equivalent of using SPF 2 to 3. Although antioxidants are no substitute for sunscreens, their presence in sun-protection formulas reduces the need for high levels of chemical filters, which are potentially irritating to the skin. Zinc, copper, manganese, selenium and super oxide dismutase are also antioxidants.

In addition to their antioxidant properties, vitamins in skin creams provide other benefits. Vitamin E is an excellent hydrating surface lubricant that supplements the barrier function of the outer layer. Vitamin C plays an important role in collagen formation. Some cosmetologists suggest that vitamin A can be turned into minute doses of retinoic acid, which can repair dam-

**EYE OPENERS:**
These lightweight, non-greasy formulas are specially formulated to care for the delicate eye surrounds.

aged collagen and elastin. Research is also being done into the use in creams of beta-carotene – a chemical cousin of vitamin A – and a potent antioxidant when taken internally.

## ENZYME *Technology*

Some enzymes in the skin build and repair tissue, others break it down. Enzyme technology is an attempt to influence the skin's natural enzymes by encouraging the function of "productive" enzymes and inhibiting the function of "destructive" enzymes, which may become over-active due to age and sun damage. Some enzymes are also

excellent exfoliants. They dissolve protein and fats, and help to loosen dead surface cells. Their action is less irritating than that of AHAs, so they make good alternatives. Products with pineapple and papaya extracts are examples of enzyme-based formulas. Heather and honey enzymes are also used in firming creams.

Do cells communicate? If they do, intercellular enzymes are the messengers. Cosmetologists theorize that signals received by one set of cells set off a chain reaction, enabling the right cells to turn up in the right place at the right time. If, for example, surface cells

are exfoliated, new cells are stimulated to migrate upward to take their place. So an important part of enzyme technology is to keep cells talking. Enzymes found in plant extracts are usually useful for this purpose.

## LIPOSOME *Technology*

Liposomes were originally used in medicine to aid the penetration of injected drugs, so their use in skin creams had contentious beginnings. Microscopic, lipid spheres (soya oil and ceramide are common ingredients), these hollow carrier molecules can be filled with other skin-care ingredients, which are then delivered to target sites in the skin. Early cosmetic liposomes were deemed unstable and useless – nothing more than oily lubricants that melted on the skin's surface. After countless refinements, however, it does seem that the liposomes of today – newer, tinier and more stable molecules – can access the lower layers of the epidermis. Most skin creams contain them.

Does skin breathe? Oxygen is the key to healthy cell regeneration and skin metabolism. Medical opinion is that skin cells receive oxygen via the bloodstream and not through the pores of the skin. An increasing number of cosmetologists, however, suggest that oxygen can be introduced into the skin via specially constructed liposomes. Sceptics hold that too much oxygen generates free radicals. Champions assert that oxygen creams are like a breath of fresh air to dull skin (especially smoker's skin) with poor circulation. The skin aerobic debate is set to continue for many years to come.

# Anti-ageing skin plan
## HOW TO MAINTAIN A SMOOTH, HEALTHY COMPLEXION

**Whichever products you use, the key to a smooth, healthy complexion is a regular routine that suits your skin and your lifestyle. These days, there's little need for complex rituals that make skin care laborious and time consuming. What most women require is a quick, efficient system that protects and enhances the skin satisfactorily.**

### CLEANSING THE SKIN: *Lotions or water?*

Should you wash your face with tap water? There are some women, such as Liz Taylor and Claudia Schiffer, who claim never to let water touch their skin. But unless your skin is ultra-sensitive and reacts to water as if it were acid, there is no reason not to wash your face with ordinary tap water.

The alkaline nature of basic, old-fashioned soaps stripped sebum from the skin and left it feeling taut, but today's cleansing bars and foaming cleansers are more gentle, formulated to respect skin acidity as well as its dry, normal or oily status. Many women love them because they're quick, easy and less messy than creams and lotions. They're easy to rinse off, too, and that final splash of water comes as a refreshing wake-up or calm-down tonic at either end of the day.

Dermatologists argue in favour of washing because water acts as a natural exfoliant, softening and sweeping away dead skin cells more efficiently than creams. If you gently whisk cleansing foam around your face with a soft brush you cleanse crevices around the mouth and nostrils, and the inner corners of the eye while also boosting exfoliative action.

The warmer the water, the more grease-solvent your wash but hot water encourages dilated capillaries. Keep the temperature just warm enough for comfort both for washing and thorough rinsing, and use several clean bowlsful. A final cold water splash, may evince a temporary glowing and firming effect, as the circulation rushes to the surface of the skin in response to the cold.

Creams and lotions, too, can be removed with warm water – a good compromise for those who like the comforting feeling of creams, followed by an invigorating splash. Use a face cloth to work creams into crevices and to speed up the rinsing off. Still loathe the idea of water? Massage your cleansing milk or lotion over your skin with your fingertips, then gently tissue off. Repeat until the tissue tests clear.

### CLEANSING THE SKIN: *Frequency*

How often do you need to cleanse the skin? Over-zealous cleansing can either disrupt the acid mantle, or excite sebaceous output – the last thing oily skin needs. Improved cosmetic formulas may mean that make-up no longer dries the skin – quite the reverse. But taking it off at night is still considered wise. Pigments can mingle with sweat and sebum to create the appearance of dingy, clogged pores, although not necesarily comedones (blackheads). The oxidized tips of solidified oil plugs, blackheads can mar even the cleanest skin. More significantly, if you remove make-up at night, you're more likely to apply moisturizer as the next step. In the morning a light cleanse removes excess night cream, kick starts the circulation and prepares the skin for moisturizer and make-up again.

A cautionary word about AHAs in cleansers. Manufacturers say that as natural exfoliators, it makes extra sense to include them in cleansers. But some dermatologists worry that as cleansing – especially washing – naturally loosens the bonds that hold dead surface cells together, AHAs may encourage bond loosening further down in the epidermis. This would make the skin even more receptive to other skin-care ingredients, which is not necessarily a bad thing. However, an overload may cause sensitivity. If you're worried, restrict use of AHA cleansers to two or three times a week or avoid them altogether.

### ARE SPECIAL EYE CLEANSERS WORTH THE EXTRA?

Yes, especially if you wear waterproof mascara, which is notoriously difficult to shift. However, if you wear contact lenses beware oil-based formulas that get into eyes and blur your vision. Most eye make-up removers dissolve shadows and mascara without rubbing or stinging – a plus for the delicate eye area. But if you are happy with your regular all-purpose cleanser, that's fine.

**CLEAN SWEEP:**
Creams, foams, buffing
grains and tonic lotions
help cleanse and refine
the skin.

### TONING: IS IT ESSENTIAL?

Applying a toner after cleansing the skin is not really necessary. Its main function is to mop up residue from the cleansing agent and help the skin regain its natural pH (acid balance). Cleansing residues that are left on the skin disrupt the pH and may cause irritation. Surfactants – binders used in emulsion cleansers – are particular culprits. However, if you are careful to remove all traces of cleanser thoroughly you will not need a mop-up agent. On the other hand, using a toner is undeniably refreshing and those that contain soothing, softening ingredients can help calm irritable skins or even prevent flare-up. So, if using a toner feels good, use it.

### EXFOLIATION: THE ANTI-AGEING BYWORD

Five years ago, we were still fervently polishing off dull surface cells with cleansing grains. Today continual, passive exfoliation with AHA-containing products makes manual sloughing seem both primitive and unnecessary. Yet "gumption" pastes are still in evidence on beauty shelves. So, do we need both?

A few beauty experts suggest manual exfoliation a couple of times a week, preferably in the morning, helps remove cells that an AHA cream has previously loosened. However, dermatologists warn that as AHAs can sensitize, manual scrubbing may cause skin to become irritated. The message seems to be don't do both. Either massage lightly, avoiding the eye zone, with a manual exfoliator – smooth polymer or plastic grains are gentler than scratchy nut kernel chips. Or let your AHA cream do the job for you. And if you choose manual exfoliation dermatologists warn against using "pan scourer" cleansing pads, which can scratch the skin surface.

### MASKS: DO THEY WORK?

Most masks increase blood circulation in the skin to give a pleasant afterglow. Clay-based masks draw sebum and debris from the skin's surface, unplug blocked pores, are mildly exfoliative, and can tighten the skin slightly.

Moisturizing masks are deeply soothing and can be a real relief to sore, taut skins, making the surface better hydrated and more supple. Effects are usually only temporary, but the feelgood factor may see you through an evening. You can turn your moisturizer into an emergency mask by applying it extra thick, leaving it on for 10 minutes, then tissuing off the excess.

### MOISTURIZING: HOW MUCH IS ENOUGH?

New York celebrity dermatologist Patricia Wexler is wary of moisture overload. She feels that older women with dry skin tend to panic and apply heavy creams in excessive amounts. She points out that too much moisturizer makes the skin sag, especially around the eyes, and encourages blocked pores. During the day, she suggests, ease up on the layers: if your foundation has an in-built moisturizer, use a light moisturizing formula underneath. And make sure your moisturizer contains a sunscreen.

Do you need to use a night cream? A good moisturizer can be used round-the-clock, obviating the need for a night cream. However, if your skin is very dry, you may prefer to wear a richer textured moisturizer than you would normally under make-up, to prevent overnight moisture loss and to soften dead surface cells, ready for exfoliating in the morning. If your dermatologist has recommended exfoliating with a high-value AHA product, it is essential to apply a moisturizer at night. Some form of moisturizer is advisable at night so that the skin is not dehydrated during its early-morning growth spurt.

# Care of high risk zones

## HOW TO MAINTAIN A SMOOTH, HEALTHY COMPLEXION

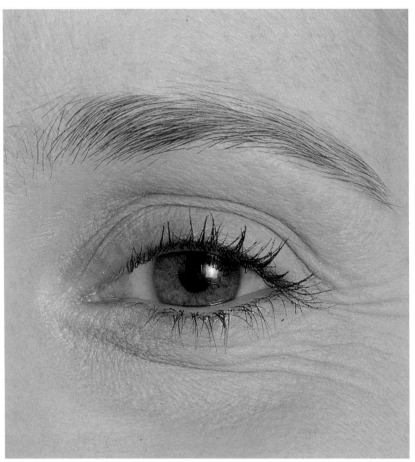

**BETWEEN THE LINES:**
Highly mobile zones, such as the skin around the eyes, are vulnerable to wrinkling. Apply a lightweight moisturizing cream that will not over saturate this zone's delicate skin.

### SPECIAL CARE FOR
### *Eye zones*

The skin around the eyes is extra sensitive and the first to register signs of ageing. It can react badly to heavy handling and heavy creams, and requires special care.

The skin around the eyes develops lines faster than the rest of the face because continual facial movement – smiling, squinting, and frowning – stresses the thin, delicate skin. Bright, ultraviolet light worsens the problem and is a prime hastener of crow's feet. (Nothing looks more starkly ageing than white furrows contrasting with a leathery, tanned skin texture.)

Under-eye "bags" result from decreased muscle tone in the lower lid, and herniation of the underlying fatty layer. Dark circles appear when stress, fatigue, chronic UV exposure, and persistent swelling weaken delicate blood capillaries to breaking point. Exhaustion and illness hamper circulation in the surrounding facial skin, causing a washed-out complexion that highlights dark circles under the eyes. Puffiness, or oedema, results from poor lymphatic circulation. Excess fluid floods the spaces between subcutaneous fatty tissue, particularly after long periods lying down, hence the occurrence of early morning puffy eyes.

Can creams cope with all this? Creams containing sunscreens and temporary firming agents like squalene can improve the quality of the skin's surface, but beware rich, oily-textured creams, which supersaturate thin skin, making puffiness worse. Look for light, rapidly absorbed creams that

### INSTANT *Firmers and brightness boosters*

Granny used egg white to firm and brighten the skin. Modern equivalents are gel and gel-cream formulas that tighten the skin and give a smoothing, brightening complexion boost. Sadly, the effect is temporary. However, for weary nights out and sag-eyed mornings, they are indispensable.

Beauty therapists recommend using serums as a recovery course after exposure to excess sun or extreme weather conditions or after illness. Serums are concentrates of the "active ingredients" of their parent skin care range. Packaged in ampoules, they have an impressive clinical image. Worn under regular moisturizer, they are supposed to give the skin an extra "fix". However, whether they do more than temporarily firm and stimulate the skin is debatable.

won't stray into the eye itself – crucial for contact lens wearers. Some beauty experts recommend avoiding applying cream to the upper lids completely.

The most effective way of minimizing puffy, tired-looking eyes is to sleep with your pillow raised, and to get more exercise. With a healthy blood and lymph circulation, skin is less likely to become fluid logged and glowing skin cancels out dark shadows. A cool eye mask (or chilled camomile tea bags) allowed to rest on closed lids for around 10 minutes may help reduce any swelling.

## SPECIAL CARE FOR *Lips*

Lips have few sebaceous glands, are sensitive to low humidity and chap and flake easily. Use a conditioning salve on its own or under lipstick to protect them from moisture loss. Choose salves with sunscreens, as herpes simplex (cold sore) blisters are triggered by heat and sunlight. At night, apply Vaseline thickly: it really is the best softening, moisture-sealing agent for dry, rough lips. In the morning, a very light scrub with a damp toothbrush (a Cindy Crawford tip) sloughs off flakes and floods lips with rosy circulation.

If you have any pucker lines around the lip contours moisturize them with regular anti-ageing creams. Some experts recommend using eye creams on the lips for their lightweight firming effects. Avoid glossy lipsticks that creep into lines around the lip line, accentuating wrinkling, and choose warm, natural-looking tones, such as rosewood.

**MINIMIZE FEATHERING:** Like the skin around the eyes, the lip zone is also highly vulnerable due to the high-mobility factor. Prime lips with "lipfix" formula to prevent feathering at the edges, and always use a moist-finish rather than glossy lipstick.

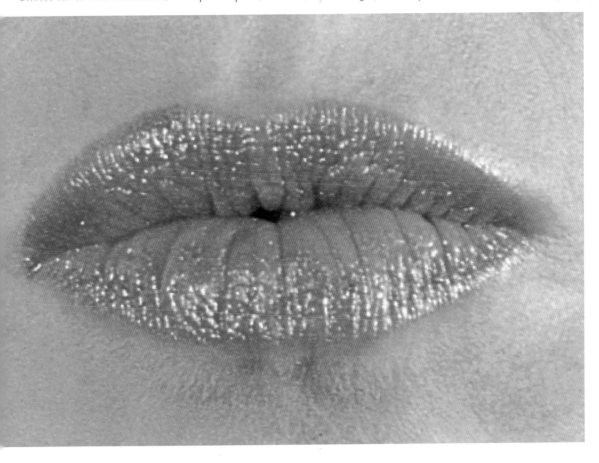

As many as 60 per cent of British women claim to have sensitive skin, according to cosmetic giants, l'Oreal, who two years ago, chose to test a new sensitive skin range in the UK. At the same time, rivals Estee Lauder launched their sensitive skin range in Europe, following acclaim in the US. Pale skins with a tendency to dryness are most likely to suffer sensitivity. But what does "sensitive" really mean?

# Strategies for problem skins

## TAILORING YOUR SKIN CARE

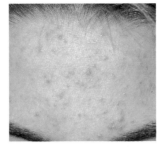

**OILY SKIN:** Stress and hormone imbalance can cause acne.

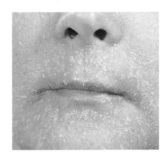

**DRY SKIN:** Overly dry skin may be an early sign of eczema.

## SENSITIVE *Skin*

A genuine sensitive or irritant reaction can be caused by sun, wind, rough handling and even water. Redness, itching, swelling and stinging are common and rapid responses, but the same trigger may not provoke the same reaction another time. However, sensitive reaction can lead to fully blown allergy. Years of chronic irritation weakens the skin and causes significant ageing. An allergic reaction occurs each time the skin comes in contact with the trigger. Perfumes, preservatives, colourings, detergents and surfactants, and sunscreens such as PABA are all common cosmetic allergens. Responses vary: blistering, cracking, oozing, scaling and redness are all common. Allergies are individual and idiosyncratic – it does not follow that if you react to one agent, you'll react to them all.

Hypo-allergenic and sensitive skin-care ranges exclude ingredients most likely to irritate, while including agents to calm and strengthen the skin against environmental attack. If you have sensitive skin avoid creams containing AHAs, which are notorious irritatants. US dermatologist Albert Kligman used glycolic acid to devise a test for skin irritancy, which is now used the world over. When choosing a new product, do a patch test before you buy.

## OILY *Skin*

Theoretically, the problem of oily skin should lessen with age. Production by the sebaceous glands varies according to hormone activity, and the main cause of increased production is testosterone, which surges at puberty. However, according to Dr Anthony Chu, consultant dermatologist to the UK Acne Support Group, stress combined with testosterone activity is a common cause of acne in women far beyond the age of puberty. Oestrogen counteracts testosterone, so some contraceptive pills are effective in controlling oily skin and acne. In contrast the progesterone-only "mini-pill" can cause acne as the body metabolizes progesterone into testosterone. Pre-period spots erupt in the progesterone phase of the menstrual cycle and outbreaks of spots may also occur as oestrogen levels dwindle toward the menopause.

New York dermatologist Patricia Wexler believes oily skin should neither be pampered nor punished. Alcohol-based astringents help remove oil from very oily skins, but they can also strip out moisture and cause a reactionary surge in oil production. Many oily skin ranges use oil blotters in toners to minimize the risk of aggravaton.

Combining products containing Retin-A and AHAs (both prescribed by dermatologists) controls severe problems in oily skin by exfoliating blocked pores and discouraging them from becoming distended, while normalizing the skin's lipid barrier. Over the counter, AHA-based cosmetics can also help regulate moderately oily skin. Toners and spot control lotions containing salycilic acid (a BHA) are effective exfoliants and de-greasers. For stubborn spots, use a benzoyl peroxide treatment, keeping it well away from the surrounding skin. Use an oil-free moisturizer on drier zones only.

## DRY *Skin*

Dry skin becomes the more common problem as skin ages, especially after the menopause when sebaceous output drops and skin loses its integral ability to retain moisture. A tendency to have dry skin is inherited, although central heating, air conditioning and temperature oscillation don't help skin retain moisture. Ultraviolet ligh also disrupts cellular cohesion, unpicking the tight, defensive mesh of cells in the epidermis, so that moisture can escape. As a result the skin's surface becomes flaky and lines more ingrained.

Dermatologists urge that it is vital to keep dry skin adequately moisturized to prevent it from developing sensitivities. An excessively dry skin could be an early warning of atopic eczema, warns Dr Ian White, consultant dermatologist at St Thomas's Hospital, London. Gentle exfoliation – AHA products help here too – keep the surface smooth and receptive to moisture. Creams don't have to be greasy to work well: choose a cream with a texture that feels comfortable. Lanolin is often used in skin clinics as an excellent therapy for chronically dry skin. Humidifiers also help prevent dry, itchy skin.

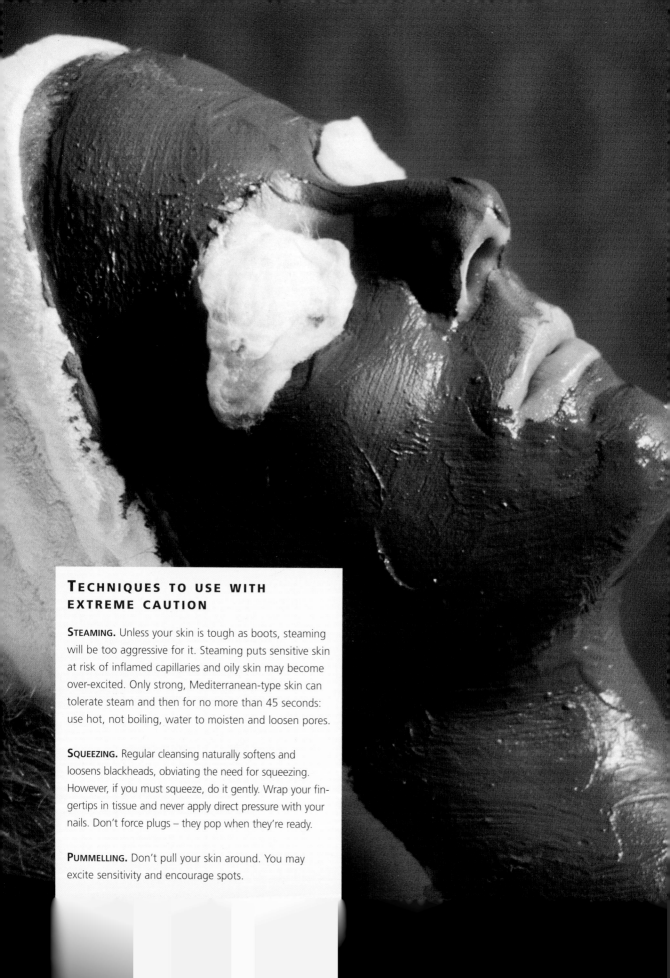

## TECHNIQUES TO USE WITH EXTREME CAUTION

**STEAMING.** Unless your skin is tough as boots, steaming will be too aggressive for it. Steaming puts sensitive skin at risk of inflamed capillaries and oily skin may become over-excited. Only strong, Mediterranean-type skin can tolerate steam and then for no more than 45 seconds: use hot, not boiling, water to moisten and loosen pores.

**SQUEEZING.** Regular cleansing naturally softens and loosens blackheads, obviating the need for squeezing. However, if you must squeeze, do it gently. Wrap your fingertips in tissue and never apply direct pressure with your nails. Don't force plugs – they pop when they're ready.

**PUMMELLING.** Don't pull your skin around. You may excite sensitivity and encourage spots.

# The art of facials

## WHY HAVE A FACIAL?

**Do facials work? If you enjoy them they do. Taking an hour out for yourself is one of life's luxuries and a professional facial is so relaxing your face is bound to look better afterward. But what of the long-term benefits of a professional cleansing and facial massage?**

### THE BENEFITS OF *Facials*

Certainly massage can help lymphatic glands clear swelling and puffiness, maintains Dr David Fenton of St Thomas's hospital, London. However, the afterglow is short term as it is due to a temporary blood circulation boost. He also believes that the effects of a firming facial, which uses electrical currents to stimulate the skin, last only a matter of hours – days at most. And if you have very greasy, acne-prone skin, he suggests avoiding stimulating facials completely as they can aggravate sebaceous glands.

Professional beauty therapists argue that treating yourself to a facial is extremely worthwhile as it is usually the beginning of a better relationship with your skin. As facials are invariably diagnostic, therapists use products best suited to your skin type and recommend a programme for home use.

### WHAT HAPPENS DURING A *Facial?*

A classic facial includes cleansing, exfoliation, massage, mask, toning and moisturizing. Usually, a treatment lasts about 60 to 90 minutes, including time to relax while the mask takes effect – say, 10 to 15 minutes. Some treatments are entirely manual, others use electronic massage equipment to stimulate facial muscles. Purists hold that fingers are most sensitive and therefore efficient; modernists assert that machines have a deeper stimulating action. Before you select a particular type of facial the beauty therapist will conduct a detailed consultation concerning your health, diet and lifestyle.

### TYPES OF *Facial*

**BASIC FACIALS.** These involve manual massage with a variety of skin-care products. Some may also include mini hand, shoulder or foot massages.

**AROMATHERAPY FACIALS.** These involve essential oils or products manufactured from them. Essential oils are said to have an affinity with the skin's natural oils and can be used to supplement or regulate sebaceous output. Therapists often use pressure point massage to encourage their efficacy. Oils are also used to stimulate and relax.

**ELECTRONIC FACIALS.** Electrotherapy is said to enhance the action of skin-care products. The best-known electrotherapy method is called Cathiodermie and was established in the 1960s. It involves two types of low-voltage current being applied with tiny fork-like electrodes. Galvanic current ionizes both skin and gels, improving absorption. High-frequency faradic current massages the skin's surface, boosting circulation and producing anti-bacterial ozone.

**NON-SURGICAL FACE LIFTS.** Controversial – and hugely popular – these high-tech treatments use electronic massage techniques to boost both muscle and tissue tone. Electric microcurrents compatible with the body's own stimulate the 30 muscles of the face. They also ease fine lines, and boost the circulation and lymph. However, to keep muscles "exercised", treatments, which are expensive, must be regular.

### DIY WEEKLY FACIAL TREATMENT

For a basic home facial you can do yourself, simply follow these simple steps:

**1** Cleanse with cream or foam, massaging the face with circular movements. Rinse with tepid water and a soft sponge. Blot the skin damp, not dry.

**2** Exfoliate using a gentle granular or latex-based "gommage", concentrating on problem zones. Rinse and pat dry.

**3** Massage with a nourishing oil or cream (see p.32).

**4** Apply a mask (see p.25) directly over your moisturized skin, to encourage the cream to penetrate further. Soak cotton pads in eye make-up remover, or use cold camomile tea bags, and place over the eyelids. Relax for 10 minutes.

**5** Remove mask and apply toner.

**6** Moisturize with your regular day or night formula.

# **F**acial massage

## SMOOTHING OUT SIGNS OF TENSION

Massage improves the circulation, which makes your skin look fresher and more glowing. It can discourage tension frowns and furrows by de-stressing facial muscles, easing headaches and lifting tiredness. It's therefore a good idea to massage your face whenever you can find the time.

### INSTRUCTIONS FOR A COMPLETE *Facial massage*

Cleanse the skin first and be very gentle: don't drag the skin. A light oil blended to suit your skin type allows the fingers to slip over the skin and encourages more fluid massage movements than creams that tend to "sink in". Use brisk movements for a morning wake-up massage and slow, soothing strokes for an evening calm down.

**2** Stroke firmly upward from collar bone to chin using each hand alternately. Tilt your head to the left and stroke the right side of your neck, then repeat on the other side.

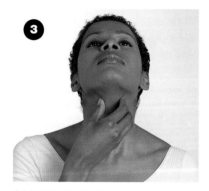

**1** Rest the palms of your hands on your face with the fingers touching your forehead and the heels of your hands on your chin. Hold for a moment, press gently, then slowly draw your hands out toward your ears, as though smoothing away tension. You can use this palming technique on its own whenever you feel the need to soothe and refresh a tired mind or eyes; it is especially helpful if you regularly use a VDU.

**3** Using both hands pinch along your jawline with your thumbs and knuckles of your index fingers to help prevent a double chin. Start at the chin and work out to your ears. Pinch close to the bone so you don't stretch the skin.

**4** Slap gently under your chin with the backs of both hands while keeping your tongue curled back in your mouth. This stretches the skin under your chin.

**5** Make an "O" shape with your mouth and curl your lips tightly over your teeth. With both index fingers, make small pressures over your chin and round each side of your mouth.

**6** Using both hands stroke outward from the corners of your mouth across your cheeks to your ears, releasing tension in the powerful cheek muscles.

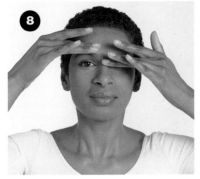

**7** Close your eyes, then with one hand following the other stroke from the bridge of your nose over your forehead to the hairline, smoothing away those tension lines.

**8** Massage away frown lines. Make short, firm strokes upward from the bridge of your nose, across to the start of the eyebrows, then diagonally back down to the bridge of the nose.

**9** With your fingertips make circular pressure movements over your forehead. Work from the bridge of your nose to your temples, covering the entire forehead up to your hairline.

**10** Stroke your forehead gently with your fingertips to soothe it. Work from the centre out to the temples. Finish by lightly pressing the temples. Clench your teeth slightly to strengthen your jaw muscle as you do this.

**11** Circle your eyes with your middle fingers. Stroke firmly from the bridge of your nose outward over your eyebrows. Press on the temples, then stroke very lightly under your eyes with the gentlest of touches.

**12** Pinch along both eyebrows from above the bridge of your nose to the temples. Gently press into the indentations in the browbones just under the eyebrows. Finish the massage by repeating step 1.

# **F**acial workout

## EXPRESSING THE LINES

Do facial exercises amount to nothing more than grimacing into the mirror? Surprisingly, some dermatologists rate them more highly than muscle-stimulating facials. Daily exercises beat machines, they say, for firming up slack jawlines and maintaining good blood circulation. Muscles are the same all over the body – keep them working and they stay firm.

Here is one non-surgical face-lift technique that costs nothing to try. Find a warm room in which you will not be disturbed. Cleanse your face and relax. Now you are ready to start the workout. Repeat each sequence three times.

### **ELIMINATE A DOUBLE CHIN**

**1** Sit at a table and, with a closed, relaxed mouth, jut your chin forward and slightly upward.

**2** Rest one elbow on the table and clench your fist. Balance your chin on your clenched fist. (A)

**3** Slide your lower lip out and over your top lip. (B)

**4** Press the tip of your tongue against the roof of your mouth behind your top teeth. Increase the pressure over a count of five. Hold. (C)

**5** Slowly release the pressure over a count of five.

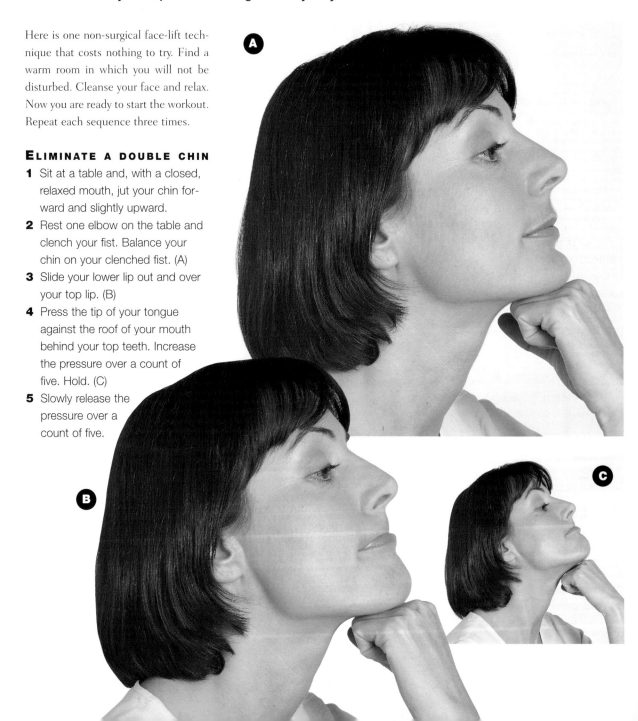

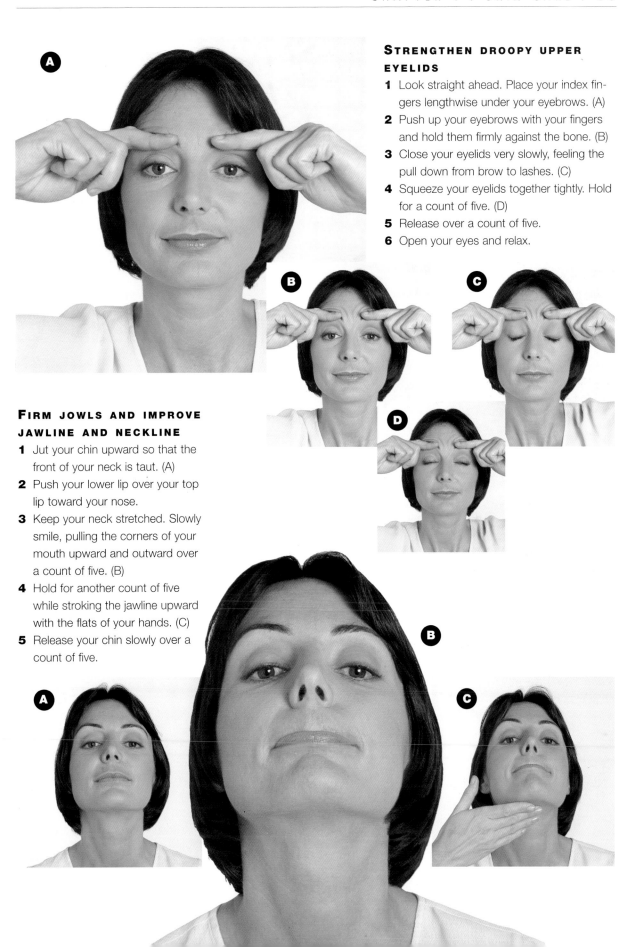

**A**

### STRENGTHEN DROOPY UPPER EYELIDS

**1** Look straight ahead. Place your index fingers lengthwise under your eyebrows. (A)

**2** Push up your eyebrows with your fingers and hold them firmly against the bone. (B)

**3** Close your eyelids very slowly, feeling the pull down from brow to lashes. (C)

**4** Squeeze your eyelids together tightly. Hold for a count of five. (D)

**5** Release over a count of five.

**6** Open your eyes and relax.

**B**

**C**

**D**

### FIRM JOWLS AND IMPROVE JAWLINE AND NECKLINE

**1** Jut your chin upward so that the front of your neck is taut. (A)

**2** Push your lower lip your top lip toward your nose.

**3** Keep your neck stretched. Slowly smile, pulling the corners of your mouth upward and outward over a count of five. (B)

**4** Hold for another count of five while stroking the jawline upward with the flats of your hands. (C)

**5** Release your chin slowly over a count of five.

**B**

**A**

**C**

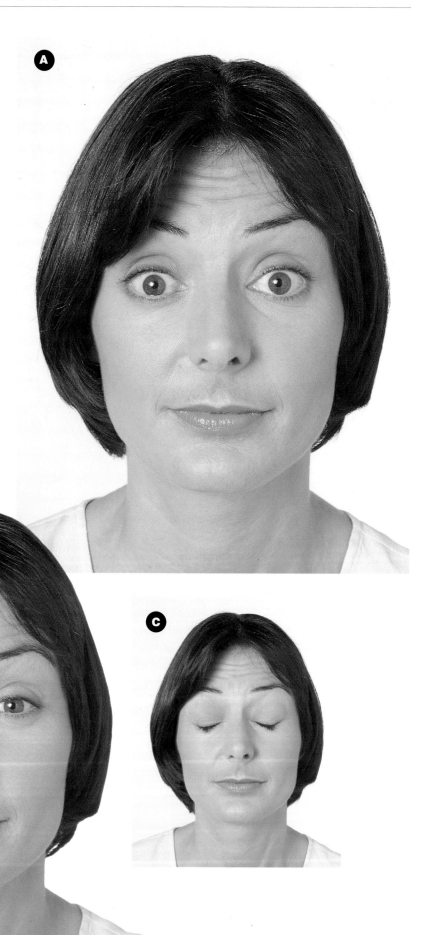

## STRENGTHEN LOWER EYELIDS TO ELIMINATE BAGS AND PUFFINESS

**1** Looking straight ahead, raise your brows (A).

**2** Raise your lower lids in five movements. (B)

**3** Close your eyes gently and squeeze upper and lower lids together. Hold the squeeze for a count of five. (C)

**4** With your eyes still closed, release the lower lid muscles in five movements.

**5** Open your eyes, then slowly relax your face.

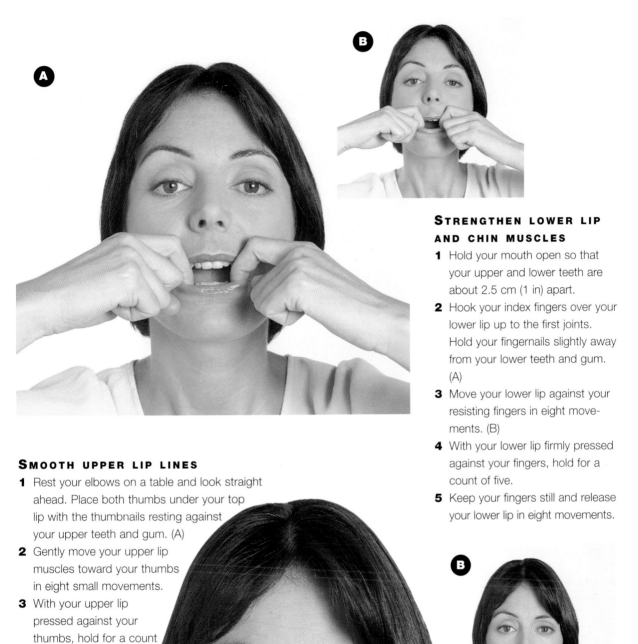

## STRENGTHEN LOWER LIP AND CHIN MUSCLES

**1** Hold your mouth open so that your upper and lower teeth are about 2.5 cm (1 in) apart.

**2** Hook your index fingers over your lower lip up to the first joints. Hold your fingernails slightly away from your lower teeth and gum. (A)

**3** Move your lower lip against your resisting fingers in eight movements. (B)

**4** With your lower lip firmly pressed against your fingers, hold for a count of five.

**5** Keep your fingers still and release your lower lip in eight movements.

## SMOOTH UPPER LIP LINES

**1** Rest your elbows on a table and look straight ahead. Place both thumbs under your top lip with the thumbnails resting against your upper teeth and gum. (A)

**2** Gently move your upper lip muscles toward your thumbs in eight small movements.

**3** With your upper lip pressed against your thumbs, hold for a count of five. (B)

**4** Keep your thumbs still and release your muscles in eight slow movements.

**NECK** – Dry skin here is vulnerable to environmental damage. Protect with a sunscreening moisturizer to prevent ring lines and "turkey neck" sagging. Toning massage and exercise help keep skin firm and your neck flexible.

**CHEST** – Consistent sun damage causes "V-neck" furrowing and crêpiness around the cleavage. An AHA-based moisturizer plus a good sunscreen protect and may retexturize the skin surface.

**BREASTS** – Heavy breasts consistently lose uplift, especially after pregnancy. Make sure your bra affords the right support without constricting breasts or shoulder muscles. Toning exercises won't significantly firm, but they can improve your profile. Health-check your breasts every month, examining them carefully.

**STOMACH** – This zone loses tone the fastest and most noticeably, especially after pregnancy. Regular exercise helps keep muscles toned and the stomach flat. Firm stomach muscles also help to support the lower back, preventing aches and damage. Gentle massage helps break down fatty deposits and relieves bloating. Good posture also refines your profile.

**HANDS** – Frequent exposure to detergents dries and roughens the skin and may damage nails. Sun damage causes slack skin tone and hyper-pigmentation – or age spots. A sunscreening hand cream protects and prevents dehydration. Simple manicure keeps nails trim and attractive. Massage and exercise keeps fingers nimble and joints flexible.

**LEGS** – Heaviness, swelling and varicose veins are all caused by a sedentary lifestyle, leading to poor circulation. Overweight, constipation and pregnancy pressurize veins; exercise and a fibre-rich diet relieve congestion and maintain veinous health. Massage stimulates lymphatic drainage and eases swollen ankles.

**FEET** – A lifetime of ill-fitting shoes causes hard skin build-up, corns and calluses. Regular home pedicure keeps skin supple and feet comfortable. Comfortable shoes limit the damage. Massage soothes soreness and eases swelling. Exercise maintains foot and toe flexibility.

**HIPS AND THIGHS** – Cellulite, or orange-peel skin, is caused by the shape and formation of fat cells beneath the skin's surface. Hormonal activity, pregnancy and the Pill precipitate its appearance and few women escape it! Cellulite may diminish after the menopause, but HRT can perpetuate it. Diet and exercise may not eradicate it, neither will so-called "slimming" creams. Careful massage helps to strengthen the skin, making dimples less obvious.

# YOUR TOP-TO-TOE CARE PLAN

# CHAPTER 2

# Body care

Understanding your body's strengths and weaknesses is the first step to ensuring that it grows older gracefully, attractively and healthily. Regular and informed body care is the key to maintaining a physique to be proud of – whatever your age. Regular exercise builds and maintains all-round fitness and helps keep your weight stable. The calories burned in an hour of activity increase in proportion to your weight and how energetic your exercising is.

**BODY BASICS:** From contouring creams to deep moisture treats, there's a formula for every zone of the body.

# Neck, chest and bust

## MAINTAINING THIS MOST REVEALING OF ZONES

**Lines on your neck can date you like rings on a tree. Skin here is thinner and drier than the face, with fewer naturally protective sebaceous glands to guard against moisture loss. Soaps, detergents and perfumes all dehydrate and sensitize the neck to other irritants, such as scratchy roll necks and scarves, and extremes of temperature. Breasts – your most obvious feminine assets – need support to maintain a firm, yet gently curving profile.**

### CARING FOR *Neck and chest skin*

Cleanse your neck and chest gently, using your facial wash or cleanser. Concentrate on the hairline especially at the back, where hairstyling products rub off and may irritate. Use a gentle exfoliant to disperse tiny sub-skin spots and rough patches. Then tone with a mild alcohol-free toner, such as rosewater, sweeping firmly upward with a saturated cotton pad.

Moisturize the neck with a serum or light lotion, both of which are absorbed fast and don't rub off on clothes or attract grime. If your skin is tolerant, use an AHA-based lotion to help smooth and prevent crêpey, "turkey neck" skin. A sunscreen is

**AGE REVEALER:** Perhaps even more than your face, your neck and chest can give your age away. Do not neglect this frequently exposed zone.

vital – check there's one in your moisture formula or top up your moisturizer with an SPF 15 lotion. Chest skin is thin but oilier than necks, thanks to a denser concentration of oil glands. An AHA-based moisturizer helps keep pores clear while smoothing furrows and crinkles. Once again, a good sunscreen is vital.

## HOW TO EXAMINE YOUR BREASTS

Your doctor should check your breasts each time you have a cervical smear. But you should also check them yourself. Breasts vary in texture at different points of your menstrual cycle. The best time to check is two or three days after the end of your period, and at the same time each month so that you get a feel for what is normal or unusual.

**1** Stand naked in front of a mirror and scrutinize your breasts for any change in shape, and any puckering or dimpling of the skin.

**2** Lie on your back with your head on a pillow. Check the left breast first. Place a folded towel under your left shoulder and your left hand under your head. This helps spread the breast tissue to make it easier to examine.

**3** Press the flat of your right hand systematically and gently over your entire breast, feeling for lumps or unusually dense areas.

**4** Check your armpit for lumps, starting in the hollow and moving down toward your breast.

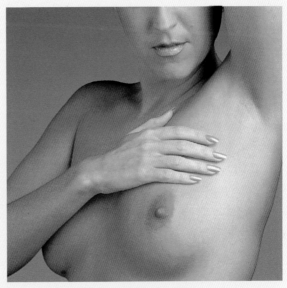

**5** If you think you've found something, check the same area in the other breast: if both breasts feel the same, it's probably just your shape.

**6** Repeat the sequence for the right breast.

**If you're worried, see your doctor as soon as you can.**

## LENDING SUPPORT TO YOUR *Breasts*

Breasts are largely supported by the Cooper's ligaments, which run from the nipples to the outer edges of the breasts. The pectoral muscles run from the outer edges of the upper breasts to the armpits, so the breasts are literally suspended. With age and breast-feeding, breasts may become pendulous, taxing ligaments and muscles and stretching the skin. After the menopause, when body fat begins to diminish, breasts lose weight and begin to take on a flatter, more hollow appearance. The once-supportive skin loses its elasticity and breasts sag. When this happens rashes can occur on the underside of the breasts as a result of perspiration building up beneath them.

Clearly it is important to wear a well-fitting bra, especially when exercising and post-surgery. In addition, for extra tonic effect, you could splash breasts with cold water before stroking on a cream. Moisturizing lotions condition the skin, helping to preserve its elasticity and prevent stretch marks. Regular stroking massage also boosts healthy breast awareness but don't knead, prod or press too deeply. Once a week, gently exfoliate the breasts by dry brushing or using a body scrub. AHA lotions also help to maintain surface smoothness.

**THE PERFECT FIT:** Your breasts should fill the cups without spilling out, and the underband of the bra should be firm without digging in. Underwired cups are the most supportive.

# **B**ust toning exercises

Help raise the profile of your breasts by toning the pectoral muscles just above them and the anterior deltoids at the back of the shoulders. Repeat each exercise as many times as you like, and repeat the sequence at least twice a day.

### **HALF PRESS-UPS**

Kneel in doggy position, arms straight, hands ahead of and slightly wider apart than shoulders. Bend the arms until your chest nearly touches the floor and straighten without locking elbows.

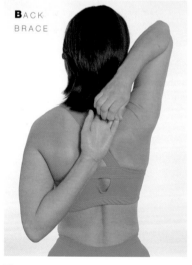

**B**ACK BRACE

### **BACK BRACES**

Raise your right elbow and drop your hand behind your back. Bring your left hand up behind your back to meet it. Clasp hands and hold for five seconds, then change sides. If your hands don't meet, bridge the gap by grasping a washcloth.

### **ISOMETRIC PRESSES**

Sitting or standing, keep your back straight.

**1** Raise your elbows out to shoulder level and hold them about 10 cm (4 in) in front of you. Squeeze as hard as you can for a count of five. You could do this holding a ball.

**2** Bring your elbows together in front of you and hold just above your head. Squeeze and hold for a count of five. (A)

**3** Bring your elbows out to the side again and raise over the crown of your head. Squeeze and hold. (B)

**4** Push arms straight out in front of you and, keeping your arms at shoulder height, squeeze and hold for a count of five. (C)

4

## TONING AND FIRMING THE NECK

Follow this routine every time you apply body lotion or throat cream. Toning massage and exercise help keep skin firm and your neck flexible.

**1** Using the backs of both hands alternately, lightly stroke from your chest up the front of your neck, under your chin and over your jawline. Do at least 10 strokes with each hand.

**2** Quickly and lightly slap under your chin with the back of one hand 30 times.

**3** Using one hand, place the fingertips on one side of your throat and the thumb on the other. Make firm and rapid, but gentle, circular movements up and down your throat five times. Repeat with the other hand.

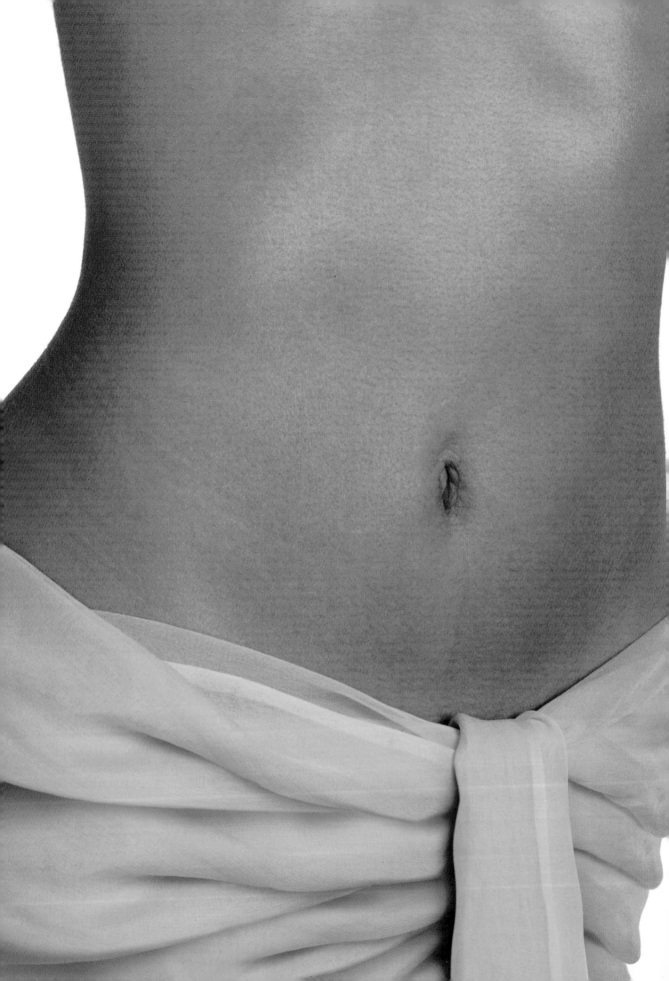

# **S**tomach

## ACHIEVING A TONED, FIRM STOMACH

**Most women feel least confident about this body zone. By the time they reach 40, few women can boast the flat taut tummy of their teens – if indeed they had them then! But even after having children, regular exercise can limit the damage.**

If you think of the extent to which your stomach expands during pregnancy, it's an awesomely accommodating zone. Keeping the skin well moisturized and conditioned goes a long way toward helping to prevent stretch marks as does avoiding rapid weight gain. In the initial red stages, retinoic acid may help avert stretch marks, but once they're white and established nothing save surgery will shift them.

Getting the stomach back into shape and maintaining its tone is an epic of hard work. However, toning slack muscles with regular exercise not only results in a smooth profile, it also means that the lower back is better supported. Keep stomach muscles well tuned and you stand a better chance of avoiding agonizing back pain while you're looking good in your lycra.

Try the stomach workout on page 47 and make it a regular part of your exercise routine. To encourage commitment to exercise try joining a body conditioning class at your local gym. Warm-ups often include low-impact aerobics. The main moves are a specific sequence of toning exercises involving hand weights, rubber tubing or the resistance of your own body weight. Many of the exercises will be aimed specifically at toning the stomach muscles. Circuit training with Nautilus equipment also gives fast results.

### EXERCISES TO IMPROVE YOUR POSTURE

Good posture can take 3 kg (7 lb) off your body image.
Reprogramme your alignment by conditioning your body with this basic exercise. Repeat three times a day, so that good posture becomes second nature.

**1** Stand about 30 cm (12 in) away from a wall, facing the room; your knees should be relaxed and feet hip-width apart. Pull your stomach muscles in toward the wall. Breathe out and press your head, shoulders, upper back and hips into the wall.

**2** Hold your spine straight and stomach muscles taut. Push away from the wall with your hands into a free-standing position. Look straight ahead without raising or jutting your chin. Relax your shoulders without slouching. This is what perfect posture feels like.

**BACK SUPPORT:** Good posture encourages firm stomach muscles, which then help to support the lower back, preventing aches and damage.

# The stomach massage

Use this massage sequence to ease cramps, constipation and bloating, while toning the skin texture It also relaxes nervous tension in the solar plexus zone. Lie down comfortably, resting a pillow under your knees to ease back strain.

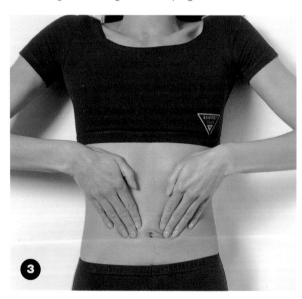

**1** Working from hips to rib-cage, massage each side of the stomach with the fingertips, then the flats of the hands in gentle raking and sweeping movements.

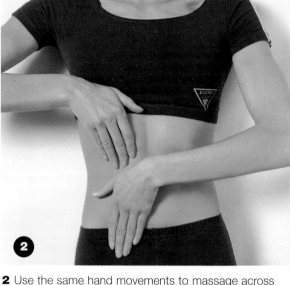

**2** Use the same hand movements to massage across the stomach from right to left, just below the rib-cage. Then massage the sides again, as step 1.

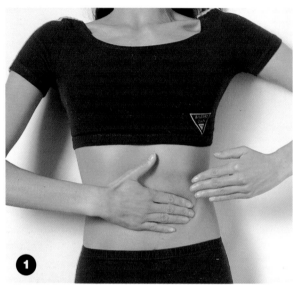

**3** Starting just under the rib-cage, stroke firmly downward to the navel several times. Repeat, sweeping down and out toward the sides.

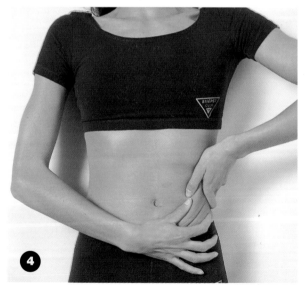

**4** Pick up any loose flesh and roll it between your fingers and thumbs, working outward from the centre to the sides. This helps break down fatty tissue.

**1** Lie on your back, legs bent, feet hip-width apart, and rest your hands on your thighs. Pull your stomach muscles down toward the floor. Slide your hands to your knees as you curl your body upward and raise your head and shoulders off the floor. Repeat 10 to 25 times.

**3** Lie on your back and stretch your arms out on the floor above your head, palms up. Cross your ankles and tuck your heels into your bottom, then bring your knees toward your chest. Draw down your stomach muscles toward the floor. Slowly roll your hips up toward the ceiling and lower in small, controlled movements, keeping your shoulders on the floor. Repeat 10 to 15 times.

**2** Lie on your back and rest your right foot over your left thigh above the knee. Pull in your stomach muscles and put your hands behind your head. Raise your body, aiming to touch your left knee with your right elbow; keep your left elbow on the floor. Slowly lower your body and repeat 5 to 15 times on each side.

# The stomach workout

**This sequence works all your stomach muscles and helps strengthen a weak lower back.**

# Legs

## ACHIEVING FIRM, TONED LEGS

**The chair is the legs' greatest enemy. Long periods of sitting means that joints may become stiff through under use and remaining too long in one position. Circulation is restricted, causing problems with veins, especially if you habitually cross your legs.**

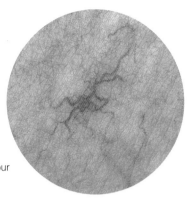

**GENETIC THREAD:** Telangiectasia (thread veins) may be part of your genetic inheritance.

### PROBLEMS WITH *Veins*

There are two main vein conditions that affect the legs. The first, and less problematic, is the appearance of spider or thread veins (telangiectasia) on the thighs and inside knees. These are not "broken" veins but capillaries whose walls have lost their elasticity and so remain permanently and obviously dilated. Such veins may be genetically inherited or induced by long-term use of steroids, pregnancy or being severely overweight. The most common treatment for spider veins is sclerotherapy, where an inflammatory fluid is injected into the capillaries to seal them off. Laser treatment that vaporizes the capillaries is also becoming popular.

The second is the appearance of varicose veins from mid-life onward. The main cause of varicose veins is overweight, as it leads to increased pressure bearing down on the legs. Pregnancy also triggers them, owing to the extra weight and hormonal changes, which relax and dilate the vein walls to accommodate the 50 per cent increase of blood in the body. Veins that become varicose are in fact superficial "feeder" veins, which supply the deep veins and arteries. These veins contain valves that prevent blood from flowing back, and when they fail problems begin: blood pools, pressure rises and the veins dilate, lengthen, twist and become knotted.

### TREATMENT AND PREVENTION OF *Varicose veins*

Varicose veins are both ugly and painful. They can cause throbbing, aching, night cramps and swollen ankles especially in hot weather, during menstruation and when standing for long periods. Treatment may be sclerotherapy, which seals the veins, although the pressure of blood may force them open again in a few years and the recurrence rate after 10 years is

as high as 90 per cent. The more permanent solution is surgery, involving tiny stab incisions, which allow the veins to be stripped out either in sections or in total. The circulation is then diverted to other veins.

You can help prevent varicose veins by exercising or swimming to boost circulation and avoiding sitting with your legs crossed or pressing on a hard chair edge. Put your feet up at regular intervals during the day and especially in the evening. Eat a fibre-rich diet to prevent constipation. Aloe vera juice is also an excellent bowel tonic. Supplements that may help include circulation-boosting gingko biloba (see p.103) and vein-strengthening silica.

### DEALING WITH *Swollen ankles*

As you grow older, slightly swollen ankles at the end of the day become increasingly common. If your ankles become very puffy and the skin is taut and shiny, check with your doctor that the problem is not liver, kidneys or heart-related.

According to J. F. Lazartigue's Paris-based Institut des Jambes, in addition to a sedentary lifestyle, overweight and pregnancy, some types of the Pill and even electric blankets can cause swollen ankles by encouraging leg veins to dilate and become less efficient at draining excess fluid. Exercise – especially walking up and down stairs and cycling – is the obvious antidote. In addition, support tights with graduated compression from foot to thigh work like a passive massage to pump blood and lymph back up the legs to minimize swelling and take the weight off varicose veins.

Reflexology (see p.116) is a gentle means of reducing leg swelling during and after pregnancy and generally stimulating lymphatic drainage. Cooling aromatherapy gels and sprays – especially if they contain peppermint – are a stimulating, on-the-spot tonic for jet-lagged or land-locked legs. At the end of the day, reduce swelling fast by soaking legs up to the knees in alternate buckets of cold and luke-warm water, with a little added sea salt. After the cold, the warm water feels momentarily boiling – and really gets the circulation going.

# The leg workout

**These exercises tone the back and inside thighs, where flabbiness is most obvious.**

**1** Stretch your leg muscles first by sitting cross-legged with your palms on the floor in front of your feet. Bend forward as far as you can and hold for five counts.

**2** Position yourself on all fours, resting on your forearms. Stretch out your left leg and point your toes. Lift it as high as you can, cross it over your right leg and touch the floor. Lift it back again. Repeat eight times for each leg. (A)

**3** Lift your left leg up behind you, bending the knee. Keep the foot flexed and raise your heel toward the ceiling. Lift and lower in a pump action eight times for each leg. (B)

**4** Lie on your right side, resting your head on your hand. Keep your left leg straight and bend your right leg, so the knee and foot rest on the floor in front of you. Flex your left foot and raise and lower the leg eight times without touching the floor. Repeat on the other side. (C)

**5** Now, with your left leg bent, so that the foot is planted flat on the floor in front of you and the knee is pointing to the ceiling, hold the left foot and move your right leg slightly forward eight times. Then raise and lower the right leg eight times without touching the flloor. Repeat on the other side. (D)

**6** Finish by lying on your back and bringing your right knee as far as you can into your chest, clasping your hands around the calf or ankle. Hold the stretch for five counts then swap legs. (E)

**THE LEG MASSAGE**
**Every time you apply body lotion repeat this massage sequence to improve circulation and skin texture, and ease stiff knee joints.**

**1** Sit on the floor, legs out in front of you. Bend the knee of one leg, keeping the foot flat on the floor. With hands either side of your leg, stroke smoothly and firmly upward from your ankles to the tops of your thighs. Repeat five times on each leg.

**2** With alternate hands, kneed each thigh, rhythmically squeezing and releasing. Then stroke upward several times from the knee, one hand following the other.

**3** Massage around each knee with circular fingertip movements. Stroke gently at first, then apply gentle pressure as you stroke. Finally stroke gently upward behind the knee.

**4** Kneed each calf muscle with both hands, gently lifting and squeezing it away from the bone. Then stroke gently up the back of the leg.

# Your top 10 toners

## STAY FIRM AND FLEXIBLE WITH THIS 30-MINUTE DAILY WORKOUT

Your body is designed to keep moving. Stop for long periods and it simply loses its full mobility potential: most mobility problems endured in old age have their roots in sedentary habits established by the middle years. Experts estimate that keeping fit can extend your life by about two years. Any form of movement – from dancing to yoga – counts as healthy exercise, so long as you do it regularly.

HAMSTRING STRETCH

CALF MUSCLE STRETCH

THIGH STRETCH

**WARM-UP AND WIND-DOWN**
Gentle stretching and flexing before and after a workout helps prevent strain and injury to the muscles and joints. Hold each stretch for 15 to 20 seconds.

**1** Loosen your neck and shoulders. Stand straight with your feet shoulder-width apart. Relax your shoulders back and down. Very gently tilt your head to the right, feeling your neck stretch. Hold for 10 seconds, then tilt to the left and hold. Centre your head. Raise your right shoulder up toward your ear. Rotate back, down and up again three full times, then repeat forward. Repeat with the left shoulder.

**2** Stretch your arms. Rest your right hand on the back of your neck.

With your left hand, gently pull your right elbow back and down until you feel the stretch in your upper arm. Change arms and repeat the stretch.

**3** Stretch the shoulder muscles. Clasp your hands loosely in front of you and raise both arms up above your head.

**4** Stretch your hamstrings. Step forward with your right leg and straighten it. Keep your heel on the ground and raise your toes. Bend your left leg, keeping your heel on the floor. Hold your back straight and relaxed and rest both hands on your right thigh. Keeping your weight on your back leg, ease into the stretch. Hold for 10 seconds. Change legs and repeat.

**5** Stretch your calves. Step forward with your right leg, keeping your left leg straight. Both heels should be on the floor and toes pointing forward. Keep your back straight and hips to the front. Keeping your weight on your right leg, rest your hands on the thigh, bend your knee and ease into the stretch. Hold for 10 seconds. Change legs and repeat.

**6** Stretch your thighs. Stand on your right leg, gripping a chair with your right hand if you need to. Keeping your hips square, bend your left leg and catch the toes of your left foot with your free hand, easing it up toward your bottom. Hold the stretch for 10 seconds. Now change legs and repeat.

## 2 FLATTEN YOUR STOMACH

**REPEATS:** 10 building to 20 times.

**ACTION:** Lie on your back, knees bent, feet flat on the floor hip-width apart. Supporting – but not pulling – your head with your hands, curl your upper body forward off the ground. At the same time breathe out and pull in with your stomach muscles. Slowly lower your back to the floor, breathing in.

## 1 TONE YOUR WAIST

**REPEATS:** 15 building to 25 times each side.

**ACTION:** Stand with your feet shoulder-width apart, knees slightly bent. Rest your hands on your hips and keep your back straight and shoulders down. Facing forward, bend your torso to the right until you feel the stretch in your left side. Straighten up and repeat to the left.

## 3 FLATTEN YOUR STOMACH

**REPEATS:** 10 building to 20 times.

**ACTION:** Lie on your back, arms at your sides. Bend your knees and raise your legs in the air, crossing your ankles. Breathe out and pull your stomach muscles in as you roll your hips up toward your ribs in a tiny, controlled movement. Hold and breathe in. Then breathe out as you roll your hips back down. Always keep your back pressed to the floor.

# The daily work-out

### 4 TIGHTEN YOUR BUTTOCKS

**REPEATS:** 15 building to 25 times each leg.

**ACTION:** On all fours, place your knees below your hips and your elbows below your shoulders with your forearms forward for balance. Straighten your right leg out behind you and lift it to hip level. Slowly lower. Keep your stomach muscles pulled in throughout this exercise.

### 5 SHAPE HIPS AND LEGS

**REPEATS:** 10 to 15 times each leg.

**ACTION:** Stride forward with your right leg. Keeping your back straight and hips forward, bend both knees until the left almost touches the floor behind you and the right leg is at right angles. Feel the stretch.

### 6 FIRM FRONT OF THIGHS

**REPEATS:** 15 to 20 times each leg.

**ACTION:** Holding a chair for support, stand straight and turn your legs out slightly from the hips so your knees face outward. Raise the right leg as high as you can in front of you, aiming for waist level. Lower slowly.

### 7 FIRM INNER THIGHS

**REPEATS:** 15 to 20 times.

**ACTION:** Lie on your back, legs bent. Raise your knees to directly above your hips and lift your lower legs so that they are parallel to the ground. Press your back into the floor. Part your legs as far as you can to the sides then squeeze them back together. Rest your arms out at your sides for balance, or place your hands on your inner thighs for resistance.

## 9 TONE FRONT OF ARMS AND SIDE OF BACK

**REPEATS:** two building to three sets of eight repetitions, both arms.

**ACTION:** Sit on a stool and place the weight – ½kg (1lb) building to 2¼kg (5lb) – on the floor next to your right foot. Rest your left forearm over your thighs for support. Lean forward, flattening your back. Pick up the weight with your right hand and draw it up to your armpit. Lead with your elbow and keep your arm close to your side. Slowly lower without letting the weight touch the floor.

## 8 TONE BACKS OF ARMS

**REPEATS:** two to three sets of eight.

**ACTION:** Sit knees hip-width apart. Hold a weight in your right hand and raise, straightening your arm. Place your left hand below your right elbow and lower the weight behind you until your elbow points upward.

## 10 SHAPE YOUR SHOULDERS

**REPEATS:** three sets of eight repetitions.

**ACTION:** Stand with feet hip-width apart, toes forward. Holding a weight – ½kg (1lb) to 1½kg (3lb) – in each hand, start with hands in front of your thighs, palms inward. Leading with your knuckles and keeping palms facing down, raise arms out at the sides to shoulder level. Hold for a count of five, then lower slowly. Rest between each set.

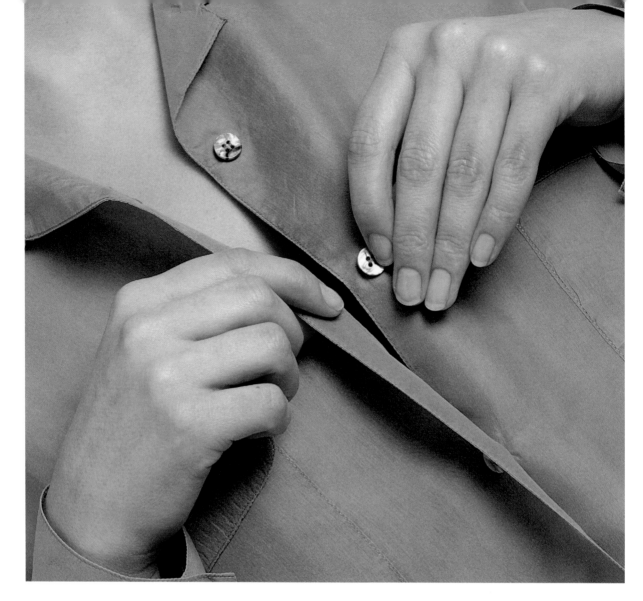

# **H**ands

### KEEPING THEM GRACEFUL

Because they are so exposed, hands are the first part of the body to show signs of ageing and the hardest to disguise. Protection is crucial when caring for hard-working hands. Moisturize liberally with hand cream, preferably after every time you wash them. Wear an SPF 15 sunscreen even on dull days – some hand creams contain this factor. Avoid contact with detergents and always wear gloves for housework and gardening.

Smooth general roughness and get rid of grime and stains by massaging with the same exfoliant that you use on your face, paying extra attention to the knuckles. Help counteract any redness by applying a green-tinted facial moisturizer that sinks in imperceptibly. Keep fingers nimble and flexible with a regular massage and exercise routine (see p.58), and keep nails attractively and simply groomed.

### **COPING WITH** *Age spots*

Ultraviolet damage is hands' worst enemy, causing skin slackness, loss of tone and solar lentigines – the classic age spots, which the French so charmingly call "cemetary medals". These flat brown spots are due to uneven clumping of melanin pigment and can be faded to a certain extent. Used regularly, creams containing hydroquinone (2 per cent strength is the legal limit in both America and Europe) work by breaking down the pigmentation just below the skin's surface. The body then metabolizes it as any other waste.

## NAILS – *Protective accessories*

Nails fulfil the vital function of protecting your extra-sensitive fingertips and improving your ability to pick up. Experts believe it's taken over 300 million years for the sheets of horny keratin protein that form the nails to evolve into smooth, translucent plates. What appears pink and sheeny is mostly composed of dead cells: the soft matrix at the base is the only living part of the nail. Here, new cells grow and push up older, dying cells that harden into protective shields.

Unlike hair that grows in cycles, nail growth is continuous, although rates vary. Children's nails take six to eight weeks to grow from base to tip; adults' three to four months. After the age of 40, nails become more horny and ridged as cell turnover slows. Nails grow faster on your writing hand, probably due to increased circulation to the fingertips. They also grow faster in summer than in winter, when cold weather hampers circulation, especially to the extremeties. Pregnancy, sunlight and exercise also speed growth.

## THE IMPORTANCE OF *Diet and moisture*

Strong, healthy growth relies on a good diet. Keratin contains high levels of sulphur and selenium and moderately high levels of calcium, potassium and trace minerals. Iron and zinc deficiencies cause brittleness, as might a lack of sulphrous amino acids, vitamin B1 (thiamine) and vitamin C. Tests on smokers' nail clippings have found all the vital minerals to be in lower concentrations than non-smokers', possibly because smoking inhibits circulation. But it's a myth that gelatine strengthens nails and white spots are more likely to be caused by past prodding and damage to the base than a lack of calcium. Research by manufacturers of nutritional supplements for hair and nails shows that the trace mineral silica helps strengthen the cross links that bond the keratin layers together and so helps prevent splitting and flaking.

A nail's water content is crucial: if it contains less than 12 per cent water it will flake, split and snap. Detergents strip protective oils from the skin and nails, so they are unable to conserve their own moisture. This is devastating in winter, when central heating indoors and freezing temperatures outside mean critically low ambient moisture levels. Regular massage with a little oil followed by lashings of hand cream help rehydrate both hands and nails. Protect them by wearing gloves in cold weather and rubber gloves to do the housework, especially hand washing.

## GROOMING YOUR *Nails*

Long nails are synonymous with elegance – they make short fingers look longer and give the hands a well cared-for look. But if they're too long they tend to look ludicrous worn with today's paired-down, simpler fashions. Shorter nail shapes also look less claw-like on older hands, which may have thinner fingers and pronounced knuckle joints.

Keeping nails at a practical length is a way of preventing breaks and splits, as the longer the nail, the greater its flexibility will be tested. An ideal, flattering length is just beyond the fingertips, where the "white" edges can be shaped to echo the curve of the half-moons at the base. Forget nail extensions: they damage the natural nail plate, are expensive to maintain and rarely look natural.

## HAND AND NAIL TROUBLESHOOTING

**SOFTEN ROUGH, DRY HANDS:** Massage in plenty of hand cream. Slip on cotton gloves (from photographic shops) then latex surgical gloves (from pharmacists). Leave for two hours or overnight.

**STRENGTHEN WEAK, BRITTLE NAILS:** Paint with a protein or polyester resin formula (from pharmacists or salons). Massage oil into the nail base daily and moisturize well.

**MEND SPLIT NAILS:** File down nail to minimize snagging. Patch each split with a waterproof, transparent nail bandage (from pharmacists or salons). Then apply polish or nail strengthener.

**SEAL FLAKES:** File down nail as far as you can. Prevent split from deepening by buffing off the top layer of the nail at the tip until it's smooth and even. Top with nail strengthener.

**SMOOTH RIDGES:** Buff the nail surface smooth with the fine, sandy side of a buffer. Polish with the smooth side. Use a ridge-filling base coat under polish.

# Finger flexes

Massage and exercise keeps wrists, hands, fingers and nails healthy by maintaining good circulation and joint flexibility. Do these quick massage and exercise routines every time you apply hand cream, or with a little olive or almond oil last thing at night.

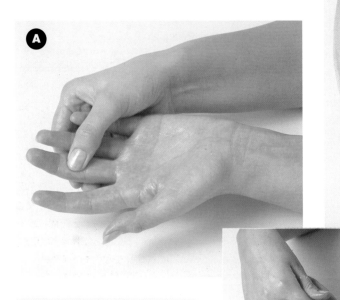

## THE HAND WORKOUT

1   Rotate each finger gently three times in each direction, manipulating it between the thumb and first finger of your other hand.
2   Gently rotate the wrists in each direction in turn.
3   Gently bend each wrist backward in turn by pushing the heel of your other hand against the palm.
4   Finish by letting your arms hang loosely by your sides, relaxing your hands, wrists and fingers.

## THE HAND MASSAGE

1   Drop a little hand cream or oil into the palm of one hand. Using the thumb of the other hand, massage the cream between and along each finger with firm, circular movements. (A)
2   Scissor each finger with the first and second fingers of the other hand, pulling firmly and gently from base to tips. (B)

3   Apply a little more hand cream or oil, then massage the palm of one hand with the thumb of the other, using firm circular movements.
4   Using firm, upward movements, stroke excess oil from palm to elbow. Lift the hand away at the end of each stroke.
5   Massage the forearm from the wrist to below the elbow with circular thumb movements. (C)
6   Repeat the sequence massaging the other hand.

# The 6-step manicure

Doing your nails doesn't have to turn into an epic. Even if you don't regularly wear polish, a once-weekly session keeps them well-groomed.

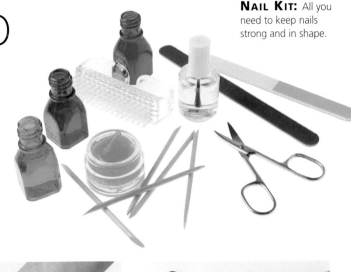

**NAIL KIT:** All you need to keep nails strong and in shape.

**1** Clean off any old polish with a gentle, acetone-free solvent that helps prevent nail brittleness and dry-out.

**2** Soak nails in a glass of warm, soapy water for two minutes. Blot dry and gently ease back the cuticles with a hoof stick wrapped in cotton wool. Don't jab the nail base.

**3** Clean under the nail tips with an orange stick. Rinse and file with a fine-textured emery board. Make long, sweeping strokes to shape, then lightly flick along the nail.

**6** Apply a protein-enriched base coat to strengthen weak nails and help prevent splitting, flaking and nail polish staining. Finally, choose a polish that flatters your skin tone.

**4** Rinse again and pat dry. Dot a drop of oil on to each cuticle and use the pad of the thumb of your other hand to massage it well into the nail bed.

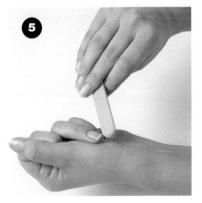

**5** Buff the nails with a smooth buffer. This boosts the circulation, helps even out ridges, seals nail tips to prevent fllaking, and leaves a natural, healthy-looking sheen.

## Foot first aid

**Foot bath for sore feet:** Add 1 drop of peppermint and 4 drops of lavender oil to a bowl of warm water. Soak feet for 10 minutes to ease swelling and burning.

**To treat blisters:** Sprinkle a few drops of lavender oil on a cold compress or plaster and place over blisters and tender spots. Leave for at least 10 minutes.

**To relieve painful itching:** Massage tea tree oil between the toes or around cracked heels.

**To treat cracked heels:** Seal deep cracks with Friar's Balsam, then moisturize three or four times daily to prevent further splitting and bleeding.

**To "kill" corns:** Relieve pressure and treat impacted dry skin with a proprietary disc plaster impregnated with salicylic acid. Avoid pastes and solutions that can migrate to surrounding healthy skin and cause irritation.

# Feet

## MAINTAINING HEALTHY FEET

Feet are the body's balancing act. Their tiny bones are delicately articulated to flex, splay, arch and grip in order to keep you upwardly mobile. If your feet are compromised, so is your posture. Foot problems can stress other joints and throw the entire body off-balance. A headache, for example, may have origins in the way you walk. Reflexologists believe that the foot contains pressure points relating to the entire body (see p.116). Their welfare then, is crucial to your comfort.

### CHOOSING THE RIGHT *Shoes*

Good style and good sense aren't always compatible in footwear for women. However, it's worth hunting for a creative compromise. According to the *American Journal of Bone and Joint Surgery*, 75 per cent of foot problems are caused by constantly wearing high heels which force toes forward, overarching the foot and imposing the body weight on the heels and balls of the feet. This unequal weight distribution means that the feet can't fully shock-absorb the impact of movement. Tension reverberates up the spine as you walk and may cause back pain and headaches.

A burning sensation on the balls of the feet is caused by the feet sliding into the narrowest part of the shoe as you walk – pitched forward by very high heels – and is an early warning sign of hard skin build-up. Corns and calluses ultimately form to protect the bones and joints from this type of shock.

Reverting to "flatties" may not be the answer. Habitually wearing high heels shortens the tendons in the back of the leg, so suddenly dropping down several centimetres can be agony. If you are used to wearing high heels, switching to shoes with a low heel of around 2½ – 5 cm (1 – 2 in) is often more comfortable than totally flat shoes, as the slightly raised heel is less likely to jar the foot and is more able to take the pressure off the lower back. Alternating high- and low-heeled shoes is the most practical answer to keeping muscles and tendons flexible. When you're running, walking or exercising always wear trainers with good, shock-absorbing soles.

### KEEPING FEET *Flexible*

To exercise feet, chiropodists recommend walking barefoot around the house or, more pleasurably, on the beach. Gripping damp sand exercises the toes and acts as a natural dead skin exfoliator. Exercise sandals are fashionable, but if you buy a pair, make sure they fit. Your heels should be cupped by a support ridge on the in-sole and grip bars should encourage the four smaller toes to curl while leaving the big toe flat. Bars or ridges that go right across the in-sole compromise the big toe and throw the foot off-balance.

In summer, prevent hard skin on heels from drying and cracking by moisturizing regularly. During winter "closed" shoes trap perspiration, keeping feet soft and hydrated. But they also need regular airing. Don't wear the same pair of shoes two days running – try to alternate as much as possible.

### THE IMPORTANCE OF *Hygiene*

The most common and insidious foot problem is athletes' foot – a fungal infection that attacks five million sufferers yearly in Britain alone. Although you don't have to be an athlete to catch it, gyms and swimming pools are high-risk zones because warmth and moisture provide the ideal environment for fungal spores to thrive.

Symptoms usually first appear between the fourth and fifth toes where the skin becomes itchy, sore and inflamed. Cracking and weeping may occur if early symptoms aren't treated. If left, infection spreads over the entire foot and can transfer to the hands around the fingernails.

Some strains of athletes' foot are resistant to over-the-counter creams, so it's best to treat it medically with broad-spectrum anti-fungal preparations containing ingredients such as terbinafine and griseofulvin. If infection keeps recurring, you may have to consider changing your footwear. Fungal spores feed off keratin and can live on shed nail and skin fibres trapped in shoes and socks for up to two years!

Efficient hygiene measures can prevent you from catching it in the first place. Bathe and check your feet daily and dry them thoroughly, especially between the toes, and use an anti-fungal powder. Wear flip-flops in communal showers, poolsides and changing rooms. Don't share towels or borrow trainers or shoes. Always wear your own tights or socks: never borrow the shop's when you're trying on new shoes.

# Footwork

Keep feet flexible and hard and dry skin to a minimum by following the massage, workout and pedicure routines outlined on this two pages. Incorporating ankles and the lower leg into your care routine helps improve circulation and eases aches and heaviness.

## PRACTICAL PEDICURE

Groom your feet at least once a week. Try incorporating it into your bath routine.

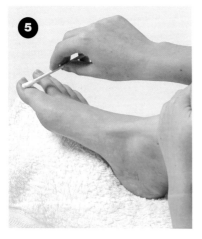

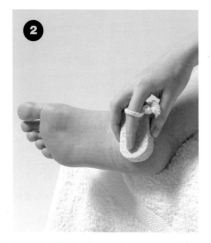

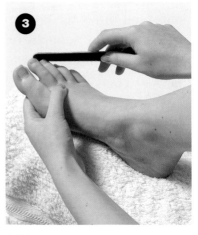

**1** Soak feet in a bowl of warm, soapy water. Blot dry with a towel.

**2** Rub off dead skin from around the heels, balls of the feet and under the big toes with a pumice stone. Don't use metal files – they can damage and irritate tender skin zones.

**3** Trim the nails with a toenail clipper. Cut straight across to minimize the risk of splitting or encouraging ingrowing nails. Buff edges smooth with the fine side of an emery board.

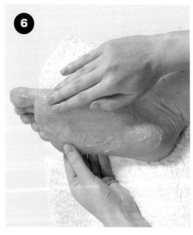

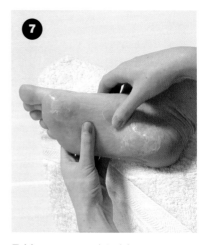

**5** Apply cuticle cream and massage into the base of each nail with your thumb pads. Use a small stick wrapped in cotton wool to ease back the cuticles.

**6** Gently massage exfoliating cream or damp sea salt all over the feet, using circular fingertip movements. Rinse and dry thoroughly, especially between the toes.

**7** Massage a moisturizing cream over the feet, especially the heels. Avoid between the toes, which must be kept dry and infection-free. Use talcum powder here instead.

**FOOTWORK:** Here are all the basics to shape your toenails and keep dry skin to a minimum.

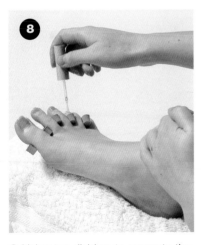

**4** Use the rough side of the emery board to refine any dry skin around the toes.

**8** Using toe dividers to separate the toes, apply a protein-enriched base coat to the nails to strengthen them and help prevent splitting, flaking and nail polish staining.

### THE FOOT MASSAGE

An aromatherapy foot massage is a thoroughly uplifting experience. Use 1 drop of peppermint oil to 5 ml of almond carrier oil to cool and refresh tired, swollen feet and boost your spirits. Other excellent oils for the feet are anti-fungal tea tree and soothing, deodorizing lavender.

**1** Spread a small amount of oil over the feet, using deep sweeps from toes to ankles. Support your right foot with your fingers. Use both thumbs to massage gently between the toes, along the sole of the foot and around the heel with circular movements. Repeat with the left foot.

**2** Use your thumbs to apply a series of pressures from mid-heel along the inner arch to the base of the big toe on each foot.

**3** Take the right foot in both hands and use thumbs to slide down the soles from the base of the toes to the heels, several times. Repeat with the left foot.

**4** Taking each foot in turn stroke upward from toes to ankle, using firm but gentle raking movements to reduce puffiness.

**5** Starting from each ankle, continue the firm, but gentle massage upward to the knee.

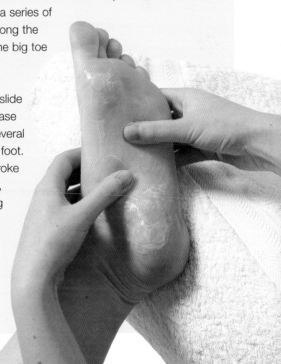

# **H**ips and thighs
## TACKLING THE PROBLEM OF CELLULITE

**Cellulite – or orange peel skin – affects 80 per cent of women some time in their lives. Yet medics are loathe to admit that the puckered, dimpled, blotchy surface skin that mars so many female buttocks, hips and thighs is anything more than just plain fat. So how come dieting doesn't always shift it? More to the point – is there anything out there that does?**

### WHAT CAUSES *Cellulite?*

Cellulite is an essentially female problem – men rarely suffer unless they're seriously, clinically obese. On average, women have 35 billion adipocytes (fat cells) compared to 28 billion in men. Deposited around the muscles, adipose fat plays an essential role in controlling body temperature and providing survival rations during pregnancy should food become scarce. Cellulite gurus also implicate highly refined foods, fizzy soft drinks, alcohol, coffee and smoking, and a sedentary lifestyle.

Hormones are thought to govern cellulite formation. Surges of oestrogen levels dwindle along with fat reserves that store the hormone. Taking some forms of HRT and the contraceptive Pill can encourage both cellulite and the fluid retention that accompanies it. Cellulite can also be hereditary.

### TWO STAGES OF *Cellulite formation*

Research at Laboratoires Elancyl pinpoints two stages of cellulite formation, both hormone-induced: water cellulite and fatty cellulite. Water cellulite occurs during the first phase of the female cycle as the body stores water and fats prior to ovulation. Oestrogen slackens blood vessel walls, so the dermis and adipose tissue is flooded and fluid leaks to neighbouring tissue. If more water than fat is stored, bloating results. At the end of the cycle, fluid returns to the lymphatic circulation and fat is burned as energy.

**PINCH AN INCH:** Early signs of cellulite are clearly visible when you pinch the flesh. Do your thighs pass the squeeze test or do you have classic "orange peel" dimples?

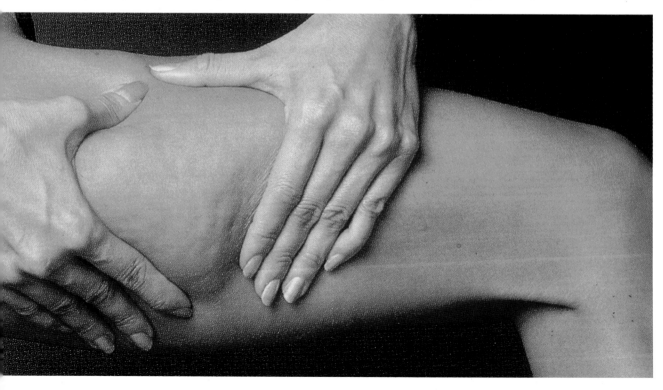

## SMOOTH MOVES

**SKIN BRUSHING:** Use a soft but firm, natural bristle brush
to sweep dry skin upward from the soles of the feet, over
thighs, hips and buttocks. It's thought this boosts lymph
circulation – it certainly exfoliates and leaves a glow on
the skin surface. Brush daily for tough cellulite or three or
four times weekly to keep skin smooth. Shower afterward, using cool jets as a massage tonic.

**MASSAGE:** Pummelling is now thought to damage and
weaken skin rather than "break down" fat deposits.
Gentle massage, though, encourages normal circulation
and aids the penetration of cellulite creams. For at least
three minutes on each leg daily, work in circular movements, kneading flesh between thumbs and fingers.
Finish by sweeping firmly upward with the flats of your
hands.

**EXERCISE:** Stress and a sedentary lifestyle encourage fat
lay-down. But avoid specific muscle-building workouts
that could worsen dimples by pushing fat pockets upward
into the skin. Concentrate on energy burners and circulation boosters, such as power walking, cycling, step aerobics, skipping and rebounding.

If you have water cellulite, when you pinch the flesh, the surface skin is curved, taught and sheeny. When you press it,
your finger sinks into the puffy surface. You may also feel generally bloated. Catch water cellulite early, and you can halt its
progress to the second stage. Adopt lymphatic drainage techniques such as skin brushing, massage and exercise. Body or
"inch" wraps may also help temporary bloating.

Fatty cellulite occurs as the female cycle becomes less
efficient. Fats that accumulate in the first half of the cycle
remain unburned. Fat cells swell with fatty acids and sugars.
Surrounding capillaries are compressed, vessels become con-
gested with fluids and circulation slows. Elastin and collagen
fibres are also compressed, causing loss of tissue tone.

If you have fatty cellulite, when you pinch the flesh, it
has the classic "orange peel" dimples. Prod and it hurts – the
fat cells compress nerve endings, too. Poor circulation also
means the skin bruises easily and feels cooler than cellulite-
free zones. Discourage fatty cellulite from becoming impacted by stepping up exercise and modifying your diet, especially during the second half of your cycle. Massage may help. A
skin-conditioning cream will improve surface smoothness.

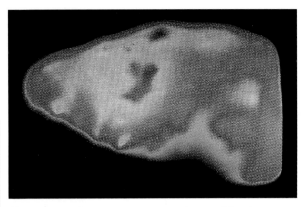

**FAT CHANCE:** This ultrasound scan shows cellulite tissue
before treatment.

## THE ANTI-CELLULITE DIET

Concentrate on low-fat, simple fibre-rich foods, which are
easier than refined foods for the body to break down, use
and eliminate as waste. Food combining also helps simpli-
fy metabolism and improve food efficiency. Eat little and
often to maintain energy levels, prevent bloating and discourage fat lay-down.

- Major on fresh fruit and vegetables, steamed or raw
  for maximum vitamins and minerals. Well-cooked pulses such as lentils, mung beans and red kidney beans
  are good sources of fibre.

- Choose proteins wisely. Avoid red meat – its dense
  connective tissue takes too long to digest. Opt for
  chicken, or best of all, fish. Restrict or avoid all dairy
  foods. Limit eggs.

- Avoid sugars and starches, including biscuits, cakes,
  pastries, sweets and chocolate.

- Try not to flavour foods. Limit salt, sugar and spices.
  Substitute herbs and seeds.

- Avoid animal fats, such as butter, and limit vegetable
  oils and spreads.

- Drink 1½ to 2 litres of still water daily. Strictly limit or
  avoid coffee, tea, fizzy drinks and alcohol. Substitute
  herb teas.

- Give up smoking – it hampers circulation.

## THE BENEFITS OF *Contouring creams*

Traditional "firming" creams have been replaced by new formulas, such as Dior's Svelte Body Refining Gel, which promise a smooth solution without pain: you don't even have to massage them in. What all the new contouring creams do well is to make the skin's surface look and feel smoother. On a good day it might even feel firmer. However, the British Advertising Standards Authority takes a tough line on cellulite creams with "over exuberant" claims. "Avoid miracle-sounding creams that imply cellulite can be removed just by applying them," warns Caroline Crawford, the ASA's Director of Communication.

Daniel Maes, Vice President of Estee Lauder Research & Development cautions: "We don't yet know what it takes to eliminate cellulite. But our view is, the key is to rebuild the skin's surface – not to remove fat." Ultrasound tests at Lauder labs reveal collagen and elastin breakdown in the skin's foundations, leaving "black holes" for fat to poke through. He recommends stroking on a cocktail of AHAs and antioxidants, to help fill in the dimples by encouraging stronger skin growth. Perhaps the most futuristic formula is one from Lancaster, which aims to magnetize fat cells. Microcrystals with a permanent charge create a static magnetic field, forcing disorientated cells to readjust. In the process, they burn fat.

## WHAT'S IN YOUR *Creams?*

How do contouring ingredients work? Adipocytes (fat cells) contain lipase – a lipid-regulating enzyme activated by cyclic AMP molecules. "Fat-busting" ingredients stimulate cyclic AMP; diuretics encourage fluid drainage; and strengtheners help firm and smooth skin tissue.

- **ALGAE** – seaweed inhibits fluid retention by improving lymphatic circulation.
- **ANTIOXIDANTS** – vitamins C and E inhibit free-radicals, so help preserve collagen, elastin and skin firmness.
- **AHAs** – smooth and help strengthen the skin's surface. May also encourage deeper collagen production.
- **CARNITINE** – enhances fat metabolism.
- **ESSENTIAL OILS** – rosemary and basil stimulate circulation; fennel, cypress and juniper are diuretic.
- **PLANT EXTRACTS** – horse chestnut boosts circulation; ivy reduces fluid retention and inflammation; ruscus

strengthens drainage vessels and capillaries.
- **SOFT CORAL** – inhibits inflammation associated with elastin loss.
- **VITAMIN A PALMITATE** – boosts collagen production.
- **XANTHINES** – burn fat and curb storage: all caffeine derivatives, aminophylline, theophylline and kola are star performers; mate and guarana are also used.

## SALON TREATMENTS *For cellulite*

**BODY WRAPS:** Treatments may include exfoliation, pressure-point massage with algae or clay-based creams and gels, plus a firming seaweed body mask that targets hips and thighs. Skin feels smooth after one treatment, but five to eight are usually recommended. Back-up formulas for home-use are always available.

**ULTRASOUND:** A system adapted from medical methods of breaking down fatty deposits, kidney and gallstones. Sound waves penetrate tissue, causing fat cells to oscillate a million times per second. This mini-internal massage breaks down fat ready for removal by the lymph. Noticeable results are claimed after three treatments; 10-12 are recommended.

**ELECTROTHERAPY:** Two or three sessions a week, each lasting around 20 minutes, are recommended, up to a total of between 10 and 20 sessions, depending on the severity of the cellulite. Regular maintenance treatments are also recommended. If you have a heart pacemaker, or any metal implants in your body (including a coil), are pregnant, have circulatory or skin problems, check with your doctor before embarking on a course of electrotherapy.

Two types of electrical pulse can be used individually or combined to tone tissue and help break down cellulite. Faradic, also called Electronic Muscle Stimulation (EMS), is the current used in the original passive exercise machines. Electrodes sheathed in fabric or plastic pads are strapped to muscles. When impulses are sent to the electrodes, the muscles automatically contract. In this way muscles are progressively toned. High-frequency faradic current also stimulates the lymph and has a temporary draining "inch loss" effect.

The second type of current is galvanic, also called iontophoresis. It alters the skin's resistance barrier and pushes

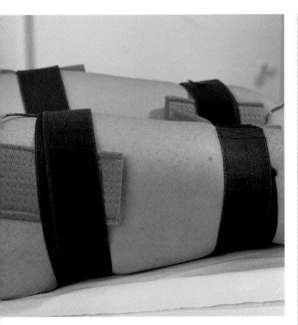

**SHOCK TREATMENT 1:** Electrodes sheathed in padding are here strapped on to the thigh muscles during a course of electrotherapy treatment for cellulite.

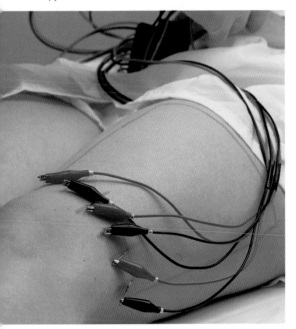

**SHOCK TREATMENT 2:** Electrodes are attached to electroylsis-type needles inserted just beneath the skin in this more radical electrotherapy treatment for cellulite.

moisturizing and fat-dissolving treatment formulas in deeper. Metal probes or rollers move gently over the skin's surface, spreading the current along with the cream. Micro-current is an interrupted, low-frequency form of galvanic current, which is used to tone flabby skin and leave it looking smooth, plump and "lifted".

## CLINIC *Solutions*

If you've tried everything and the cellulite still won't shift, cosmetic surgery may be the solution. Lose weight first if you need to – these treatments may be drastic but they're no couch potato's substitute for sane body maintenance. Neither are they permanent solutions.

**CELLULOLIPOLYSIS:** Thin electroylsis-type needles are inserted just under the skin and attached to electrodes. Weak electric current forces fat cells to burn energy by sheer resistance. Under medical supervision, you control the current's strength but it can still be uncomfortable. Some bruising is inevitable due to the needles. Diet recommended. "Top-ups" advised every 18 months or so.

**MESOTHERAPY:** Air pressure and tiny sub-skin injections introduce droplets of thyroid-mimicking drugs (such as aminophylline, enzymes and vasodilators) to remind fat cells to burn energy. Circulation and lymph is also boosted. 10-15 sessions recommended. Patients often have two or three "top up" sessions at the start of each summer.

**LIPOSUCTION:** The final and most permanent solution to saddlebag thighs and "fat in a string bag" skin texture. A cannula is inserted deep into the skin and the fat is sucked out. Up to 2½ litres can be removed in one session. The surgeon moves the cannula vigorously back and forth and from side to side to generalize the suction and prevent furrowing – the technique's greatest drawback. A general anaesthetic and an overnight stay is needed and a lycra compression garment must be worn for a fortnight to control bruising and swelling. Fat reduction is obviously immediate, but it takes up to a year for the area to settle, showing final results. Liposuction is not usually suitable if you're over 50 as your skin may not be sufficiently resilient.

# CHAPTER 3

# Make-up

Why do you use make-up? There is no single answer: it depends on how you feel. You use make-up to make a statement about yourself; to raise your social profile; to boost your confidence; to give you the strength to face the world; to get that bit closer to how ideally you want to look. As you grow older, some of the fantasy element goes out of making up. Like clothes, extremes in make-up styles are the preserve of the very young. But that doesn't mean you can't move with the fashions, updating and adapting your make-up to present a confident, contemporary profile.

A fact long acknowledged by psychologists is that make-up's feelgood factor is as potent as a drug. It's well known that the first sign of clinical depression is that sufferers lose interest in personal appearance and grooming. One of the first signs of recovery is that they look in the mirror again.

# The psychology of make-up

**GROOMING IS GOOD FOR YOU**

## THE FEELGOOD *Factor*

Dr Jean Ann Graham, who pioneered research into psychotherapeutic cosmetology at the University of Pennsylvania, discovered that when depressed women were shown how to apply make-up well, it dramatically boosted their optimism. In workshops across America, the highly successful Look Good, Feel Better campaign hosts hospital workshops for cancer patients to learn make-up skills and ways of disguising post-chemotherapy hair loss. Not only does make-up boost the morale of patients, but, according to *FDA Consumer* magazine, it can actually reduce the need for chemotherapy and radiotherapy.

In Japan, the link between using make-up and feeling "up" has been even more closely studied. During trials, after cleansing their faces, a group of women had their saliva tested for levels of human secretory immunoglobin, which indicates activity levels of the immune system. They then applied full make-up. Forty minutes later, the saliva tests were repeated. The results showed that the concentration of immunoglobin rose significantly after the application of make-up. So make-up not only boosts your mood, but it can also strengthen your immune system.

## SKIN-ENHANCING *Ingredients*

A further therapeutic aspect of make-up is that today much of it contains similar skin-enhancing ingredients as found in anti-ageing creams (see p.19), albeit to a lesser degree. For example, sunscreens and moisturizers are present in most types of foundation; eyeshadows, lipsticks and blushers often contain the anti-ageing vitamins A, C and E; and some types of mascara contain keratin protein which strengthens and moisturizes lashes.

However, so-called protective ingredients in make-up can undermine the work of the cream beneath, warn dermatologists. For example, an SPF 10 foundation actually dilutes an SPF 15 moisturizer to around SPF 12.5, cautions Nicholas J. Lowe, clinical professor of dermatology at UCLA School of Medicine. Consequently, if you intend wearing foundation in strong sunlight, it's best to skip the moisturizer completely and put a proprietary SPF sun lotion on first thing in the morning. Leave it for 15 minutes to bind with the skin's surface, then apply foundation.

## ADAPTING YOUR MAKE-UP *To suit you*

Successful make-up has a lot to do with being open to new ideas and to creating a look that doesn't clash with your age. Deborah Hutton in her *Vogue* Futures column expresses it excellently: "The more defined, more polished looks that work to such an effect on the older face does not mean denying the changes that age brings – but rather acknowledging and taking account of them. Often it also means having the confidence and courage to let go of an earlier look, which can operate as a sort of cosmetic security blanket."

One of make-up's greatest blessings is the warmth and vitality it can bring to complexions of any age. Once you're into your 30s, this aspect of make-up plays an increasingly important role. At this stage you need to reassess the shade of your foundation base, perhaps opting for a shade warmer. You probably also need to soften dramatic eye make-up which by now might look harsh rather than vibrant. And you must reconsider your lip tints. Are they too pale to pull their weight, or so glossy they're now impractical?

## GETTING THE *Surface right*

The right base becomes more and more important as the face develops less even, more lived-in characteristics. Quantum leaps in formulations over the past five years or so have made available firmer, more stable textures, which are less likely to gather in the lines, wrinkles and crevices everyone would rather not accentuate. But the maxim is still "less is more". Heavy make-up is least reliable – rest assured, the cracks will show. If you use the lightest possible touch for the job, make-up stays fresher and looks more plausibly attractive for longer.

As your face loses plumpness, and lines, dark shadows and angles begin to reveal themselves, you'll want to use concealer. But don't expect to hide these unwanted features altogether – that's impossible. Concealer goes a good way to soften blemishes and discrepancies but it should never be regarded as the perfecting tool to hide behind. A far more practical and rewarding way of reducing the impact of imperfections is to accentuate the features you're happiest with. For example, if you're proud of your smile, major on your lips. Remember, the most attractive face is one that is full of confidence, warmth and easy humour. The more natural your face looks, the more approachable you seem.

# Foundation basics
## YOUR HARDEST-WORKING MAKE-UP ALLIES

Your base is the most crucial stage of your make-up. It's the bedrock for the rest of your look. Make-up simply doesn't sit smoothly on an uneven skin tone. A basic team of complexion primers helps subsequent colours to glide on and stay true. Get your priming right and your skin will look smoother, fresher and younger.

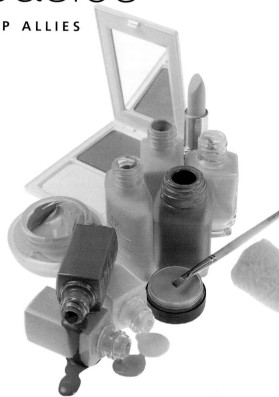

### FOUNDATION TROUBLESHOOTER

**YOU'VE POWDER-SET A TIDEMARK?** Try sweeping inward from face edges with a clean latex sponge. Still there? Work in a tiny bit of moisturizer, then tissue off. Sponge-blend the area, then fluff over with powder again.

**FOUNDATION HAS SUNK INTO CREASES?** Use a cotton bud to clean out and re-blend.

**THE BEST OF BASES:** Foundations, complexion primers and concealers all help perfect your skin's tone and texture.

### FOUNDATION HOW-TO

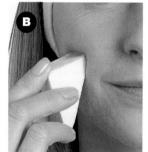

1  Wait 10 minutes for moisturizer to settle before applying foundation.
2  Stroke on colour primer, sponge-blending it evenly into your cheeks, forehead, chin and nose, until there are no patches. (A)
3  Dab foundation on the cheeks, chin and forehead. Use a dry latex, or slightly damp natural sponge to smooth over the face, including nose and eyelids. Work into inner eye crevices and around nostrils. Blend well. Finish by sweeping inward from the hairline and jawline to rub out tidemarks. (B)
4  Stroke tiny amounts of concealer under the eyes, along deep lines and over spots. Blend with a flat brush, or dab lightly with fingertips – don't rub. Look up to blend out creases under the eyes and puff out your cheeks to smooth laughter lines. Press over loose powder to set, then dust off the excess. (C)
5  Use a puff to press powder lightly over the entire face, then buff into the foundation with a complexion brush for a natural demi-matt finish. (D)

**POWDER POWER:** A light dusting makes your base stay longer.

## FOUNDATION – YOUR SECOND SKIN

The ideal base looks so natural it's almost invisible. Very sheer bases only work for naturally smooth skins. Heavy-coverage formulas have a high powder quota, giving them an opaque texture and a matt finish, which can look a little "cakey". Go lightly with powder-cream foundations, which may be difficult to blend. Oily skins suit oil-free bases. Rich, moisture-cream formulas maintain the satin finish on dry skins that "drink in" bases. Best all-rounders are the newest, light fluid, medium-cover polymer and silicone formulas that glide on evenly and "cling" to the skin's surface longer. Those containing light-reflecting titanium particles give the skin an extra dewy finish.

## CONCEALER – EXTRA COVER FOR TROUBLE SPOTS

Concealers pick up where foundations leave off. Their ultra-dense textures are applied selectively to blot out blemishes. Solid, lipstick-like bullets are concealer classics, although some tend to be greasy and unstable. Easier to use are the automatics – dryish-textured fluids with their own sponge applicators, ideal for dabbing over spots and large freckles, or lentigenes – sun induced "age spots". Fluid, polymer-based concealers are perfect for covering larger areas such as under-eye shadows, veiny lids and high-coloured cheeks.

## PRIMERS AND HIGHLIGHTERS – RADIANT SOLUTIONS TO DULL SKIN

Tinted primers or colourwashes even out the complexion before applying foundation. Green primer calms a ruddy complexion; mauve lifts sallow, olive skin; peach warms pasty skin; and white endows skin with a porcelain quality. Use sparingly and centralize colour on the cheeks, chin, nose and forehead. Titanium microparticles have revolutionized bases to "lift" shadows, balancing a dull complexion with a softer finish. Highlighters have a high titanium quota. Use them sparingly to enhance natural "highs" such as cheeks, browbones and lip contours. Don't attempt to conceal spots with them – they accentuate bumpy surfaces.

## POWDER – THE SMOOTH FIX

Heavy, cakey powder makes skin look older, drier. But carefully placed, microfine translucent loose powder gives the base a professional finish. Powder sets cream and fluid foundations and prevents concealer from creeping into lines or wearing off. Powder is also the dry base that supports powder blushes and eyeshadows, making them easy to blend and keep in place.

## SMOOTH APPLICATORS – TOOLS FOR SUCCESS

Sponges – natural or latex – spread foundation more evenly and give a lighter finish than fingers. They work bases well into crevices and make a little foundation go a long way. Latex sponges are especially efficient at rubbing out "tidemarks" from around the jawline. Use a firm, flat eyeshadow-sized brush to blend concealer with your foundation. A flat velour puff is best for pressing loose powder into foundation. Use a flat complexion puff to whisk off any floury excess that could dull the skin finish.

### FOUNDATION TIPS

- Test foundation on your cheek as the backs of your hands are darker, and the inside of your wrists paler, than your face. Check in daylight.

- Match your concealer to your foundation. If it's too pale, it will highlight the blemishes you're trying to hide.

- Don't try to warm a pale skin with a darker base – your face will contrast with your neck. Use a complexion primer or a slightly warmer shade of powder.

# **B**lusher

## YOUR INSTANT, HEALTHY-LOOKING GLOW

More than simply colour for the cheeks, a well-chosen, well-applied blusher can endow skin with a fresh, young-looking bloom that enlivens the entire face. "I always take my blushers everywhere I go. They cheer me up because they give me a healthy look. I feel, and probably look, prettier," says American make-up artist and cosmetic queen, Bobbi Brown. Most women – whatever their age – need a blusher to freshen their complexion, especially when they're tired or under the weather. Then, as skin loses pigment and pinkness with age, blusher becomes essential. The perfect one-stop cosmetic, lightly dusted on cheeks, browbones, chin and hairline, blusher transforms "bare" foundation basics into a face full of warmth and vitality.

**GLOWING**
Blushers ma
complexion
more radian

### BLUSHER TIPS

- Check the colour of your cheeks after exercise and use the shade of blusher to match. Usually, it's sandy-pink on fair skins; tawny-rose on medium skins; fresh rose on yellow-based skins and deep rose on dark skins.

- Bronzing powders make good blusher substitutes on all skin tones: choose pale, medium or dark according to your complexion.

### TEXTURE FOR SUCCESS – POWDER, CREAM OR GEL?

Microfine powder blushers give the lightest, most controllable colour veil. By far the most popular type of blusher, they're easiest to brush on, re-touch, calm down or build up. Creams initially look dewy-fresh but tend to sink into dry skin. Gels are trickiest of all to handle. As they dry quickly on skin contact, they need fast, deft blending to avoid a blotchy stain. The new powder-cream blush formulas that combine vibrant, fresh-looking colour with a long-lasting demi-matt finish are highly su cessful. More densely pigmented than powders, a little goes a very long way, so be econom ical if you choose this option.

### WHERE TO BLUSH – FINDING THE HIGHS AND LOWS

Blushing is a subtle and selective business which aims to mimic the pinched-cheek fresl ness of a brisk walk in the country. Check your face after exercise, making love or laughte that's the look you need to recreate. Make a note of where the natural pinkness is mo intense – that's the point at which you start blending. Blusher looks most youthful whe dusted on the cheek muscles. Before applying blusher, UK-based make-up artist Ariar Poole asks her models to smile to push up the cheek muscles – a useful tip if your face lacl prominent cheekbones. Apply blush to the browbones to give warmth to the eyes, and acro the brow close to the hairline to relieve a high forehead and gaunt temple hollows. A touc on the chin softens a pointed, or chiselled jawline and balances the face.

### SHADING – IS IT NECESSARY?

The seventies trend for striping the face with bands of blusher, highlighter and shaper was surely one of the most time-wasting, disaster-prone and potentially unflattering phases in cosmetic history. If you feel your face lacks shape bronzing powder is the best answer. It's easy to use, does the trick subtly and gives your skin an extra-healthy glow. Start from slightly under your cheekbones and dust upward. A touch along the jawline detracts from jowls or a double chin and a very faint whisper softens the tip of the nose. Add your regular blusher to cheek apples only.

### BRUSH SENSE – CHOOSING THE RIGHT ONE

Most blush mistakes are made because the brush is wrong. Brushes provided in blusher compacts are a waste of space – too thin, not wide enough and guaranteed to give you stripes. The ideal brush is fat, round and soft enough for the bristles to flex with your facial contours.

## BLUSHER TROUBLESHOOTER

**YOU'VE OVERDONE IT.**
Powder over the top to dull the blush. Still too much? Use a damp cosmetic sponge to blend in a touch more foundation. Then re-powder to give a natural flush finish that blends edges imperceptibly.

**TOO FAINT NOW?** Lightly retouch cheekbones only with the colour remaining on your blusher brush.

**DO BROKEN VEINS ON YOUR CHEEKS SPOIL YOUR BLUSH?** Make them work for you. Calm veins with concealer, then powder. You'll be left with a faint rosy glow. Dust similar-toned blusher very faintly on cheek domes for a more controlled flush.

## BLUSHER HOW-TO

1 Apply blusher over foundation. Apply a cream blusher before face powder and a powder-cream or powder blusher after face powder.
2 Pick up less blusher on the brush than you think you'll need – sometimes just touching the compact gives you enough colour. Remember it's easier to add than to dilute blusher once it's on the skin.
3 Dust over cheeks in a circular motion. Sweep upward from just under cheekbones to blend the edges.
4 Echo the effect more faintly on brow-bones, temples and hairline.

# Eye make-up

## YOUR EXPRESSION MAKERS

Eye make-up makes or breaks an overall look. Use a heavy hand and you'll pile on the years; apply subtle, natural tones and you'll achieve a warm, approachable, fresh appearance.

## EYE MAKE-UP TIPS

- Shadows glide smoothly and are easy to blend on foundation and powder-primed lids. Pull lids smoother with fingertips to work shadow well into eyelid creases.

- The older you get, the lighter the shade of your eye shadow should be. Some women in their fifties onward prefer to leave their lids almost bare, using the merest hint of mascara for definition.

- Stop just short of the socket line with eye shadow to prevent deepset eyes from looking sunken.

- Mascara is likely to blob if the wand is overloaded. Tissue off the excess before applying.

### EYESHADOW – SHADE NOT SHINE

As you grow older it is likely to be your eyes and delicate surrounding area that give the game away first with a display of crow's feet, bags, droopy lids, crinkles and wrinkles. The make-up priority here then, is gently to maximize your eyes' best expression without accentuating their less attractive facets.

### EYESHADOW – SHADE NOT SHINE

Forget high-pearl and frosty finishes, especially on dark skins. Matt finishes are kinder to older skins and easier to blend. Which texture should you choose? Creams tend to run into creases. Powder-creams are long lasting but tend to dry so fast on the lids, you barely have a chance to blend them evenly. Powder eye shadows are by far the safest bet as you can vary their intensity by applying them dry or damp, directly over powdered lids, or you can mix them on the back of your hand with a spot of foundation and then apply.

### EYE LINER – FINE DEFINITION

A heavy outline looks hard and stark, especially if it's black, but as eyes seem to "shrink" or become deepset with age, they do need extra definition, especially if the eyelashes have begun to thin out. Automatic liquid liners are less than smooth operators on crepe-paper lids, leaving a wobbly line. For best results use a khol pencil and smudge-blend close to the lash roots, to give depth of tone without harshness. You can achieve a similar, crease-resistant effect by tracing dark powder shadow next to the lash roots with a sponge-tipped applicator.

**THE TOTAL VISION:** Tools to groom brows and lashes. Colour to define the eyes.

## EYE MAKE-UP HOW-TO

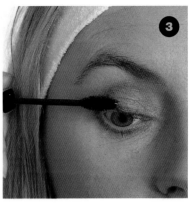

**1** With a sponge-tipped applicator, pick up a little powder shadow and stroke inward over the lids. For the most wide-awake look, the depth of colour should be darkest at the outer corners of the eyes – the inner eye corners should be almost bare. Blend with a brush.

**2** Trace khol pencil lightly along the lashline, starting a third of the way from the inner corners on both upper and lower lids and moving outward. Use a fine sponge-tip or a brush to smudge-blend the liner well into the lash roots to achieve a softly defining blur.

**3** For no-blobs mascara application, close the upper lids slowly and firmly on to the flat of the wand, forcing the colour consistently through the lashes. Wait for the coat to dry. Look up and run the tip of the wand back and forth along the bottom lash line. Brush downward to straighten.

## MASCARA – LASH GROOMING

Even short, stubby lashes need a coat of mascara – eyes look strangely bald without it. But distrust "lash building" formulas, which tend to have a gloopy, cloggy texture. Look for "natural finish" mascaras that groom in a single coat and don't dry so fast that you can't separate your lashes. Of these, polymer-based formulas glide on easily, last longest and are often water-resistant. Brown-black, rather than full black defines without looking harsh. If you invariably blob your mascara, consider having your lashes salon-tinted.

## BROW SHAPERS – ARCH EXPRESSION

Bushy brows tend to bear down on the eyes and need thinning out. Pluck stragglers from the browbone and over the bridge of the nose. The ideal brow shape starts in line with the inner eye corner, arches gently upward two thirds of the way over the eye at the browbone peak, then tapers gently just beyond the outer eye corner. Go gently when shaping eyebrows – thin, high, half-moon brows lend eyes a perpetually shocked expression. Fill out thin brows with a brow pencil that matches the colour of the brows or is a tone lighter. Use fine strokes, feathered to mimic natural hair. Use powder brow pencils: they provide a realistic finish and don't melt or shine as the day wears on. Fill in patchy brows with brown powder eye shadow. If your brows are white or fair, consider having them tinted at a salon.

## APPROPRIATE APPLICATORS – SPONGE-TIPS AND BRUSHES

Square, flat, flexible brushes endow lids with a subtle finish and are excellent blenders. Sponge-tipped applicators encourage powder shadows to go on densely, so they are good for picking up, placing or tracing liner shadow next to the lashes. Fine brushes can be dampened and used to mix powder shadow into an easily correctable "liquid" liner. Use a small, stiff brush to work powder shadows through brows. Mascaras come with their own brush wands, but it is useful to clean an old one and keep for separating and grooming lashes.

## EYE MAKE-UP TROUBLESHOOTER

**OVERDONE THE SHADOW?** Blend a dot of concealer on the centre of your lids to ease the colour.

**YOU'VE BLOBBED YOUR MASCARA?** Use a clean, damp mascara wand to separate clogged lashes, and a damp cotton bud cleans blobs from surrounding skin.

**LASHES LOOK STRAIGHT AND SPIKY?** Use lash curlers over mascara to "open up" the eyes.

**EYEBROWS TOO HEAVY?** Brush a clean mascara wand through them to diffuse the pencil tone.

# Lip tint

## YOUR FINAL TOUCH

Matt or sheer, lip colour is the signature of your face – it finishes your face and co-ordinates the rest of your shading and blending into a balanced, polished overall look.

## THE RIGHT TONE – ACHIEVING THE BALANCE

Rich lipstick warms skin tone; pale lipstick drains it. For daytime wear a shade somewhere between the two is the best working compromise. Brownish pink tones, a touch richer than your actual lip tone, suit everyone and look the most natural. Warm beige and brown shades are universally flattering – they're definite without being garish or contrasting too wildly with your skin. Reds make a bold, optimistic statement, but are demanding of pale skins. Save them for evenings when you feel you can live up to them. Alternatively, top up a basic beige with just a print of red on the centre of the lips, then blend well. Avoid blue-toned reds, pinks and magentas, which invariably look harsh on paler, older skins. And forget frosty, shiny finishes – they leach warmth from the skin tone and are definitely ageing.

## TEXTURE – WHICH LASTS LONGEST?

As we grow older, tiny puckers and wrinkles around the lip contour begin to threaten liptick's smooth finish. Preventing "bleed-off" becomes an imperative – nothing looks less polished than a smudged, "jammy" mouth. Until very recently, a lipstick's stability depended on whether its texture was gloss or matt: matt textures with a high powder quota ensured that the colour stayed put, but some formulas left lips looking dry after a couple of hours' wear; more glossy formulas tended to creep into creases or simply smear off. Thankfully, lipstick textures are improving all the time. A new generation of long-lasting, polymer and silicone-based full-pigment formulas cover lips with colour that is more likely than ever to stay where it's put. In addition, as they act on a "cling film" principle, they also seal moisturizing ingredients, to provide a supple, demi-matt finish. Many of the new sheer lipsticks that add a subtle stain of colour to gently boost your natural lip tone also seal in moisture. And, although they may not be quite as long lasting as full-pigment lipsticks, when they wear off, they do so "politely".

## CONTOURING – OUTLINING AND DEFINING

Outlining lips gives them the stronger definition they often need as they lose natural plumpness with age. The firm texture of a good pencil prevents lipstick bleeding off into any surrounding skin wrinkles. For an extremely durable finish, pencils can also be used in place of lipsticks to colour in the entire lip area softly. A final coat of lip salve lifts the dryish, matt finish to a subtle conditioning sheen.

## LIP-TINT TIPS

- Clear, lip-priming products with conditioning formulas provide a stable, no-bleed base for lipstick, while protecting the lips from drying out.

- Be wary of ultra-moisturizing lipstick formulas – their textures may be too rich to be stable. If your lips tend to dryness, try mixing a matt finish lipstick with a moisturizing salve on the back of your hand. Brush over outlined lips, keeping well within the contours.

- The stronger and brighter the colour, the more obvious it is when it starts to wear off. Subtle tones are safer.

Many women find lip liner pencils difficult to use, and it certainly takes practice to define a subtle lip contour that doesn't create a cartoon mouth. Do not try to enlarge or radically modify your lip shape. Trace your pencil along, or at most just slightly outside, the natural lip contour, to make your lips look believably plumper. Blend lip liner either with your lipstick or your lips for the softest possible edge to a well-shaped mouth.

## KEY APPLICATOR – THE INDISPENSABLE BRUSH

Applying lipstick straight from the bullet tends to overload the lips, whereas a brush gives you control, enabling you to spread lipstick evenly over the lips, working it into the natural creases to ensure a smooth, longer-lasting finish. Make a little go a long way – the less lipstick you use, the less there is to smudge. Lastly, a brush is the ultimate key to soft, even contours – it blends lipstick with lip liner and eliminates harsh, obvious edges. Easiest designs to use are slim, flat brushes with flexible bristles, neither too long and unwieldy nor too short and stubby. Many professional make-up artists use fine art sable brushes with long handles for maximum balance and control.

## LIP-TINT TROUBLESHOOTER

**LIPSTICK OVERLOAD?** Press a tissue over closed, still lips to blot off excess colour and shine.

**WOBBLY OUTLINE?** Blot the lips. Use a cotton bud to clean up the lip contours. Load a clean bud with a little concealer and trace over the outline. Blend with a fingertip, and then powder. Now re-do your lip line. Use this technique to patch up bleed-off during the day.

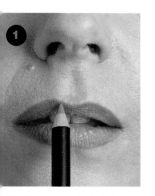

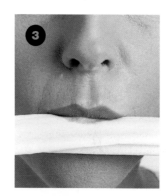

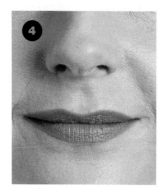

## LIPSTICK HOW-TO

To outline lips, trace the pencil along the lip contours from the corners of the mouth to the centre on both upper and lower lips. A light, feathering touch works better than a heavy, single movement. If your natural outline is puckered, pull the skin slightly tighter by placing a fingertip at the edges of the mouth. Don't smile – a relaxed mouth gives you a more accurate contour. Trace the cupids bow to a gentle inverted curve – no pointed peaks.

To apply lipstick, either work a little from the bullet on to your brush, then paint on the lips, or dab lipstick on to the centre of the lips only, and use the brush to blend outward to the contour lines. Use as little lipstick as possible, and a firm, even stroke. Blend the lip tone well with the contour line, but don't stray over it.

Blot the first coat with a tissue to absorb the excess colour. Retouch the edges without re-loading the brush.

If you feel the finished results are too subtle or too dull, print a little more lipstick on the centre of the lips only. Press your lips together, or use the brush to blend.

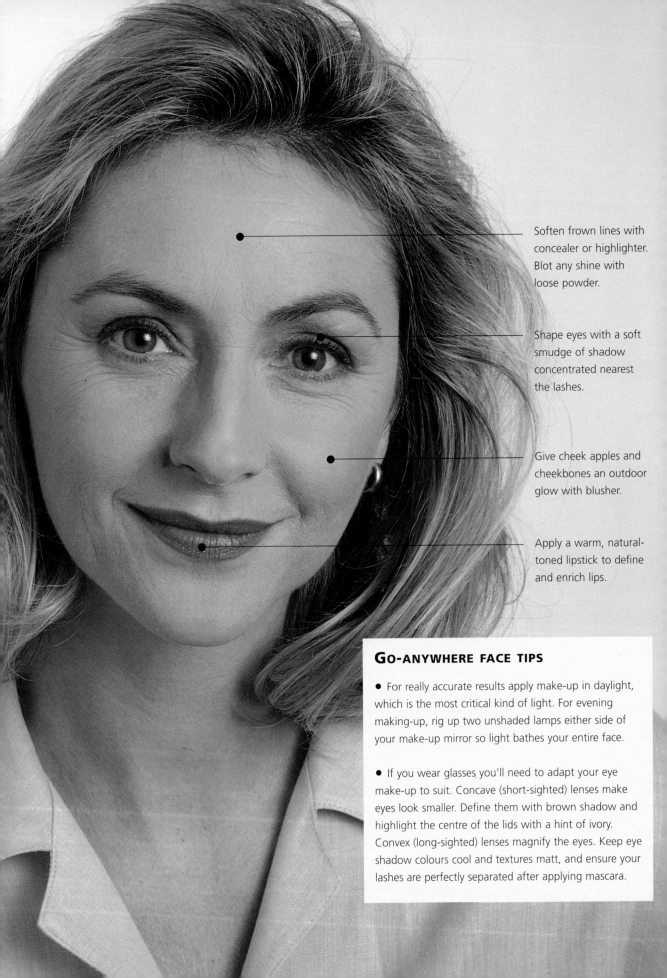

Soften frown lines with concealer or highlighter. Blot any shine with loose powder.

Shape eyes with a soft smudge of shadow concentrated nearest the lashes.

Give cheek apples and cheekbones an outdoor glow with blusher.

Apply a warm, natural-toned lipstick to define and enrich lips.

## GO-ANYWHERE FACE TIPS

● For really accurate results apply make-up in daylight, which is the most critical kind of light. For evening making-up, rig up two unshaded lamps either side of your make-up mirror so light bathes your entire face.

● If you wear glasses you'll need to adapt your eye make-up to suit. Concave (short-sighted) lenses make eyes look smaller. Define them with brown shadow and highlight the centre of the lids with a hint of ivory. Convex (long-sighted) lenses magnify the eyes. Keep eye shadow colours cool and textures matt, and ensure your lashes are perfectly separated after applying mascara.

**IN THE BAG:** The essential make-up kit to accompany you everywhere you go.

# The go-anywhere face

## AN EASY-TO-ACHIEVE LOOK THAT CONVERTS FROM DAY TO NIGHT

**The most successfully made-up face has fundamentally a natural look. The go-anywhere face is quick, simple and easy to achieve, and it gives you confidence, because you know it looks good. Rely on the basic look during the day, then adapt for stunning evening effect.**

### FOUNDATION

**DAY BASICS:** For a base that lasts with the minimum of build up caused by retouching, go for a powder-cream compact foundation, and sponge-blend lightly over the skin. Try not to overload oily or crease-prone zones. Lift off excess from the hairline and jawline with the clean side of the sponge.

**NIGHT EXTRAS:** Foundation absorbs, settles and wears off in patches, depending on how dry your skin is. Tissue-blot your skin to absorb surface oiliness and get a more accurate picture of your base. Be selective with retouching: blending lightly with a clean sponge may be enough to redistribute foundation. Check shadows and blemishes with concealer. If you need to, apply a light layer of powder-cream foundation, or fluff over a loose translucent powder. Those with light-reflecting pigments and a delicate peach or rose tinge give a soft, attractive evening glow.

### BLUSH

**DAY BASICS:** Warm cheek apples and browbones with your regular, neutral powder blush.

**NIGHT EXTRAS:** Adopt make-up artist Bobbi Brown's blush layering technique. Top up your daytime blush with a slightly brighter tone, high on the cheek domes. Buff the two together for a glowing finish.

### EYES

**DAY BASICS:** Nude-look lids are obviously the easiest to build up later. If you feel "eyeless" without some colour, choose a neutral tone, such as soft beige, over lids with deeper brown definition next to the lashes. Apply a single coat of mascara.

**NIGHT EXTRAS:** The merest touch of a sheeny shadow blended over the lid domes gives eyes sparkle. Retouch the lid line by re-blending existing colour with a cotton tip or clean sponge applicator, then adding a touch more if you need to. Strengthen your lashes with a second coat of mascara. To open up and glamorize eyes without looking too obvious, attach two or three separate false lashes to your natural lash base at the outer corners of your upper lids only.

### LIPS

**DAY BASICS:** Use a natural beige or lightened lipstick for an all-day ally that can be easily adapted. Make the lip contours as soft as possible.

**NIGHT EXTRAS:** Retouch or redefine your lip outline. Echo the blush effect on your lips – top up the basic tone with a more vibrant colour, but apply to the centre of your lips only. Alternatively, cleanse your lips, prime with foundation to blend with the surrounding skin and redo your lips with a bolder evening colour that will strengthen your entire look.

# CHAPTER 4

# Hair

The way you style your hair is one of the most eloquent aspects of your body vocabulary – it's an instantly recognizable statement of character. Perhaps this is why style is so crucial to self-esteem: a bad hair day undermines confidence. Your hair style and colour have a dramatic impact on the look of your face to others: hair length and style affects the shape of your face and hair colour affects your complexion. This is why, as you grow older, it pays to adapt your hair to suit your changing features: the right colour and cut can take years away.

# **Y**our crowning glory

## UNDERSTANDING HOW HAIR WORKS

**Hair grows from a single papilla, or bud, deep in the follicle in the skin's lower layer. The follicle is nourished by its own blood supply. Each hair shaft consists of three concentric layers: the outer layer, composed of overlapping, scaly cells; the middle layer, or cortex, which gives hair its bulk and colour; and the central core, or medulla, composed of transparent cells and air spaces. In the same way as skin cells (see p.14), hair cells move upward from the root as they mature, so that the visible part of the hair shaft is composed entirely of dead scales of keratin protein – the same substance as the skin's horny layer.**

### **PHASES OF** *Growth*

Everyone is born with a genetically determined quota of follicles – on average 120,000 per head, although blondes have slightly more, redheads fewer. The size of the follicle determines hair thickness. Fine hair tends to be straight and limp, with the exception of fine black (Afro) hair. Oriental hair is wider in diameter than Caucasian hair.

Hair grows at a seasonal rate – faster in summer than in winter. The growth, or anagen, phase of each individual hair varies from person to person but is generally between three and five years. When the growth phase ends, the hair follicle enters a resting, or catagen, phase which lasts around three months. In the final, or telogen, phase, a new hair forms in the follicle, pushes out the old hair and the cycle begins again. Hairs are lost at a rate of between 20 and 100 every day. It's also thought that hair goes through "moult" phases: you may notice more stray hairs in the sink or brush during spring and autumn.

There are always new hairs on the way to replace shedding ones, although the rate of hair growth is controlled by hormones. In women, oestrogen prevents hair growing on the face and diverts it to the head, which is why women tend to have more lustrous hair than men. Consequently when oestrogen levels drop during the menopause, hair becomes

**WELL AHEAD:** Here are strong, healthy hair shafts with smoothly overlapping cuticles.

noticeably thinner. The diameter of individual hairs begins to decrease much earlier, at the age of about 25, especially in women, accounting for the gradual loss in "body". Sadly, some women may begin to lose hair.

### **WHAT CAUSES** *Hair loss?*

Losing hair is unbelievably distressing. Who hasn't panicked when the brush seems fuller than usual? So what causes obvious hair loss? Cell division slows when you reach your thirties, and each hair spends less time growing and longer in its resting phase. Some follicles may become completely inactive. So, by the age of 50, the number of active follicles in the scalp has virtually halved. Hair colour also plays a role – the blonder your hair, the more you risk losing it.

Stress is a significant factor in hair loss as it triggers the hormone testosterone, responsible for male "pattern baldness". Tension – especially in the neck and

shoulders – restricts circulation to the scalp, and follicles may become weak and undernourished. Similarly, strict diets, periods of illness or medical treatments such as chemotherapy and radiotherapy, may cause hair to fall out. (For advice on hair nourishment, see p.88.) Rough handling is also a prime factor, along with chemical abuse – straightening, over-perming and colouring – which is also the most common cause of hair damage (see p.91). Sleeping in rollers that are too tight causes "patchy" traction hair loss, in which the hair falls out in clumps.

### WHY DOES HAIR *Turn grey?*

Hair derives its colour from granules of melanin pigment produced by cells in the hair follicle. With age melanocyte cells become less active and what look like grey hairs start to appear. In fact the "grey" is a combination of normally pigmented hairs interspersed with white ones. Hair colour eventually turns completely white when the melanocytes cease to function altogether.

Nutrition and stress also affect hair colour. Stress burns up B vitamins in the body, as does alcohol. A diet insufficient in these vitamins may also hasten the appearance of grey hairs. According to celebrity trichologist Philip Kingsley, studies have shown that large doses of B vitamins can reverse greying in three months. Stop taking the vitamins and the greying starts again. Check with your doctor before starting a course of nutritional supplements. (For advice on nutrition see p.95.)

# WASH CYCLE

Gently does it – and don't overdo it. Careful washing thoroughly cleanses hair without tangling or stressing the roots.

- Use a wide-toothed comb to untangle dry hair and prevent matting once it's wet.

- Thoroughly wet hair needs less shampoo. Wet hair with warm water and gently comb your fingers through the hair to ensure that it's really soaking.

- Rub shampoo in the palms of your hands, then smooth over your hair. Use your palms to distribute suds and your finger-tips to knead your scalp gently. Massage for around three min-utes, untangling your hair from front to back every so often with your fingers.

- Use clear, running warm (not hot) water, and don't skimp. A common cause of dull hair is insufficient rinsing, so keep going even when you think your hair's clean. If you can stand it, finish with a cold jet to tone the scalp and close the hair cuticles.

- Smooth conditioner over your hair with the palms of your hands, concentrating on the ends and avoiding the scalp. Rinse thoroughly again.

- Wrap hair in a towel and squeeze out the excess water. Untangle with a wide-toothed comb, starting from the ends.

# Hair care

## TREASURING YOUR ASSET

**Shampooing is the make or break factor of hair health, which probably explains why it's surrounded by myths and controversy. Does frequent washing damage hair? Yes, say the "once weekly" experts who believe daily washing has a similar effect on the scalp as washing your face with soap: it risks sensitizing the scalp and over-exciting sebaceous glands. No, says trichologist Philip Kingsley, who recommends daily shampooing to cleanse and stimulate the scalp, and flush away loose strands that may matt and tangle the hair. Somewhere between lies a compromise.**

**TIP-TOP CONDITION:**
Shampoos, conditioners, glosses and serums all help to maintain bounce and shine.

### WHY SHAMPOO YOUR *Hair*

Shampooing fulfils two functions – it cleanses both scalp and hair. Cleansing every two or three days would be sufficient to remove dust and sebum from hair. However, today, shampoo's main job is to remove the build up from styling products such as sticky, dust-attracting gels, mousses and sprays. Left in the hair for more than a day, they cause dryness and brittleness, make hair frizzy or lank and impossible to style. They can give white hair, which shows the dirt more in any case, a yellowish tinge. A daily shampoo clears the way for successful styling, which makes hair look so much healthier. Preserve delicate white hair's silvery sheen by washing it every other day in a mild, frequent-use shampoo.

Hair texture largely dictates your choice of shampoo. Limp, straight hair needs a "body building" protein-based shampoo to give it texture. Coarse hair needs moisturizing and softening. Curly hair – whether permed or natural – is invariably dry and requires a moisturizing formula. Coloured hair requires a special "colour protective" protein shampoo that helps keep roughened cuticles smooth and cortex moisturized, while preventing colour fade. If you swim regularly, a de-chlorinating formula will help prevent colour oxidating –

of special importance in the sun, as UV light heightens the bleaching effect.

As sebacous output diminishes with age, an oily scalp and hair problem becomes less likely. However, if it is a problem avoid detergent-based cleansers that strip the scalp and so panic it into producing even more oil, while pitting and dulling the hair shaft in the process. The new AHA-based shampoos are thought to help regulate oily scalps and prevent seborrhoic (sticky) dandruff. These provide a more practical alternative to the traditional anti-dandruff shampoos that clear the problem, but often leave the hair looking dull and greasy.

### WHAT CAUSES *Dandruff?*

A dry, flaking scalp is basically an extended dry skin problem. But stress, hormonal changes or too much sugar and salt in the diet can influence the scalp's sweat and sebum output. An increase in the skin's natural bacteria causes an increased shedding of surface cells. These flakes are oily and stick together on the scalp in clumps. A common mistake is to overdo the conditioner in an attempt to relieve a "dry" scalp, when this type of dandruff is an oily problem.

Philip Kingsley's solution to control grease at the roots and dry hair at the ends is to alternate your regular shampoo with an anti-dandruff formula, and condition the hair tips only. He also recommends that you massage your scalp with an anti-flake tonic. Make it yourself from equal quantities tonic and mouthwash. Some essential oils can also help control a greasy scalp (see aromatherapy p.114). Left unchecked, acute dandruff can cause hair loss: if your scalp becomes excessively scaly, sore or itchy, make an appointment to see a trichologist or dermatologist.

Thorough rinsing after cleansing is also crucial to keep scurf at bay. Surfactants from shampoos can irritate and dry the scalp, and turn to dandruff-like powder if left in the hair. It's a good idea to use a clarifying shampoo once in a while to deep-cleanse hair of both shampoo and styling product residue, without compromising scalp health. Always rinse with tepid water until it runs clear. It's the only way to make sure your hair is really clean.

## USING THE RIGHT
### *Conditioner*

Conditioners are basically anti-ageing creams for the hair. A conditioner's moisturizing finish smooths down the hair cuticles, prevents tangles, makes combing easier and gives hair a light-catching sheen. Conditioners replace moisture and prevent further moisture loss by buffering hair against damage heat styling and arid atmospheres. When the air is moisture-logged, conditioners can also prevent flops and frizzes.

It's important to choose the right conditioner for your hair type. Dry hair is always crying out for intense, moisturizing formulas. Afro and coarse, curly hair types may benefit from leave-in conditioners, moisturized into the tips to ensure lasting softness and flexibility. As curly hair is less able to reflect the light than straight hair, conditioner is also important for its ability to counter a dull finish by building shine. Coloured and permed hair need

moisture as well as strengthening protein to compensate for the damage of chemical processing. Coloured hair also needs to be protected with a sunscreen, to prevent fading.

Fine, floppy hair faces a dilemma. Body-building formulas are ideal for fine hair, but if your fine hair is also dry, it will need moisturizing too, although not with a product that weighs the hair down. The practical answer may be to use a moisturizing conditioner, then pump up the volume with a styling mousse (see p.93). Whichever formula you use, don't overdo it. Often a small amount of the right conditioner concentrated toward the drier hair tips is all you need. Use a lightweight conditioner on very fine white hair.

Opinions differ as to how long you should leave a rinse-off conditioner on your hair. Some experts recommend a full three minutes – longer if your hair's extra dry. Others say it hardly matters – you can rinse it off almost immediately. If your hair is not too fine the most important element is even distribution. To ensure each strand is coated, use your fingers or a wide-toothed comb to spread the conditioner through the hair right to the tips.

## BRUSHING FOR
### *Condition*

Brushing your hair is such a routine, basic function, you'd think it was impossible to get it wrong. Think again. Sharp-bristled brushes can scratch the scalp and split hair. Rubber-cushioned brushes with well-spaced, flexible bristles are the gentlest. The longer your hair, the larger your brush should be.

The thicker your hair, the denser the brush bristles. Use a brush that is composed of a mix of natural and plastic bristles: natural bristles absorb more sebum and are better "cleansers", while round-tipped plastic bristles are gentler on the scalp.

As a brush's function is not only to smooth, but also to "dust" your hair, loosening "dead" hairs, stale scalp cells and sebum as well as styling aid build-up, hairdressers suggest brushing thoroughly before each shampoo as a pre-cleanse stage. They also suggest brushing last thing at night to loosen mousse, gel and spray, while relaxing the scalp, and first thing in the morning to lift flattened hair from the scalp. Trichologist Philip Kingsley disagrees. He maintains that a brush is not a scalp exerciser and should be used only for styling. As to the mythical 100 strokes a day, everyone is agreed – if you value your hair, don't. For weak hair, over-brushing is the final straw.

## THE GENTLE *Comb*

Combs are far easier on your hair than brushes. But avoid cheap plastic made-in-the-mould types that have seams jutting out from the teeth that can slice into the hair shafts. Hard rubber or vulcanite combs with saw-cut, individually smoothed teeth are the anti-static, professional choice. Choose wide-tooth combs to distribute conditioner through wet hair. Tail combs are useful for sectioning off hair prior to blow-drying. Use a comb to untangle the hair: work from the hair tips to the roots, progressively smoothing snags with light, upward-flicking movements.

# Colour

## HAIR'S HARDEST WORKING COSMETIC

By the age of 30 most Caucasian women will have a few grey hairs and by 50 at least half their head will be grey. The fairer you are, the slower you seem to grey because there is less of a natural contrast. Grey hair can, of course, look fabulous – often more sophisticated, assured and downright sexy than hair that's carefully tinted to hide it. Think of Marie Seznec, the muse of designer Christian Lacroix and Evangeline Blahnik, ultra-chic sister of shoe designer Manolo. But it does depend on how your hair greys. There's a world of difference between gunmetal and salt and pepper. If you're glad to be grey, enhance it. If you're not quite ready to "come out" – and this often takes courage – there are many successful ways to hide it.

### CHOOSING *Your colour*

If you've decided to colour your hair avoid trying to recreate your natural, youthful hair colour. Like hair, skin becomes paler with age, and the deep, lustrous hair colour you had in your 20s and 30s may be too much of a contrast with your 40-year-old skin. Beware also going – or staying – blonder, which can contibute to an overall, washed-out impression. For best results choose a colour within your natural colour range that is warm in tone, such as a mid-brown or a rich chestnut that reflect light well and enliven skin tone. Supplement with well-placed highlights to accent and brighten your look.

**HAIR COLORANTS ARE AVAILABLE** *In the following basic forms:*

**PERMANENT COLOUR:** This covers grey completely, in whatever shade you choose, and lasts until it grows out. In permanent colour formulas, an alkaline agent, usually ammonia swells the hair and opens the cuticle to enable pigment molecules to enter the hair shaft. An oxidizing agent, such as hydrogen peroxide, releases oxygen on contact with ammonia. This lightens hair's natural pigment and causes the pigment molecules to produce the larger molecules that create the hair's new colour. A final "neutralizing" stage removes excess colour, closes the cuticle and locks in the new pigment.

**TONE-ON-TONE TINTS:** These cover up to 60 per cent grey and last up to 20 washes. They colour the hair to the same depth, or deeper than permanent colour. However, the ammonia-free, low alkaline and oxidizing formula means that tone-on-tones cannot lighten hair. They are excellent for reviving your natural hair colour.

**SEMI-PERMANENT TINTS:** These tints cover up to 40 per cent grey, enrich and deepen but won't lighten your hair. Most last up to eight shampoos. In semi-permanent tints colour molecules penetrate the hair cuticle and lodge in the outer layer of the hair cortex. Water swells the cuticle, so each shampoo releases pigment until your hair is back to its natural colour.

**HIGHLIGHTS AND LOWLIGHTS:** Highlights merge effectively with grey, camouflaging rather than covering. Highlights and lowlights that combine two or three permanent tints can be used to mimic natural hair highlights and lowlights. They are complicated and time-consuming to create. The tinter takes fine sections of hair all over the head, applying colour to each and wrapping the individual colour sections in foil. When the colours have "taken", the foils are removed to reveal subtly woven threads of colour, which last until they grow out. Re-touching the roots can be done selectively, wherever the lack of highlights is most revealing. If you tire of highlights, you can always blend them down with a tone-on-tone tint while you grow them out.

**COLOURING** *Your own hair*

Home-colour formulas have improved considerably over the past two or three years. Most are shampoo-in gel or cream formulas that are easy to apply and control. Permanent tints give fairly predictable results because they're designed to oxidize deep into the hair. If problems occur it is generally due to human error, not the formula. A common mistake is to create too dense a build-up by layering new tint over old. Avoid this by copying the professionals: re-touch your roots first, leave to develop, then comb the tint through to the ends five minutes before you rinse it off.

Do not use tints – especially permanent ones – over henna or colour-restoring lotions that claim to banish grey. There could be unpredictable chemical reactions to the metallic compounds in these substances: your hair could literally turn green. Never try to tint your own eyebrows.

**CHAMELEON CHOICE:** Changing your hair colour can affect your complexion considerably, witness the four variations at left.

## FOLLOW THESE STEP-BY-STEP GUIDELINES FOR COLOURING YOUR OWN HAIR:

### 1 Do a sensitivity test

- To check for allergic reaction, clean a 1-cm (½-in) circle of skin behind one ear with surgical spirit. Dab on a little of the tint with a cotton bud.
- Reapply two to three times, allowing the tint to dry between each dab. Leave for 48 hours.
- If there's any redness or itching, do not use the product.

### 2 Do a strand test

- You need to gauge the result, especially if your hair is already tinted or permed. Snip off a tiny section of hair close to the roots. Tape it at one end.
- Apply the colour mixture with a cotton swab and leave for the full developing time.
- Rinse, leave to dry and assess the colour.

### 3 Preparing for tinting

- Wait at least 48 hours to colour after a perm.
- Stroke Vaseline around the hairline to prevent staining.
- Always protect your hands from staining by wearing gloves. If a pair is not provided in the pack, buy surgical gloves from a pharmacy.
- Mix up the formula and use in one session. Throw leftovers away unless the instructions say you can save them. Use a plastic, never a metal, mixing tool.
- Make sure your hair is free of styling product build-up, grime and grease. Check the packet for whether to apply the tint on wet or dry hair.

## THE BENEFITS OF SCALP MASSAGE

Fashionable hair salons offer shiatsu-style scalp massage as part of the shampoo service. Experts agree that boosting the scalp's circulation benefits hair by increasing nutrient supply to the roots. It may also help prevent hair loss, although over-vigorous massage can irritate the scalp and loosen already weakened roots.

If you are trying a scalp massage yourself be careful not to rub the scalp or tangle your hair. Begin at shoulder level, as a stiff neck leads to a tense scalp. Then ease your fingertips under the bulk of your hair and work gently around the roots, kneading and pressing. Cover the entire scalp working from the base of the skull to the crown, from brow to crown and sides to crown. Finish by gently massaging the temples.

## CARING FOR
### *Coloured hair*

Even the gentlest, low-level peroxide formulas remove protein and moisture from the hair shaft, and because cuticles are ruffled in the process, hair loses softness and natural gloss. While fine, flyaway hair may actually feel thicker and easier to control, coarse hair can easily become brittle and devitalized with constant colouring. Compensate by treating hair with colour-maintenance shampoo and conditioning formulas, which help preserve the tint and the hair's moisture quota.

Leave-in conditioners are excellent as between-shampoo moisturizers that keep hair supple and easier to style. Massage them into dry hair, especially at the tips. Intensive hair packs help re-moisturize excessively dehydrated, frizzy hair. Hot oil treatments build shine. As a pre-shampoo glossing treatment, warm two tablespoons of olive oil to a bearable temperature in a bowl within a saucepan of boiling water. Comb through dry hair and wrap your head in hot towels. Leave for 15 minutes, then shampoo and condition as usual.

Sunlight, salt water and chlorine in swimming pools can all oxidize colour, cause it to fade or turn a strange shade. Use a protective, sunscreening oil or gel when swimming and sunbathing, and a neutralizing, anti-chlorine shampoo after swimming.

# **H**air style

## CHOOSING AND MAINTAINING A STYLE

**A good haircut can be as uplifting as cosmetic surgery. The key factors to consider when choosing a hair style are its suitability to your hair texture, face shape and features, and its ease of maintenance. Shorter, layered or feathered styles that frame the face have a gamine appeal and suit most people. The layers can be coaxed away from the scalp to conceal roots and give a fuller impression to fine or even thinning hair. Feathering around the hairline is more forgiving to the face than hair that is scraped back severely. And a halo of hair softens leaner features.**

If you have thick, straight and well-behaved hair, a jaw-length bob is more bouncy and flattering than longer styles, which can accentuate a longish face. But unless you're prepared to live up to them with graphic make-up, avoid "hard edge" geometric styles, which can look too angular or just plain contrived. Heavy fringes dwarf delicate features and are best broken into sections, or wisps which will soften a lined or receding brow.

For fine or limp hair a demi-wave might be the answer. This lifts the hair at the roots to build body subtly into hair without touching the drier and potentially vulnerable tips. It works especially well where the hair is layered.

### **Six** *Easy styles*

According to Brendan O'Sullivan, creative director of Regis salons in the UK, all styles stem from six basic cuts which can be adapted to suit all face shapes. They are: classic bob; round graduation; long interior-layered; short interior-layered; long graduation; and graduated bob. Meg Ryan's successful feather cut is a version of a long layered look. The Princess Diana style is based on short layers. Layers form the style's architecture, flattering the shape of your head by compensating for a flat crown, or emphasizing a well-formed occipital bone at the base.

If you have a round face avoid "pudding basin" styles and choose a graduated bob. If yours is a thin, narrow face opt for a softening fringe and layers that add width to the sides. A style that falls just below the jaw suits a square face, while a heart-shaped face can wear any style well.

**FULL COMPLEMENT:** Good use of brushes, rollers, hairdriers and hairsprays give you control over your hair's volume.

## HEAT STYLING HOW-TO

**Used wisely, your hairdrier is your greatest style ally.**

- After shampooing and conditioning, blot excess moisture with a towel. Apply a styling formula such as mousse or gel.

- Hair should be 50 per cent dry before you start precision blow-drying. Let it grow semi-dry naturally or rough-dry it with a hairdrier.

- For smooth styles, blow-dry your hair in sections. Pin the top sections out of the way and begin drying underneath, coaxing the hair around a large, round brush. Rotate the brush as you slowly and firmly pull it through the section from roots to tips.

- For more textured styles, make a spider-shape with the fingers of your free hand and gently massage the roots as you blow-dry. "Scissoring" sections of hair between your fingers from roots to tips styles more smoothly.

- Keep the drier on medium heat and hold about 10 cm (4 in) to 15 cm (6 in) away from your hair. Aim the nozzle down the hair shafts from the roots to the tips.

- Use the right attachment for the job. The nozzle of your hairdrier concentrates hot air for quick, sleek, precision styling. The diffuser distributes warm air over a wider area and is ideal for initial "rough" drying or for styling naturally curly or wavy hair.

**HIGH STYLING:**
Mousses, gels and sprays help your hair to behave the way you want it to.

## YOUR HARDEST-WORKING *Style allies*

**MOUSSES:** Classic bodifyers, mousses are, perhaps, the easiest bulking agents to use, but don't use too much or you risk dulling the hair. A golfball-sized dollop is enough for most short to jaw-length styles. Comb mousse through damp hair before styling.

**GELS:** These are the firmest styling formulas, but they can leave hair stiff. To perk up fine hair without weighing down the tips, concentrate the gel at the roots, massaging it in place with your fingertips, then combing it through so the ends are the least liberally coated. Apply to damp hair before blow-drying or styling. Gels are useful for combing and setting waves in place, then brushing out when the hair is dry.

**THICKENING SOLUTIONS:** The most recent formulas on the market, most thickening solutions contain keratin, the same protein that hair is made from. Spray them in, then blow-dry to bond the liquid keratin to the fine hair shaft. Your hair will remain thicker until it's washed.

**SERUMS:** Serums can perform reconstructive surgery. Only serums can bring back gloss to severely dry hair, or suppleness and control to frizzy hair. Be sparing in use: a single drop of the glycerine-like texture may be enough for a whole head of hair. Spread serum in the palms of your hands, then massage through dried hair after styling and before the finishing spray. Alternatively massage into the ends only to "mend" splits.

**POMADES, WAXES, PUTTIES AND STYLING CREAMS:** Specialist finishing formulas that mould the hair into place, giving texture and sheen. Pomades provide a high shine finish; waxes a more subtle polish. Stiffer putties and styling creams coax hair sections into soft peaks or ruffle them into highly textured looks. If your hair usually slides out of place when you put it up, try using them. Massage through dried hair.

**FINISHING SPRAYS:** These freeze lifted hair once you've coaxed it into place. Misted on to damp hair, they also help mould blow-dry or roller styles. Aim the spray toward the roots, where it will work the hardest. Try to avoid "rock solid" fixing.

# CHAPTER 5
# Eat Yourself Younger

Sensible eating coupled with moderate exercise are essential to fitness. Sensible eating means a balanced diet. In addition, timing meals right maintains blood sugar levels for mental and physical acuity – skipping meals, then snacking on chocolate or biscuits will send you blood sugar into soaring and crashing yo-yo mode. Eat a substantial breakfast, snack on fruit mid-morning and have lunch at midday, not later. Mid-afternoon, nibble nuts or a slice of wholemeal bread. Keep dinner light and eat it preferably before 8 p.m. Spacing meals well may also help re-educate a sluggish metabolism – if calories are consumed more consistently and used more efficiently, there is less of a risk of weight gain.

# Nutrients at a glance

## THE IMPORTANCE OF EATING A BALANCED DIET

Only by eating a balanced diet will your body gain the full range of essential vitamins and minerals it needs. The British Government's National Food Guide defines a balanced diet as comprising 34 per cent bread, potatoes and cereals; 33 per cent vegetables and fruit; 15 per cent milk and dairy foods; 12 per cent meat, fish and alternative proteins; and only 6 per cent fatty and sugary foods.

### THE BENEFITS AND *Sources of vitamins and minerals*

Compared to the macro-nutrients protein, fat and carbohydrate, the body requires only very small quantities of the micro-nutrients vitamins and minerals. Yet vitamins and minerals are essential to normal body functions and protection against disease. There are two groups of vitamins: fat soluble (vitamins A, D and E), which the body stores, and water soluble (B-group and C vitamins), which you need to take in daily. Minerals also fall into two groups: major minerals and trace elements. You need larger amounts of major minerals than trace elements but both are vital. Major minerals required are outlined below. Trace elements required are: iron, chromium, copper, manganese, selenium and zinc.

## MAJOR MINERALS

|  | NEEDED FOR | SOURCES | EC RDA |
|---|---|---|---|
| **Calcium** | Teeth and bone formation and maintenance. Healthy muscle contraction. Needs vitamin D for absorption and efficiency. | Dairy foods; green leafy vegetables like broccoli. Bones of tinned fish. Peanuts, sunflower seeds. | 800 mg |
| **Magnesium** | Needed for neuro-transmission. Helps fight stress and depression. Maintains healthy circulation. | Nuts, wholegrain cereals, meat, fish, figs. | 300 mg |
| **Phosphorus** | Bone formation and maintenance. Helps convert food to energy. | Dairy foods, vegetables, fish, meat, nuts and wholegrains. | 800mg |
| **Potassium, Sodium, Chlorine (electrolytes)** | Involved in a wide range of biochemical processes. | Best source is salt, in moderation. Lost through perspiration. | No RDA |

# VITAMINS

| | NEEDED FOR | SOURCES | EC RDA |
|---|---|---|---|
| **Vitamin A (Retinol)** | Healthy eyes and night vision. Clear, supple skin and strong nails. Fat soluble and stored in the body. | Cod liver oil, liver, kidney, eggs and dairy foods. Depleted by cooking and exposure to air. | 800 mcg. Toxic at doses over 25,000 iu. |
| **Beta-carotene** | Converted by the body into vitamin A. | Carrots, tomatoes, spinach, broccoli, mangoes, pumpkin, watercress, apricots. Depleted by sunlight. | N/A. 3 mg is equivalent to 5000 iu vitamin A. No toxic risk. |
| **Vitamin B1 (Thiamine)** | Releases energy from food. Essential for digestive and nervous systems and helps fight stress. Water soluble. | Liver, kidney, pork, milk, eggs, wholegrains, brown rice, barley and cereals. Depleted by heat, food refining and cooking and alcohol. | 1.4 mg |
| **Vitamin B2 (Riboflavin)** | Energy metabolism and development and repair of healthy tissue including skin and nails and mucous membranes. Water soluble. | Milk, eggs, cereals, liver, lean meat and fish, green leafy vegetables. Depleted by sunlight, alcohol and oestrogen-based drugs like the Pill and HRT. | 1.6 mg |
| **Vitamin B3 (Niacin or nicotinic acid)** | Converted by the body into energy-generating niacinamide. Essential for brain, nervous and digestive systems. High doses lower cholesterol but can cause itching and flushing. Water soluble. | Meat, fish, wholegrain cereals, eggs, dairy foods. Depleted by cooking and cholesterol food refining. | 18 mg |
| **Vitamin B5 (pantothenic acid)** | Releases energy from fats and carbohydrates. Necessary to the immune system and for healthy skin tissue. Water soluble. | Yeast, liver, kidney, eggs, brown rice, wholegrain cereals and molasses. Depleted by heat, light, alcohol, caffeine and oestrogen-based drugs. | 6 mg |
| **Vitamin B6 (Pyridoxine)** | Protein and amino acid metabolism. Helps manufacture red blood cells. Regulates the nervous system. Water soluble. | Meat, fish, milk, eggs, wholegrain cereals, wheatgerm, vegetables. Depleted by cooking, food refining, alcohol, oestrogen-based drugs. | 2 mg. Do not exceed 2,000 mg |
| **Vitamin B12 (Cobalamin)** | Essential for forming antibodies in red blood cells. Energizes and maintains nervous system. Water soluble. | Meat, yeast extract, seaweed (kelp). Depleted by light, heat, alcohol and oestrogen-based drugs. | 1 mcg |
| **Folic acid** | Works with vitamin B12 to make red blood cells and genetic material. In first 12 weeks of pregnancy, helps prevent spina bifida in the foetus. Needed for growth and maintenance of digestive and nervous systems. Water soluble. | Liver, kidney, green, leafy vegetables, fortified bread, bananas, oranges and pulses like lentils. Depleted by light, heat, food refining, alcohol and oestrogen-based drugs. | 200 mcg. Do not exceed 800 mcg |
| **Biotin** | Breaks down and metabolises fats. Also manufactured by intestinal flora. | Liver, kidney, eggs, dairy foods, fish, cereals, fruit and vegetables. Depleted by cooking and food refining. | 0.15 mcg |
| **Vitamin C (ascorbic acid)** | Healthy connective tissue, skin, gums, teeth and blood vessels. Aids iron absorption. Water soluble. | Fruits and vegetables, especially blackcurrants, oranges, acerola cherries, broccoli, cabbage and potatoes. Depleted by heat, light, alcohol, smoking. | 60 mg. High doses depend on bowel tolerance. |
| **Vitamin D (calciferol)** | Works with calcium and phosphorus to maintain strong teeth and bones. Fat soluble. | Dairy foods, eggs, oily fish like mackerel. Made by the skin on stimulus of sunlight. Depleted by light and air. | 5 mcg |
| **Vitamin E (tocopherol)** | Helps prevent cell damage; dissolves blood clots; strengthens blood vessels; boosts muscle strength and regulates hormones. Fat soluble. | Vegetable oils like sunflower and rapeseed. Almonds, peanuts, sunflower seeds, avocado, spinach, asparagus. Depleted by light, air and food refining. | 10 mg |
| **Vitamin K (phytomenadione)** | Essential for normal blood clotting. Manufactured by intestinal flora. | Vegetables like cauliflower, cabbage, spinach, peas and wholegrain cereals. Kelp and fish liver oils. Depleted by heat, light and food refining. | No RDA |

# Anti-ageing crusaders
## GARNERING ESSENTIAL NUTRIENTS TO COMBAT DECAY

Cells are permanently damaged by continual attacks from aggressive chemical particles called free radicals. And an estimated 80 to 90 per cent of degenerative diseases (such as cancer, heart disease, arthritis and Alzheimer's) are caused by free radical activity, according to some experts. Free radicals are a by-product of oxygen combustion: some are useful for snuffing out infection but some attack cells, causing them to become dysfunctional and eventually to die.

### COMBATTING FREE RADICALS WITH
### *Antioxidants*

By the age of 50, 30 per cent of cellular protein has been damaged by free radical activity. Accumulation of cellular damage hastens the ageing process and increases the risk of age-related illness. So what can you do? Prevent free radical overload in the body by avoiding processed foods, eating foods rich in antioxidants and taking antioxidant supplements. The key antioxidants are as follows.

### VITAMIN A AND BETA-CAROTENE
### (PRO-VITAMIN A)

Vitamin A, or retinol, is vital for the maintenance of skin, teeth, bones and mucus membranes. Beta-carotene is converted from food by the body into vitamin A as and when needed. Countless studies show that beta-carotene can lower the risk of heart disease and cancer, including breast and cervical. It may also protect against ultraviolet light, shielding you to some extent from wrinkles and skin cancer, while boosting your immunity against viral attack. Several studies have shown it helps prevent cataracts.

**FOOD SOURCES:** Retinol is found in fish, meat, dairy products and eggs. Beta-carotene is found in dark green or orange foods, such as broccoli, spinach, carrots, apricots, peaches and sweet potato.

**SUPPLEMENT DOSE:** The RDA for retinol is 800 mcg or 25,000 iu. It is toxic above 25,000 iu. There is no RDA for beta-

carotene but six units gives one of retinol, so a 3-mg dose equals 5000 iu of vitamin A. Many experts recommend from 6 mg to 14 mg daily. It is not toxic at high levels.

### VITAMIN C

A potent antioxidant, which many studies suggest can help prevent cancer. It may also prevent viral infection and cataracts, and lessen the inflammatory reaction during colds and allergic reactions by lowering histamine levels in the bloodstream. It is vital for the formation of collagen protein, which keeps skin firm by supporting and binding connective tissue cells.

**FOOD SOURCES:** Mango, kiwi fruit, grapefruit, broccoli, cantaloupe, strawberries, sweet red pepper, sweet potato, snow peas, oranges, cherries.

**SUPPLEMENT DOSE:** The RDA is 60 mg (100 mg for smokers) but most experts recommend a daily dose of at least 100 mg (1 g) and 6,000 mg to fight infections caused by colds. High doses cause diarrhoea. Calcium ascorbate crystals are gentler on the stomach and easier to tolerate than regular ascorbic acid.

**CITRUS POWER:** Oranges, lemons, limes, grapefruits – all are packed with the powerful antioxidant, vitamin C.

## THE FREE-RADICAL FIGHTING FOODS

According to Jean Carper in *Stop Ageing Now!* antioxidant-filled fruits and vegetables are the foods we should eat to protect our bodies against age-related disease. Eat them daily and raw for full potency.

**AVOCADO** – rich in glutathione, the master antioxidant that helps neutralize destructive fat in other foods. Contains potassium for blood cell protection.

**BERRIES** – strawberries, raspberries, cranberries and blueberries are rich in vitamin C. Blueberries are the richest source of antioxidant anthocyanins.

**BROCCOLI** – rich in antioxidants vitamin C, beta-carotene, quercetin, indoles, glutathione and lutein. In women it's thought to help prevent cancer by neutralizing excesses of oestrogen. It also helps guard against lung cancer, colon and cardiovascular disease.

**CABBAGE** – antioxidant indole-3-carbinol speeds the disposal of breast cancer-causing oestrogens and lowers risk of colonic and stomach cancers.

**CARROTS** – help boost immune function, lower cholesterol and reduce the risk of stroke and lung cancer. They may also help guard against age-related eye disease and dwindling eyesight.

**CITRUS FRUITS** – oranges contain cancer-fighting carotenoids, terpenes, flavonoids and vitamin C. Grapefruit contains cholesterol-reducing fibre in its juice sacs and membranes.

**GRAPES** – contain at least 20 antioxidants. Richly coloured types are the most potent; raisins are more powerful than fresh grapes. Grape antioxidants, chiefly quercetin, prevent blood from clogging, relax blood vessels and inhibit the oxidation of LDL cholesterol.

**GARLIC** – contains at least 12 antioxidants plus ajoene, an anticholesterol agent that helps prevent blood clots, and allicin, an antiviral and antibacterial agent. Garlic also stimulates immune function and may help prevent memory loss and depression.

**ONIONS** – help prevent blood clots by raising "good" HDL cholesterol levels. Red and yellow types are richest in cancer-inhibiting quercetin, which also has anti-inflammatory, anti-bacterial, antifungal and antiviral properties.

**SPINACH** – contains beta-carotene and lutein, both powerful antioxidants which help protect against cancer, heart disease, high blood pressure, strokes, cataracts and macular degeneration, which can cause blindness.

**TEA** – helps prevent heart disease and cancer, thanks to antioxidants such as polyphenols, quercetin and catechins. Tea also stimulates liver enzymes to detoxify the body of free radicals and cell-damaging chemicals.

**TOMATOES** – the richest source of lycopene, an extremely potent antioxidant that helps preserve physical and mental functions.

## VITAMIN E

Studies have linked vitamin E with the prevention of heart disease: long term it can lower LDL cholesterol and prevent its oxidation, thin the blood and prevent clots. There is growing evidence that it may protect against various cancers, including skin and lung cancer. In cases of late-onset diabetes, which occurs during mid-life and beyond, vitamin E has been shown to facilitate the use of insulin and help maintain normal blood sugar levels. It may reduce anxiety and depression, enhance immunity and skin condition, ease arthritis and prevent cataracts.

**FOOD SOURCES:** Vegetable oils, whoegrains, sweet potato, wheatgerm, brown rice, nuts.

**SUPPLEMENT DOSE:** The RDA is 10 mg or 14.9 iu. Many experts recommend 400 iu daily but it is wise to avoid supplements if you take a blood thinner such as asprin or have a vitamin K deficiency.

## BIOFLAVONOIDS

These are a group of about 500 compounds that give colour to fruit and vegetables. Some are potent antioxidants believed to work with vitamin C to keep connective tissue healthy and improve the strength of capillaries, preventing leaky walls, easy haemorrhaging and bruising. Bioflavinoids also treat allergies and asthma. They are thought to protect against heart disease and cancer – quercetin found in red and yellow onions has been shown to inhibit the activity of carcinogens and tumour promoters. They are antiviral, and in conjunction with vitamin D, they may help relieve monopausal hot flushes.

**FOOD SOURCES:** Pith and segments of citrus fruits, apricots, buckwheat, red and yellow onions, blackberries, cherries, rose hips, tea and apples.

**SUPPLEMENT DOSE:** No RDA. Usual combination with vitamin C is 500 mg vitamin C to 100 mg bioflavinoids. Take 1,000 mg bioflavonoids to 400-800 ius of vitamin D.

## BUILDING *Strong bones*

Rapidly thinning bones is one of the biggest health threats to post-menopausal women – one in four women is likely to develop osteoporosis, which makes bones – especially spinal, hip and wrist – vulnerable to fractures and breaks. Bone is composed of several minerals, including calcium, phosphorus, magnesium, zinc, iodine and fluoride. By the age of 30, peak bone mass has developed and the production of new bone cells starts to slow. After the age of 35, bones begin to lose around 1 per cent bone mass anually, rising to between 2 to 4 per cent yearly for up to 10 years after the menopause.

This loss is attributed to the decline in oestrogen, which is essential for calcium absorption. Good nutrition before, during and after the menopause is the natural solution. Soya bean products, such as soy sauce and tofu, have attracted particular interest by researchers on both sides of the Atlantic. Soya beans contain genistein, a rich source of plant oestrogens, which mimic the body's natural hormones.

Weight-bearing exercise, including walking and jogging, builds bones and boosts muscle mass, which could help cushion a potentially fracturing fall. It has been shown that combining exercise with vitamin and mineral supplements can significantly lower the risk of osteoporosis. Here are the key bone boosters.

## VITAMIN D

This vitamin is essential to allow the body to use calcium and phosphorous. A genetic inability to metabolize vitamin D may itself be the cause of some forms of osteoporosis. Sunlight stimulates certain skin oils to synthesize vitamin D in the body but consistent use of high-factor sunblocks could inhibit this natural process.

**FOOD SOURCES:** Dairy products and fatty fish oils. Milk and vegetable margarines are often fortified with Vitamin D.

**SUPPLEMENT DOSE:** The RDA for vitamin D is 200 iu. There is some evidence that 400 ius during winter when bone loss is most rapid can reduce the loss. But vitamin D is toxic at levels over 1000 iu daily, so don't exceed the RDA unless your doctor is supervising you.

**BONING UP:** Calcium-rich foods help strengthen and maintain healthy bones.

## CALCIUM

Calcium is vital for bones to reach their peak mass and maintain their strength and density. It's thought that maintaining good calcium levels throughout the 30s, 40s and 50s builds reserves to draw upon later.

**FOOD SOURCES:** Low-fat dairy products – an average tub of plain yoghurt contains aroung 400 mg calcium. But some low-fat cheeses contain phosphate, which inhibit calcium absorption. Tofu processed with calcium sulphate, sardines with bones, and broccoli are all good sources.

**SUPPLEMENT DOSE:** The RDA for calcium is 800 mg, but the American National Osteoporosis Foundation recommends 1,500 mg for post-menopausal women not on HRT. Of all the types of calcium supplement, calcium carbonate delivers most efficiently. Take it with meals for full absorption. Avoid supplements made from bone meal, oyster shell or dolomite, which may contain unsafe levels of lead.

## BORON

Research by the US Department of Agriculture shows the mineral boron can reduce loss of calcium and magnesium in urine (both are needed to build and maintain strong bones). Another USDA study suggests boron may also improve mental alertness.

**FOOD SOURCES:** Many fruits and vegetables, especially dried prunes and apricots.

**Supplement dose:** 3 mg daily (no more than 10 mg). Works best taken with a good vitamin and mineral supplement which includes calcium, magnesium, manganese and riboflavin.

## Eating the right *Fats*

Saturated animal fats are bad for you: they increase the risk of heart disease by boosting blood levels of "bad" artery-clogging LDL cholesterol; women who eat a lot of animal fat have higher levels of oestradiol, which promotes breast cancer and colon cancer; and animal fat stimulates production of inflammatory prostaglandins and leukotrienes, responsible for rheumatoid arthritis, and linked to migraine, artery clogging and psoriasis.

However some unsaturated fats are essential to health. Essential fatty acids – so called because the body can't make them and it is therefore essential to derive them from your diet – can actually prevent cancer and heart disease while protecting against osteoporisos, fatigue and even obesity. EFAs boost calcium absorption and prevent bone loss. Deficiencies register in dry skin, dull hair, disgestive disorders and more severely, depression and heartbeat abnormalities. There are two groups of essential fatty acids:

**Omega-3:** Derived from alpha-linolenic acid which is found in vegetable oils, soya beans, flax and rapeseed oil, walnuts and oily fish. Vital for brain function (60 per cent brain is fats, mostly EFAs), eye function, anti-inflammatory action and blood clotting. Research indicates prevention of heart and bowel disease, and breast cancer.

**Omega-6:** Derived from linoleic acid which is found in seeds, vegetables, sunflower, safflower and sesame oil. Needed for cell membrane production, prostaglandins and eicosanoids – hormone-like substances that control inflammation and blood pressure. But too much omega-6 is linked with arthritis, strokes, diabetes and some types of cancer.

Low-fat foods and the new "fat-digesting" slimming pills may mean we're not getting enough EFAs for our own good. Cutting out fats means limiting your intake of valuable nutrients like essential fat-soluble vitamins A, D and E and beta carotene, which need at least 25 g fat daily to absorb them. If a woman's fat intake falls below 15 per cent of calorie intake daily it can affect oestrogen production, leading to menstrual problems and risk of osteoporosis as well as general fatigue. So how much fat is good?

The WHO recommends adults take at least 15 per cent of their calories from fat (30 g for a 2,000 calorie diet) and no more than 35 per cent. For women of reproductive age, 20 per cent (about 40 g for a 2,000 calorie diet) is healthy, with no more than 10 per cent saturated fat (20 g per 2,000 calories). EFAs should provide at least 1/3 of total fat consumed.

## Fat file

- Avoid saturated animal fats, hydrogenated fats in processed foods, and margarines containing trans-fats, which all affect blood cholesterol levels. Use unrefined, cold-pressed oils or a little butter as a spread.

- Nuts and oily fish such as herring, mackerel, tuna, pilchards, sardines, trout and salmon are good sources of polyunsaturated oil and omega-3 fatty acids which balance and offset omega-6.

- Olive oil is acknowledged as a monounsaturated fat that helps prevent heart disease and breast cancer. But it's low in EFAs. Vary your oils – use sunflower, sesame and walnut for salad dressings, and olive, soya and grapeseed oils for cooking.

- Consuming more EFAs means you must increase your intake of antioxidants to prevent free radical damage. Boost your fruit and vegetables, or take vitamins A, C and E.

# Supplements

## CAN THEY STOP THE CLOCK?

**Trials consistently show that at the right potency, "natural" remedies may rival conventional medicines. German doctors often prescribe nutritional and herbal supplements as effective but gentler alternatives to conventional drugs for problems ranging from depression to indigestion. Here are 10 key anti-ageing supplements:**

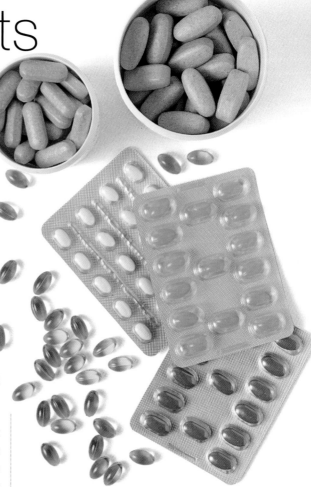

### COENZYME Q10

Coenzyme Q10 (ubiquinone) drives the fuel we need for life. Naturally present in every cell, it converts energy from food into a form that the body can store and use for both physical and mental activity. It's not present itself in food – the liver has to manufacture it from related coenzymes in proteins and green vegetables. It is believed to strengthen heart muscle and American and Japanese studies indicate it lowers blood pressure and can reduce the need for painkillers for those with angina. As an energizer, Texan and Belgian studies suggest CoQ10 can boost metabolism and help weight loss. It may also boost the immune system. It also declines with age. Swedish research compares CoQ10's antioxidant powers to "anti-ageing" vitamin E, which protects cells against sclerosis that causes membrane damage and degenerative disease.
**DOSE:** 30 mg daily.

### DHEA (DEHYDROEPIANDROSTERONE)

Produced largely by the adrenal glands, DHEA is a hormone-like substance also produced in smaller quantities by the ovaries. The "mother of all hormones", it is converted into steroid hormones such as oestrogen, progesterone, testosterone and cortisone. With age, DHEA levels decline – by the age of 60 it's barely detectable in the female body. Some 2,000 studies (mostly animal), indicate that high levels of supplementation boost energy, memory and libido and may protect against heart disease, osteoporosis, cancer, depression and aggression. DHEA may even aid weight loss and increase longevity. Side-effects of large doses are enlarged liver and facial hair in women. Wild Yam is a natural source of DHEA.

**DOSE DEPENDENT:** Food supplements contribute to health maintenance, but are no substitute for a balanced diet.

**DOSE:** There have been few side effects reported at doses between 25 and 50 mg daily.

### DONG QUAI

What we know as angelica is the premier Chinese remedy for PMS and is also called the "female ginseng". A natural adaptogen, it balances the menstrual cycle, preventing cramps, bloating, acne and irritability. It helps regulate the cycle after coming off the Pill, and reduces hot flushes, vaginal dryness and palpitations during the menopause. It is also rich in iron and vitamin E. According to some studies, dong quai can lower blood pressure, regulate blood sugar and help prevent anaemia.
**DOSE:** Two to three capsules daily.

### GINKGO BILOBA

In China, they call ginkgo biloba the plant of youth and its heart-shaped leaves and plum-like seeds are used to treat res-

piratory ailments, such as tuberculosis, asthma and bronchitis, and circulatory problems. In the west, studies indicate that ginkgo biloba yields ginkgolides and bilobalides – flavonoids that dilate blood vessels and have antibacterial and antifungal activity. Powerful anti-free radicals and anti-coagulants, these flavonoids may also help to prevent strokes, and speed brain tissue repair. Over 40 studies have also shown it to combat memory loss and poor concentration and to boost mental alertness.
**DOSE:** 120 to 160 mg daily. It may take four to six weeks to kick in. The few reported side effects include headaches, mild stomach upsets and skin reactions.

## GINSENG

The Chinese have used this most famous root for 5,000 years as a rejuvenating cure-all. It is said to improve memory and mental performance. Ginseng has antioxidant properties: Japanese studies have found that it contains compounds called saponins that inhibit the growth of cancer cells and lower cholesterol. Russian studies have demonstrated ginseng's ability to fight stress by normalizing body functions such as blood sugar and pressure levels – hence its "adaptogenic" reputation. As a menopause aid, compounds similar to oestrogen help counter hot flushes, lethargy and irritability.
**DOSE:** Take two or three capsules daily or 5 to 10 g powder mixed with liquid; and one cup of tea, preferably in the morning and an hour before eating.

## GLUTAMINE

Glutamine is the body's most abundant amino acid, especially in the brain, bones and blood. However, illness, continual stress and dieting depletes it, and cooking destroys it in food. Research reveals that glutamine is the primary fuel that prevents bone and muscle wastage and fatigue. Studies have shown glutamine to help raise the IQ of children with learning difficulties and generally boost mental performance, especially when blood glucose is low. An immune-booster, it also aids digestion and helps prevent upsets and food allergies. It can also reduce alcohol, nicotine and drug cravings.
**DOSE:** During times of stress or recovery from illness, 1 or 2 teaspoons (4 to 8 g) daily mixed with water is usual. Subtract 1 g of protein from your diet for every gram of glutamine you take so as not to overstress the liver or kidneys.

## GLUTATHIONE

Glutathione is a powerful antioxidant which is synthesized in the body from three other amino acids: L-cysteine, L-glutamic acid and glycine, all found in fruit and vegetables such as citrus fruits, melon and raw carrots. Studies have shown that it may help protect against cancer, radiation and debilitation due to smoking and alcohol abuse. It has major detoxifying properties and may help keep the immune system healthy. Other studies indicate that glutathione may act as an anti-inflammatory agent and may reduce symptoms of allergies and arthritis.
**DOSE:** 50 mg once or twice daily.

## MELATONIN

This hormone is secreted by the pineal gland in the brain during sleep. It is crucial to body rhythms, especially the circadian rhythm which regulates sleep-wake cycles. Widely used to ease the symptoms of jet lag, it can also help cure insomnia. Production of melatonin drops dramatically with age. Animal studies have shown that melatonin supplementation can prolong life by 20 per cent.
**DOSE:** An effective dose for jet lag and insomnia is one to three 3 mg tablets taken 90 minutes before bed.

## SELENIUM

An antioxidant, selenium works with glutathione to quash free radical damage and animal studies have shown it to have an antiviral action when combined with vitamin E. Selenium also detoxifies metals such as arsenic and mercury in the body. Its most famous property is as a cancer fighter. Selenium may help prevent heart disease by protecting lipids from oxidizing and "furring" arteries and preventing blood clots.
**DOSE:** 100 to 200 mcg daily. Selenium is toxic in high doses, so don't exceed 300 mcg.

## WILD YAM

This increasingly popular "anti-ageing" vegetable extract is a traditional African folk remedy for rheumatoid arthritis and colic. Herbalists also prescribe it to ease PMS and menopausal symptoms such as hot flushes, fatigue and vaginal dryness, hence its modern reputation as the alternative HRT. DHEA (see above) is also present in wild yam.
**DOSE:** Two or three capsules daily.

# CHAPTER 6

# Relax!

Stress is a major cause of physical and emotional illness. Stress weakens the immune system, increases the risk of illness and lessens the chance of recovery. It is important therefore to find ways of managing stress in an age when the "fight or flight" response built into your body is generally of little benefit. The link between state of mind and state of health has been demonstrated time and time again. Whereas negative emotions suppress the immune system, positive thinking raises your resistance and speeds healing. In short, if you believe you can cope, you probably will. Complementary therapies can help give you that extra resolve.

# Stress management

## HOW MUCH STRESS CAN YOU TAKE?

**A certain amount of stress is actually good for you. Psychologists call healthy stress "eustress" – it's the impetus behind clear, creative thinking and achievement. Sports people rely on the effects of eustress to help them surpass personal bests. However, when the pressure builds up eustress gets out of control and it becomes unhealthy stress. You feel overwhelmed and unable to manage rationally. You develop negative or self-defeating patterns, such as working too hard, oversleeping or waking up in panic, drinking and smoking, over- or under-eating. Unhealthy stress can lead to mental and physical exhaustion.**

### WHAT HAPPENS WHEN *You're stressed*

The fight or flight response is a complex chemical chain reaction, which affects the entire body immediately you suffer a shock. First the senses become heightened and the threat is magnified. Then the brain assesses information received and prepares the body for action. Hormones and electrical impulses flood both the voluntary and the autonomic systems.

At the centre of the brain the hypothalamus triggers the production of three main stress hormones. Adrenalin, produced by the adrenal glands, raises the heartbeat, blood pressure, breathing rate and blood sugar levels, energizing the body. Cortisol, also produced by the adrenal glands, increases the blood-clotting rate and energizes the organs by converting stored fat into glucose. The brain itself produces endorphins – natural opiates that kill pain and produce a euphoric "high".

Now you're all wired up, senses sharp as razors and muscles raring to go. So what's your next move? It is generally not appropriate to run away, punch the source of your shock or fall to the floor flailing and sobbing. So you make a superhuman effort to contain your feelings, thus denying both your mind and body the release it expects. Your system can dump a certain amount of the build-up. But if the stress is sustained or repeated over long periods, the body's self-defence mechanism turns inward and the self-destruction process begins.

### GAUGING YOUR *Stress threshold*

How can you determine your "elastic limit" – the maximum you can take before you break? Personality plays a major role in determining your personal stress threshold. Psychologists have identified two personality types which are most at risk of stress-related disease. The first is hard-working, impatient, competitive and aggressive, and is especially at risk of heart disease. The second is a perfectionist who may seem outwardly calm, cheerful and capable, but finds it hard to admit to feeling ill or under pressure.

Having established how much stress your personality can take you then need to look at the circumstances that tend to cause stress and see how many pertain to you. In 1967, two American psychologists, Thomas Holmes and Richard Rahe of Washington University identified 20 or so stress situations and awarded them points according to risk to the body's health. Use the scale below to gauge your own current stress levels. If you score around 100 points, you have a 10 per cent increase in the risk of illness over the next two years. A score of 100 – 300 points means a 50 per cent increase, and 300 points or more indicates a dangerous risk. Consult your doctor if you are at all worried about your score.

| POINTS | EVENT | POINTS | EVENT |
|---|---|---|---|
| 100 | Death of partner | 29 | Change in workload |
| 73 | Divorce | 29 | Child leaves home |
| 65 | Separation from partner | 29 | In-law trouble |
| 63 | Prison sentence | 28 | Major personal achievement |
| 63 | Death of close family member | 26 | Partner starts or stops work |
| 53 | Injury or illness to self | 26 | Child begins or ends school |
| 50 | Marriage | 25 | Change in living environment |
| 47 | Loss of job | 24 | Change in personal habits |
| 45 | Reconciliation with partner | 23 | Problems with the boss |
| 45 | Retirement | 20 | Change in working hours or conditions |
| 44 | Illness in the family | | |
| 40 | Pregnancy | 20 | Moving home |
| 39 | Sexual problems | 20 | Child changes schools |
| 39 | Arrival in the family | 18 | Change in social activities |
| 39 | Major changes at work | 16 | Change in sleeping habits |
| 38 | Change in finances | 15 | Change in number of family reunions |
| 37 | Death of friend | | |
| 36 | Change of job | 15 | Change in eating patterns |
| 35 | More arguments with partner | 13 | Going on holiday |
| 31 | Taking on a large mortgage | 12 | Approaching Christmas |
| 30 | Mortgage or loan foreclosed | 11 | Minor violations of the law |

## TEN WAYS OF DEALING WITH STRESS

**1 TALK ABOUT IT.** Where you feel you can, discuss your problems with your partner or close friend in order to see the situation more objectively.

**2 PLEASE YOURSELF.** Make sure you do something you really enjoy at least once a day.

**3 LAUGH IT OFF.** Laughter is a fabulous healer and encourages social bonding. The act of laughing also increases the oxygen supply to the lungs, stimulates the production of endorphins and can produce a feeling of euphoria. Occasionally it may also open the gates to tears – another positive release.

**4 EXERCISE.** Burn off the energy that stress generates before it burns you up. A study at the University of British Columbia, Vancouver, shows that 20 to 30 minutes of aerobic exercise that raises your heart rate to about 120 beats per minute at least three times a week can lower depression and anxiety within 12 weeks.

**5 SAY NO.** Make space for yourself and get some respect. State your opinions clearly and calmly. Don't wait to be asked, then feel angry and overlooked if you're not.

**6 BE CREATIVE.** Women often feel stressed, frustrated and depressed when family or business management pushes creativity out of the picture. Taking up a stimulating new interest helps you to keep an open and progressive mind.

**7 GET REAL.** Accept your personality, don't try to alter it. Instead, learn to manage your strengths and weaknesses. Likewise, stop chastising yourself for past mistakes. Learn from them – then let them go.

**8 PLAN AND PRIORITIZE.** Organize your life better by tackling important issues early to get them off your mind, and don't take on too much.

**9 THINK POSITIVE.** Approval-seeking and self-doubt both erode self-esteem. Tell yourself you can do things not merely to stay popular but because you genuinely enjoy them.

**10 BE KIND TO YOURSELF.** When you're stressed, give yourself physical and emotional support. Treat yourself to your favourite foods. Pamper yourself in an aromatherapy bath or book in for a relaxing massage.

# DE-STRESS BY *Breathing*

During stress or panic attacks, rapid, extremely shallow breaths cause hyperventilation in which too much oxygen is taken in and too little carbon dioxide is expelled. The body responds by shutting down the lungs until oxygen levels normalize. This creates a feeling of tightness, rather like an asthma attack, and heightens the panic. Inhaling into your own cupped hands or a paper bag for a couple of minutes regulates your air balance by forcing you to re-inhale carbon dioxide. A way of preventing a panic attack in the first place is by learning breath control.

## BREATHING EXERCISE

1 Lie on a bed or the floor. Rest both your hands on your diaphragm just below your ribs with the fingertips almost touching.

2 Breathing through your nostrils, inhale deeply so that you can feel your diaphragm pulling out and down, your ribs expanding and your stomach rising. Your fingertips should also move up and apart.

3 Hold your breath for a count of five.

4 Breathe out smoothly, ensuring that all the air is expelled. Feel your ribs collapse down and in, your stomach sink back and your fingertips almost touch again.

5 Start the sequence again and repeat three or four times. If you feel dizzy during the deep breaths, relax and breathe naturally before starting over.

# DE-STRESS THROUGH *Muscle relaxation*

Possibly the most effective and simple de-stressing technique is based on the yoga asana of the corpse. This exercise teaches systematic muscle relaxation, promotes total mind and body awareness and helps you identify where areas of tension are most deeply rooted. It helps shut out the world and promotes an exquisite feeling of inner harmony. Do jt whenever you can spare half an hour or so, or use it to get to sleep.

## MUSCLE-RELAXING EXERCISE

1 In a quiet, darkened and warm room, lie down on a bed or the floor. Place a pillow or cushion under your head and knees to take the strain off your spine. Let your arms rest at your sides.

2 Take two deep breaths as you relax. Sigh out tension.

3 When you're ready, starting with your toes, travel up the body, telling every centimetre to relax. If one area is difficult, try tensing and relaxing it to experience full stress release.

4 The face is often the most difficult zone to relax. Yawn, opening your mouth widely. Purse your lips tightly, then blow air through them as you relax. Frown like you mean it, then release the emotion. Raise the eyebrows to shift the scalp and let go. Screw up your entire face – mouth, nose, cheeks, eyelids brow – then relax them all.

5 When your whole body is relaxed, concentrate on that warm, heavy feeling. Breathe rhythmically, telling yourself you feel more relaxed with each breath.

6 Stay that way for around 15 minutes. Then gently come to, stretching and moving your limbs until you feel ready to get up and go once again.

# DE-STRESS THROUGH *Massage*

Massage is one of life's most deeply relaxing luxuries. Studies show that massage lowers levels of adrenalin and cortisol. Try this simple relaxing massage on yourself. The soles of your feet harbour reflex points that relate to your entire body (see Reflexology, p116).

## FOOT MASSAGE

1 Take off your socks. One at a time, rest a foot on the opposite thigh. Rub your bare foot briskly between both your palms. Hold it.

2 With your index finger and thumb, gently tug and roll each toe, working from the base to the tip. This relieves headaches and facial tension.

3 Use the middle finger of each hand to massage the sole – from ball to heel – in firmish, circular movements. This progressively relaxes chest, middle, stomach and pelvic zones.

4 Finally, hold the foot firmly with both hands, with thumbs on top and fngers underneath. Pull the hands firmly from heel to toe, several times.

5 Heighten the effect by lubricating each foot with aromatherpy oils, such as lavender, cypress, jasmine and neroli (see aromatherapy, p.114).

# Relaxation therapies

## FINDING THE THERAPY TO SUIT YOU

**The most successful relaxing therapies and practices aim to harmonize physical, emotional and spiritual wellbeing. Most derive from eastern philosophy, which maintains that if the spirit becomes detached from the body, the imbalance is psychically disabling. The holistic mind, body and spirit approach is ultimately the most unifying and healing. Use one or more of the techniques described below – whichever appeal to you most will be the most successful.**

### AUTOGENICS

Devised by German psychiatrist Johannes Schults in the 1930s, autogenics is like putting yourself into a light hypnotic trance. You command your limbs to feel heavy and warm, your breathing and heart rate to steady, your stomach to relax and your forehead to feel clear and cool. Then you repeat the command most relevant to your stress symptoms; for example, you tell your forehead to cool to ease a headache. As you repeat this command, cross your fingers. With practice this action will eventually become a relaxation trigger.

**GOING WITH THE FLOW:** Chinese women practise T'ai Chi every morning to balance energy and maintain mobility.

### MEDITATION

Meditation is an ancient Eastern technique that switches off the mind, preventing overload. There are several methods you can use to shut out the world. Begin each by finding a comfortable position and make sure you can stay warm and quiet for at least 20 minutes.

Breath meditation is a simple technique. Begin with deep breathing (see breathing exercise, p.109) until your body begins to relax. Empty your mind of everything but your breathing and concentrate on your breath as it comes in and goes out. Allow yourself to feel your ribs and stomach rising and falling. If you have trouble concentrating, try counting your breaths in sequences of ten.

Mantra meditation is the method taught in Transcendental Meditation (TM). Purists believe your mantra, or personal secret word, can only be given you by a guru. Certainly the word should have no intellectual meaning or relevance, but it still works if you choose it yourself. If you can't decide on a mantra, the classic "Om" (the Eastern seed word for the infinite, or universal love) is a powerful relaxation ally. Repeat your mantra slowly and steadily in time with your breathing. Concentrate on the sound of it and nothing else. If conscious thoughts float into your mind, breathe them out and focus on your mantra again.

Object meditation focuses on a small object instead of a word. Traditionally, this is a candle, but you can use a crystal or stone, which is easy to carry around. Place it a few feet away from you at eye level or just below to prevent the eye muscles becoming tired. Concentrate on the object's shape, texture and smell. Sense its weight and energy.

### VISUALIZATION

The imagination has been used to heal and relax for centuries by traditional shamen, or tribal healers. Make sure you're comfortable and imagine a pleasant scenario. It might be somewhere where you've been happy or relaxed or a totally fictitious destination, such as a desert island. Let the colours, sounds and scents flood your mind's eye and wash over you. You may find it helpful to repeat positive affirmations, such as "I am safe, at peace with myself and relaxed".

As you become expert, allow your subconscious mind to take over from active visualization. Try imagining that you're walking through a gateway into a beautiful garden. Lie down on the grass and allow new images to present themselves. This process can be extremely insightful and can put a fresh perspective on problems. If you don't enjoy what you see, you can always change your mind.

## T'AI CHI

Tai Chi Chuan is an ancient Chinese technique combining Taoist philosophy with the art of movement. Practised by millions of Chinese daily, it encourages the balance of yin and yang energies so that chi, or life force, can flow through the body smoothly (see Traditional Chinese Medicine, p.117). It consists of a series of fairly complex postures and breathing techniques, performed slowly in a balletic sequence. All improve muscle control, but are not strenuous. Their main aim is to promote grace, tranquility and full use of your energy.

Ideally, T'ai Chi should be practised in the open air, on grass, first thing in the morning to prepare you for the day ahead, although indoor evening classes are popular and effective.

## YOGA

This most famous Indian technique has inspired countless Western methods and is one of the most popular and successful means of de-stressing, strengthening and unifying the mind, body and spirit. The asanas, or postures, are a series of gentle stretches which promote balance, flexibility, strength and muscle control. They work the entire body, including the internal organs, which are "massaged" by specific movements.

**1**

## YOGA ASANAS

**1** This asana is called the tree pose. A concentration exercise to promote balance and stability of body and mind, it is also designed to improve your basic posture.

**2**

**2** The half lotus also improves posture. It is designed to strengthen the digestion and reproductive systems and improve mental discipline and concentration.

**3**

**3** Known as the open-leaf pose, this asana is designed to stretch the spinal column. It relieves lower back tension.

# Complementary therapy

## HELPING YOURSELF TO GOOD HEALTH

**Complementary therapies used to be thought of as too alternative to make sound, healthy sense. But attitudes are changing fast. In Britain, the past five years have seen a steady increase in people seeking not merely alternatives to mainstream medicine, but soothing, drug-free, complementary support to whatever the doctor ordered. In 1993, osteopathy was the first complementary therapy to gain medical status. Other therapies, such as acupuncture, aromatherapy, remedial massage and homeopathy are recommended by orthodox doctors, especially where the patient has a persistent or chronic problem that drugs alone fail to relieve.**

## MAINTAINING YOUR *Energies*

The tenets of complementary therapies evolved from a time when wellbeing embraced both body and mind. Allopathic or orthodox medicine still tends to treat medical symptoms as separate from any emotional problems. Although stress is a nineties buzzword, the concept of "energy imbalance" has yet to gain broad acceptance.

Most ancient cultures hold that in addition to the tangible circulation of blood and lymph, there exists the circulation of a more subtle energy. Call it chi, prana or life force, it is this energy that generates vitality and connect the body and mind to the spirit. A "spirited" person exudes vitality and seems happy, healthy and well-balanced. If there is an imbalance, or blockage, in this energy system due to physical or mental trauma, the whole body is thrown out of kilter.

To the Chinese, subtle energy, or chi, flows through meridians – invisible channels, or arteries. Vedic (ancient Indian) texts identify chakras, or energy centres, relative to specific physical, emotional and spiritual areas, and crucial to the free-flow of prana.

These energy systems form the basis of a broad range of complementary therapies, including acupuncture and acupressure, reflexology and, to some extent, aromatherapy, all of which work to keep the "channels" free of blockages.

## THE POWER OF *Touch*

Another important aspect of complementary thearapies is touch. Too easily associated with invasion or, at worst, aggression, touch is overlooked as fundamental human need. Studies last century demonstrated that children who are held thrive better and are more resistant to illness. Recently, Dr Tiffany Field at the University of Miami Medical School has found that daily massage helps premature babies gain weight faster and leave hospital sooner. Basic massage can go beyond de-knotting tense muscles to give emotional reassurance. To a lonely or emotionally isolated person, re-established contact can be an affirmation of self-worth.

Counsellor and nurse Jean-Sayre Adams is also senior tutor of Therapeutic Touch (TT), a controversial hands-on healing technique. Over the past ten years, she has successfully trained around 1,500 nurses and health workers in Britain and has helped to establish TT as part of a complementary therapy degree programme for nurses and midwives at Manchester University. Also known as the Kreiger/Kunz Method, TT is based on the theory that illness is caused by blocks in the patient's energy field. Through a series of stroking movements, TT rebalances energy, relaxes the patient and allows their own life force to do the healing.

The "feelgood factor" may also be chemical. There is growing evidence that skin is a well-stocked pharmacy housing potent natural opiates, such as endorphins, which are released to suppress pain. According to Dr Peter Collett, a research psychologist at New College, Oxford, having your skin rubbed releases chemicals that can help immunize against illness and disease.

## EMOTIONAL *Rescue*

As well as physically easing tension, touch is also a powerful catalyst to emotional release. Earlier this century, psychoanalyst Wilhelm Reich put forward the idea that psychological trauma could be stored in bone and muscle. Reich believed that tissue has memory – traumatize it and each time that zone is touched, the memory of impact is released. If you don't like being touched in a particular area, you could be

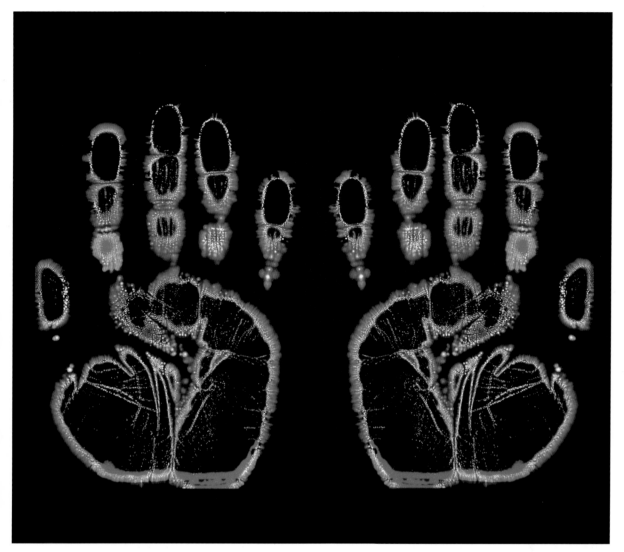

**HANDS ON:** Kirlian photography reveals energy transmitted by the hands during healing.

subconsciously associating it with a traumatic incident from your past which your conscious mind has blocked. Likewise, a classic hunched, defensive, tense-shouldered posture may be caused by chronic low self-esteem. Reichian massage evolved to release the underlying emotional cause through easing the muscular block and restoring the free flow of orgone energy, Reich's term for life force.

Gerda Boyesen, a Norweigian Manipulative Therapies psychologist and Reichian analyst who developed the technique as Biodynamics in the UK and elsewhere, also found that blocked energy builds up in the form of fluids trapped between muscles and nerves. Once the fluid is dispersed, spontaneous peristalsis in the intestine processes it. She likened this "gut reaction" to the Chinese concept that every

organ has two functions – physical and esoteric, or "meaningful". Stress, then, is meaningfully digested by the intestines.

Reichian therapists listen to the intestines through steroscopes as they work. To them, stomach rumblings, churnings and gurglings are positive signs that stress is being released and digested. A stress-free system, they say, sounds like a smoothly babbling brook.

Virtually all complementary therapies uphold Reich's theories on stress. There are countless anecdotes of spontaneous emotional releases such as sobbing, laughing or flashes of grief or anger as long-suppressed memories begin to surface. Many therapists also have counselling skills, or may recommend a course of "talking therapy" for specific emotional problems. It's not unusual for phychotherapists to combine some form of touch with talk. And if you're mortified because your stomach rumbles the moment you hit the couch – don't be. It's like music to a therapist's ears.

# **A** summary of therapies
## HOW TO GET THE BEST FROM COMPLEMENTARY THERAPIES

### DE-STRESSING AND *Cleansing therapies*

#### AROMATHERAPY

**GOOD FOR:** An excellent stress-buster, which helps counteract anxiety, insomnia, PMS and depression. Oils can be blended to control and rebalance skin problems, ease muscle strain, circulation and respiratory problems, and strengthen the immune system. They also make excellent natural first-aiders.

**THE LOWDOWN:** Clinical studies confirm constantly that specific essential plant oils have a potent physiological and psychological effect. They soothe and sedate, stimulate and dispel depression. They also regulate body functions and some have potent antibiotic, antibacterial, antifungal and antiseptic actions.

Aromatherapists use around 300 oils blended according to the condition being treated. They can be massaged into the skin, after which they are carried by the bloodstream to the organs. Oils can also be inhaled, reaching the brain, and therefore affecting mood, via the olfactory nerves in the nose. After six hours or so, oils leave the body through the usual elimination channels. An aromatherapy massage may include the face and feet.

#### FLOWER ESSENCE REMEDIES

**GOOD FOR:** Treating the emotions underlying physical conditions. Flower essences are widely used for stress, anger, grief, lack of confidence and low self-esteem.

**THE LOWDOWN:** Flower remedies were first devised in the 1930s by pathologist and bacteriologist Dr Edward Bach. Intuition told him that specific flower essences could balance mood and personality traits, allaying the negative, encouraging the positive and stimulating resistance to stress and disease. Bach initially captured the essence of 38 flowers by bottling the dew on their leaves and petals. Later he used spring water in which petals floated for three hours in full sunlight. The energized water was then strained and preserved.

Essences are either dropped on to the tongue, rubbed on to the forehead, lips, wrists, soles and palms or added to bath water, moisturizer or body lotion. Bach's most famous tincture, Rescue Remedy has become something of a cult cure-all. A blend of rock rose, busy lizzy, clematis, star of bethlehem and cherry plum soothe you after shock, calm panic or ease grief and depression.

**PLANT POWER:** Aromatherapy essences ease aches and tension and are powerful mood enhancers.

#### HYDROTHERAPY

**GOOD FOR:** Muscular tension, joint pain, rheumatism, arthritis and bronchitis; chronic fatigue syndrome (ME). Avoid if you have heart disease, high blood pressure or are allergic to iodine in seaweed.

**THE LOWDOWN:** Steam rooms and Turkish baths ease muscle strain and sinus pain as well as deep cleansing the skin. Alternate hot and cold bathing, showering and foot bathing all pump up the circulation by constricting and dilating arteries and veins. Sitz bathing (sitting in cold water with your feet in hot, then changing round) tones the lower body, stimulates spinal chord reflex and increases pelvic circulation. It is used to treat menstrual and menopausal problems and chronic fatigue syndrome. Wet towel packs and warm blanket wraps encourage detoxification. Bracing treatments like these are also thought to strengthen the immune system.

More relaxing balneotherapy involves total body immersion for 20 minutes in water at 32 °C (90 °F). Adding pine oil aids respiratory problems; adding oatmeal soothes skin irritation, psoriasis and eczema; adding a type of peat called Austrian Moor deeply relaxes muscles; and adding seaweed strengthens skin and boosts the metabolism.

## COLONIC HYDROTHERAPY

**GOOD FOR:** Acid and inflammatory conditions, such as arthritis; digestive and elimination problems; skin disorders such as acne, eczema and psoriasis. Colonic exponents also claim this therapy enhances energy levels and maintains good health.

**THE LOWDOWN:** Also known as colonic irrigation, practitioners of this therapy believe that years of smoking, drinking alcohol and eating an acidic Western diet of sticky processed food and mucus-forming dairy products chronically impairs the digestive and elimination processes. The bowel and large intestine become impacted with rubbery waste matter and unhealthy micro-organisms. Because the walls of these organs are so permeable, the body re-absorbs toxins in a self-poisoning process known as autointoxication.

The treatment is literally to flush away the toxic debris. You lie on a couch, while a tube is inserted into your rectum. Under gentle, gravitational pressure, alternate warm and cold water floods the large intestine, softening and dislodging the debris, which is carried away in a separate evacuation tube. Therapists also counsel a change of diet – less glutenous and acidic with more raw fresh fruit and vegetables – and recommend herbs that aid regular elimination. Treatment should result in increased energy, glowing skin and sparkling eyes.

## TOUCH AND *Posture therapies*

### OSTEOPATHY

**GOOD FOR:** Back and joint pain, aches and strains; rheumatism, sciatica, arthritis, sports injuries; PMS; and asthma.

**THE LOWDOWN:** Osteopathy deals not only with bones, but also with the tendons, ligaments and muscles that hold them in place and allow them to move. In a healthy musculo-skeletal system these interact smoothly but poor posture, a lifetime of carrying heavy loads, strain or injury can throw the system out of balance, causing restricted mobility and pain.

It's the osteopath's job to relieve that strain by systematic massage and manipulation. Practitioners ease joints back into place by positioning and supporting the body in a series of rhythmic movements and deep stretches. They prod or "palpate" tissues, muscles and joints to test their temperature, tension, shape and reflex. They check your standing, sitting and lying posture to determine the origins of the imbalance.

## CRANIO-SACRAL THERAPY

**GOOD FOR:** Headaches, migraine and sinus problems; stress and posture-related shoulder and back pain.

**THE LOWDOWN:** An offshoot of cranial osteopathy that uses extremely subtle manipulation to free tension between the bones of the head and spine. The region from the cranium (top of the head) to the sacrum (base of the spine) has an energy system with its own subtle pulse. Tension blocks can affect the entire body, as every organ, muscle and tissue group is linked by nerves to points on the cranio-sacral system. Similarly, feedback from a stiff limb joint can upset the subtle cranio-sacral circulation and throw the body off balance.

The touch is featherlight and deeply relaxing. Therapists believe that the body tenses in defence against rough handling, and yields more readily to subtle coaxing. Their role is simply to support the head, spine and occasionally other zones and allow tension to uncoil. At the end of a successful session, you feel refreshed and pleasantly expanded.

An important part of cranio-sacral work is with babies and children. Therapists recommend that infants are checked within six months of birth to ensure the soft platelets in their skull have recovered from compression in the birth canal or from forceps during a breach birth. Babies who are treated sleep and eat better and seem better adjusted.

### SHIATSU

**GOOD FOR:** Emotional and physical stress, which often underlie other symptoms; back and shoulder tension; rheumatism, arthritis; digestive problems; migraine; asthma; and insomnia.

**THE LOWDOWN:** Shiatsu is a Japanese form of acupressure – acupuncture without needles. Points along the body's subtle energy channels, or meridians, are stimulated to clear blocks and re-balance energy flow, and also to disperse lactic acid and carbon monoxide that accumulates in muscles, causing stiffness and cramped circulation. Freeing muscular tension also liberates the skeletal system and internal organs and often prompts emotional release.

Massage takes place fully clothed, except for shoes. At the start of the session, the practitioner gauges your general state by taking your pulse and gently prodding your back and stomach. In shiatsu, the hara (abdominal zone) is seen as a map of your entire wellbeing. Massage can be quite vigorous and occasionally painful, or extremely gentle – it's up to you and your body to call the pace. The practitioner rubs, strokes and presses the acupoints and lifts, moves and stretches your limbs. He may also hold you in various positions with his hands, arms, knees and feet to encourage the flow of ki through individual meridians.

## REFLEXOLOGY

**GOOD FOR:** Health and energy maintenance; problems with digestion, constipation; fluid retention, such as swollen legs and puffy ankles; menstrual bloating, cramps and irregularities; menopausal symptoms; stress, fatigue and migraines; skin problems.

**THE LOWDOWN:** A technique of treating the entire body by massaging reflex points in the foot and occasionally the hands. Because the body's six major meridians (energy channels) all end in the feet, each part of the foot relates to a body zone. Imagine the toe as your head, your instep as your waistline and your heel as the base of your spine. By stimulating relevant points, the therapist eases tension, dissolves blockages and boosts the circulation of energy, blood and lymph to and from the organs.

For one hour to 90 minutes the bare feet are manipulated while you lie back fully clothed. The therapist applies firm finger and thumb pressure over the sole and around the heels and ankles. Reflexologists say that congestion feels like granular crystals underneath the skin, which they aim to break down and disperse. To you, the zone may feel sensitive, ranging from mildly tingling to downright sore.

## REIKI

**GOOD FOR:** Relaxation; muscle strain, general aches and pains; immune-related conditions such as ME and HIV. Reiki is also a powerful self-development tool.

**THE LOWDOWN:** This controversial hands-on healing system is one of the fastest-growing therapies in the West. Developed in the mid-1800s by Dr Mikao Usui, Reiki loosely means the free flow of universal energy or ki – the Japanese chi. Practitioners act as conductors for universal energy.

Practitioners believe that Reiki has a balancing effect on the body. During 90 minutes of treatment, the practitioner places his hands, for up to 10 minutes at a time, over the

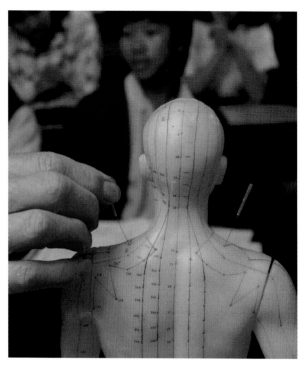

**TAPPING THE CHANNELS:** Acupuncture needles are inserted along the body's subtle energy channels, called meridians.

entire head and body, front and back. Individual areas can also be treated – a painful joint, say, or an aching head. The patient usually feels intense warmth, tingling sensations or gentle pulses of energy. Afterward you feel deeply relaxed or energized and in far less pain.

## ALEXANDER TECHNIQUE

**GOOD FOR:** Anxiety, arthritis, asthma, lower back pain, depression, fatigue, stiff neck and shoulders, stomach ulcers, high blood pressure, repetitive strain injury (RSI), breathing disorders, headaches and gynaecological problems.

**THE LOWDOWN:** Alexander technique is a postural new way of life. The system teaches how to sit, stand and move efficiently and gracefully without straining any area of your body. Everyone develops constricting postural habits that limit their full health potential. Stiff joints, shallow breathing, restricted circulation, back ache and the classic "dowager's hump" are common symptoms of this sedentary age of hunching over keyboards. Poor posture often has psychological links – depressed people tend to collapse into themselves and rarely keep their "chin up". An Alexander session is usually on a one-to-one, teacher-pupil basis. During the first session, your standing, walking, sitting and lying posture is assessed, while the teacher gently guides you into optimum positions that your body will eventually learn with practice.

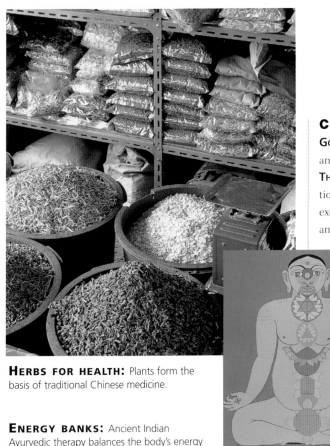

**HERBS FOR HEALTH:** Plants form the basis of traditional Chinese medicine.

**ENERGY BANKS:** Ancient Indian Ayurvedic therapy balances the body's energy centres, or chakras.

## CHINESE AND *Indian therapies*

### ACUPUNCTURE

**GOOD FOR:** back pain, headaches, sinusitis, asthma, menstrual and menopausal problems, and colitis. It can also treat stress, chronic fatigue and myalgic encephalomayelitis (ME), depression, arthritis and rheumatism, allergies and digestive problems. Acupuncture is also useful for treating addictions, such as smoking, compulsive eating, drug and alcohol abuse.

**THE LOWDOWN:** Acupuncture is an important aspect of traditional Chinese medicine. It is believed that chi, or life energy, flows through the body through 14 main meridians, or channels, running from the hands, feet and trunk to the head. Along these channels are some 2,000 acupuncture or energy points where chi enters and leaves the body.

Chi can only flow smoothly through the body when the passive energy, Yin, and the active energy, Yang, are balanced. When off-balance due to stress, poor diet, grief, infection or strain, chi is restricted and the body vulnerable. Acupuncture rebalances and stimulates chi by inserting fine, stainless steel needles $\frac{1}{2}$ cm ($\frac{1}{4}$ in) into the skin, along the meridians.

### CHINESE HERBAL MEDICINE

**GOOD FOR:** Skin conditions, digestive disorders, menstrual and menopausal problems, and chronic fatigue and ME.

**THE LOWDOWN:** Herbalism is an important aspect of traditional Chinese medicine, which also incorportes diet and exercise. Herbs are chosen to maintain the yin/yang balance and facilitate chi circulation.

Yin and yang are divided into eight principal patterns, such as hot-cold and empty-full, which characterize the type of imbalance underlying disease. "Hot" symptoms might be a red face and fever, requiring cooling herbs; "cold" symptoms might manifest in a slow pulse and pale tongue, requiring strengthening, stimulating herbs. Traditional Chinese medicine also addresses the emotional root of physical problems. Ancient texts state that strong emotion can attack an associated body organ: joy and shock affect the heart; anger weakens the liver; worry and intense concentration affects the spleen; grief injures the lungs; and fear attacks the kidneys.

### AYURVEDA

**GOOD FOR:** A complete system for physical, emotional and spiritual wellbeing.

**THE LOWDOWN:** India's traditional medicine, ayurveda dates from 3,000 years ago and preaches balance of mind, body and spirit. Ayurvedic principles relate to the balance of various energies, or gunas. These are divided into three qualities — sattva, wise and unifying; rajas, active; and tamas, passive. There are five elements, or doshas, each relating to a part of the body. Bio-energies, or tridoshas, are derived from these. They are: pitta, which produces heat and governs the metabolism; kapha, which governs growth and structure; and vata, which generates all bodily movement.

An important aspect of ayurveda is diet, which is used to correct imbalances in the doshas. Different food groups have their own light, passionate or sluggish qualities and can influence physical energy as well as subtle emotion. Massage, meditation and exercise make ayurveda a holistic philosophy. It's best-known and most popular aspect is yoga (see p.111).

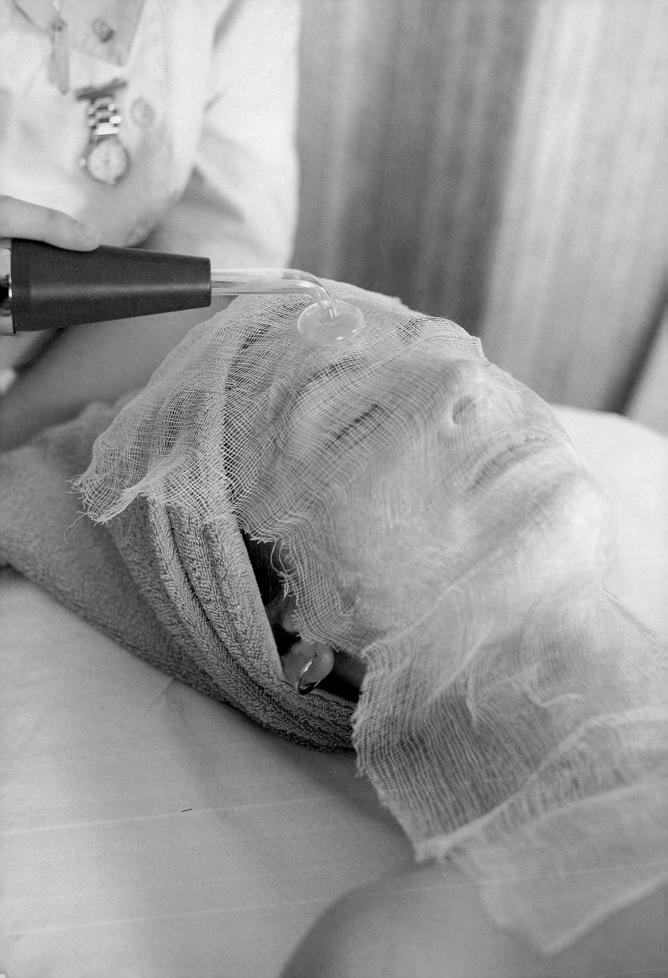

# CHAPTER 7

# High-tech Treatments

There is a bewildering range of surgical and para-surgical treatments now available. It's estimated that 100,000 cosmetic surgery operations are carried out in Britain each year and in the US each week. But what can the various high-tech treatments achieve? This chapter outlines the options so you can start to evaluate whether cosmetic surgery is the answer for you. If you decide to pursue the options further remember that reputable cosmetic surgical practices carry out full consultations prior to surgery. Check your surgeon's credentials: is he endorsed by an approved body? Is he a Fellow of the Royal College of Surgeons (FRCS)? What is his speciality and how experienced is he? Be realistic in your expectations: an ethical surgeon will discuss what is practical and achievable for you. Understand the operation fully, including the stages and length of recovery.

# **F**ace lifts

## IN SEARCH OF THE MORE YOUTHFUL-LOOKING FACE

Face lifts are the most popular cosmetic surgery procedures. The ideal age for a face lift is in your 40s when the skin is still elastic and bone structure is well defined, making it possible to postpone signs of ageing for around 10 years. A face lift raises your profile, brightening your expression and giving your face a pleasantly optimistic, less "miserable" overall look. However, a face lift won't remove superficial lines such as crow's feet and wrinkles around the lip contours, and the effect on nose to mouth furrows may be minimal. Also, the eyes may still look heavy and baggy – many people have their eyes lifted at the same time as their faces to complete the youthening effect.

### **FACE,** *Brow and eye lifts*

There are six types of face lift, each tailored to ease problems in different facial areas, plus a brow lift and an eye lift. The table on the opposite page provides all the salient details, so you can evaluate the pros and cons of each one.

If you decide to have a face lift you are generally out of commission for around three weeks – three days in hospital and at least two weeks recovering at home. After surgery your face will feel bruised, swollen, taut, numb, stiff and painful for at least 14 days. You may suffer headaches, itching and depression. Avoid the sun as much as possible and do not undertake any strenuous activity, which could cause internal bleeding. In two months your face will probably have settled back to normal. Bear in mind, though, that there is a slight risk of permanent nerve damage: numbness may last up to six months. In addition, scarring, the appearance of red spider veins, an altered hairline and dark areas that remain long after bruising has subsided can all be long-term problems.

**TWELVE WEEKS LATER:** The face looks softer than before the operation, less stressed and tired, and more alert, rather than younger.

**FIVE WEEKS LATER:** Bruising under the eyes and pinkness around the mouth area are the only remaining visible signs of surgery. Make-up is effective in concealing both.

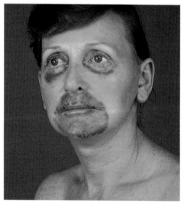

**THE OPERATION:** One week after blepharoplasty for the eyes, dermabrasion around the mouth and a lower face lift.

# EIGHT BASIC LIFTS FOR THE FACE

| | SUITABLE FOR | INVOLVES | RISKS | RECOVERY TIME |
|---|---|---|---|---|
| The mini face lift | Those who wish to avoid extensive surgery. | A line cut from the temples down in front of the ears, then behind into the scalp. The skin is then lifted, stretched taut and the excess trimmed off. | May have only a short-term effect. Ears may become distorted when they are pulled downward by contracting scars six months later. | About two weeks. |
| The SMAS face lift | Jawline problems, such as jowls, double chin or loose neck skin. This is the standard face lift. | A deeper cut allows skin and the SMAS (superficial musculo-aponeurotic system) to be pulled up. Muscles in the lower face and neck are tightened so that skin is re-draped over more youthful contours. | Possible obvious scarring. A small risk of damage to facial nerves. | About three weeks. |
| The extended SMAS or deep plane lift | Deep nose-to-mouth grooves, sagging cheeks or jowls, loose neck skin. | An even deeper incision toward the nose. The SMAS is lifted right off the cheek ligament to tighten the lower half of the face and neck. | An increased risk of nerve damage, but swelling may be less than after the standard SMAS lift. | Two to three weeks. |
| The composite lift | Drooping brows, eye and cheek bags to nose-to-mouth furrows, jowls and saggy neck. | A major operation combining the extended SMAS lift, brow lift and lower eyelid surgery. | Increased risk of facial nerve damage and altered scalp sensation. | Up to six months for swelling to subside. |
| The basic mask lift | Eye area and nose-to-mouth lines. | Cuts inside the mouth free the cheeks. Incisions over the top of the head from ear to ear allows the surgeon to tunnel down under the bone covering to move deepest layers of fat upward together with muscle and skin. | Infection in the cheek area. Hair loss around the scalp incisions, plus permanently altered sensation. Results are dramatic – the face takes on a slightly Oriental look with flatter cheeks and upward-tilting eyes. | Swelling lasts from six to twelve weeks. |
| The endo-scopic mask lift | The upper two thirds of the face. | A refinement of the basic mask lift that uses keyhole surgery. Five small incisions are made in the scalp and tiny cuts are made inside the lower eyelids. A fibre-optic light with endoscopic camera are inserted through one cut. A fine chisel instrument is entered through another cut to lift fat from bone. | As with the basic mask lift. Areas of permanent numbness may persist over cheeks and forehead. Endoscopy leaves less scarring, but as this technique is new to cosmetic surgery, it's not yet known how long results last. | As the basic mask lift: restrictions in facial movement usually ease after around six weeks. |
| The brow lift | Bad-tempered, sad or tired expressions, heavy brows and hooded eyes. Brow lifts can modify the appearance of horizontal frown lines, ready for laser or collagen treatment. | This is an endoscopic technique. Incisions are made in the front of the scalp, the skin is lifted off the bone and pulled up. The brows are surgically glued or fixed with screws which are removed four to six days later. The muscle which anchors the brows is weakened. | Impaired natural movement of the forehead, loss of ability to raise brows, or a permanently surprised look; uneven brows, with one higher than the other. | Bruising subsides in about 10 days. In 14 days sensation should return together with the ability to raise your brows. Hair grows back around the cuts in about three months. |
| The eye lift (blephero-plasty) | Hooded lids, puffy lids and under-eye bags. But not for easing dark circles under eyes (see laser treatment below) or crow's feet – although lines may be softened. | Surgery to remove excess skin and fat from upper lids, or fatty pouches (festoon bags) from under the eyes. Upper lid scars are hidden in the creases. Fat is removed from the inside of lower lids or through a cut close to the lash line, so scarring is minimal. A scalpel is standard procedure, although lasers are increasingly being used as surgeons believe they give more accurate results with less scarring. | Damage to the lid muscle, causing drooping. If too much skin is removed, the lid is tight. Too much fat removed from lower lids causes "scleral show" where the inner rim peels back, revealing too much eyeball. Scars can swell. The shape of the eyes may be changed. Eyes can water or have difficulty closing, so they feel gritty and dry. | Blepheroplasty requires a general anaesthetic and an overnight hospital stay. Swelling and bruising should subside within 10 days, but lids may lose sensation for up to three months. |

# Body surgery

## IN SEARCH OF THE PERFECT BODY

Wise preparation and careful aftercare can do much to speed healing and minimize the damage caused by cosmetic surgery, and to boost your chances of achieving the result that you want. So prepare your body for cosmetic surgery by taking the following steps: lose weight if you need to; stop smoking; limit alcohol, cutting it out entirely two weeks before the operation; supplement your diet with vitamin C twice daily two weeks prior to surgery, arnica four times daily from one week before and echinacea extract before and after surgery; avoid aspirin two weeks before and three weeks after surgery. In addition, rest your body before and after surgery; and use extra virgin olive oil on damaged skin to relieve pain and reduce scarring.

## EVALUATING *High-tech treatments*

What does cosmetic surgery achieve? Lifts don't ultimately defy gravity: the average life expectancy of a face lift is 10 years when you're in your 40s and only five if you're in your 60s. Cosmetic surgery won't stop your partner leaving if he's already decided to do so; neither will it make you look 20 years younger or stop the clock. However, cosmetic surgery will help you to age at your preferred pace.

Listed below are the most common signs of ageing treated by cosmetic surgery together with the range of high-tech options for dealing with them. Some of these are "para surgical" solutions. For example, collagen injections for lips and lines; botulism toxin injections for frown lines; laser surgery for lifting and peeling treatments; chemical and fruit acid peels for badly sun-lined skin.

**DROOPING FACE** – six types of face lift for specific zones. Plus brow lift, lid lift and lower lid reduction brighten the eye area (see p.121).

**LINES AND WRINKLES** – lasers, chemical and AHA peels clarify skin and ease wrinkles. Botulism toxin injections paralyse frown muscles and smooth lines. Collagen injections and Gore-Tex implants smooth wrinkles around the mouth.

**DOUBLE CHIN** – liposculpture removes fat from immediately below the skin.

**TURKEY NECK** – face lift "tightens" any loose skin.

**NECK RINGS** – a face lift, plus a chemical or AHA peel may soften, but not erase rings.

**SAGGING BREASTS** – breast reduction shrinks them; uplift moves them up the chest wall.

**SMALL, FLAT BREASTS** – implants augment or reconstruct after mastectomy.

**FLABBY ARMS** – arm reduction takes up slack skin, but scars are obvious.

**WRINKLY HANDS** – skin removal is largely unsuccessful. Laser and chemical peels remove age spots, help smooth and slightly tighten loose skin.

**SAGGING STOMACH** – abdominoplasty or "tummy tuck" removes stretched muscles, loose skin and excess fat. Liposuction removes fat from pot bellies.

**DROOPING BOTTOM** – a buttock lift raises their profile, but scars show in time.

**LUMPY HIPS AND THIGHS** – liposuction removes excess fat from "love handles" and "saddlebag" thighs.

**VARICOSE VEINS** – laser treatment, vein stripping and sclerotherapy offer varying success.

**FAT KNEES AND ANKLES** – liposuction reduces fat in these zones.

## IMPROVING YOUR BUST LINE

| | SUITABLE FOR | INVOLVES | RISKS | RECOVERY TIMES |
|---|---|---|---|---|
| **Reduction** | Heavy, pendulous breasts which are painful or embarrassing. | Cutting away part of the underside of the breast and repositioning the nipple. The scar circles the nipple, then runs downward from the nipple to the underside crease and along the crease itself in an anchor shape. Breasts scar more than any other zone. | Lopsided breasts; nipples placed unnaturally high. Nipples may become temporarily numb and very occasionally infected, resulting in removal. Breast-feeding is affected if milk ducts are damaged during surgery. | One or two nights in hospital and two to three weeks off work. Breasts stay bruised for about 12 weeks and you need to wear a support bra. |
| **Uplift** | Drooping breasts and downwardly mobile nipples after pregnancy and breast-feeding. Advisable only after you have finished having babies. | Pulling the breast tissue further up the chest wall, reducing the underside skin and repositioning the nipple. The breast then looks pert, but there is no increase in size. If breasts end up looking too small, the surgeon may suggest implants. | Scarring similar to breast reduction: the vertical scar may initially be so tight that it pulls the breasts flat and square before it relaxes to allow a more naturally round shape – in up to six months. Loss of sensation in both breast and nipple. | As for reduction. |
| **Augmentation** | Breasts that have shrunk or drooped after pregnancy. Naturally small breasts. Reconstruction after mastectomy. | A small incision is made in the armpit or around the aureola (coloured nipple surround). Keyhole surgery is also now used and scarring is tiny. Implants are inserted either in front or behind the chest wall, depending on the natural shape of the breast and the fullness, shape and feel desired. | Lopsided breasts; loss of nipple sensation; burst implants; thickened internal scar tissue that forms around the implants and causes hard, painful breasts. | An overnight stay in hospital. Pain and soreness subsides within a week; you can drive after 10 days and exercise after three weeks. You must wear a support bra for a month. |

## HIPS, THIGHS AND STOMACH

| | SUITABLE FOR | INVOLVES | RISKS | RECOVERY TIMES |
|---|---|---|---|---|
| **Liposuction** | Women under 40 whose weight is within 6.5 kilos (1 stone) of their ideal. Liposuction is a zonal fat removal operation: saddlebag thighs, love handles and pot bellies respond best. It can also reduce fat knees and ankles. | A rigorous operation. Small cuts are made in the skin and hollow canulla instruments are inserted. Fat-dissolving saline plus adrenaline which parts fat from muscles is injected. But fat cells in the hips and thighs are quite tough and the surgeon has to ram the canulla vigorously back and forth to scramble fatty pockets prior to suction. Lasers and ultrasound are also used to liquidize fat cells. | No more than 3 litres (5⅛ pints) of fat should be removed in a single operation, or the patient could go into clinical and potentially fatal shock. Blood vessels may become damaged. Surface puckering may worsen if the skin is slack; ridging may occur if channels of fat have been obviously and unevenly removed. Ultrasound can burn skin black and leave it numb for up to a year after surgery. | An overnight stay in hospital plus 24-hour wearing of compression garment for at least three weeks. Up to 1.5 litres (2½ pints) of fat can be removed without an overnight stay. Pain and stiffness is usual. Swelling takes three to six months to subside. |
| **The tummy tuck (abdominoplasty)** | Stretched muscles, loose skin and fat accumulation especially after pregnancies. The "apron" of skin or scarring after Caesarian section or hysterectomy. This operation should only be considered if you've finished having children. | A hip-to-hip cut above the pubic bone and around the navel, which is left intact. Liposuction removes excess fat, and skin and fat is separated from the underlying abdominal muscle, which is tightened. Surplus skin and fat is trimmed off and the new edges are sewn together. A hole is made for the navel which is pulled through and repositioned. A "mini-tuck" version using endoscopy is sometimes possible for women under 40. | Major pain and scarring. Your stomach may never seem smooth again. Nerve damage and numbness. Chest infection resulting from the opening in the body cavity during surgery. | At least one night in hospital. Pressure garment must be worn for at least three weeks afterward. Swelling can take up to six months to subside. Scars can take 12 months or more to fade. |

# TYPES OF *Para-surgical solutions*

## COLLAGEN

Hugely popular in the US, where 2,000 injections are performed each week, collagen instantly fills nose-to-mouth creases, frown lines, acne pits and sunken scars. A diluted form is used for crow's feet and around the eyes. Collagen is the protein that gives skin a firm, plump foundation. A purified extract from cowhide is injected with ultra-fine needles into the dermis where the skin has collapsed into lines. Two or three treatments, two weeks apart, may be needed to fill the area fully. The area will then need to be topped up every three to six months. Collagen can also be injected directly into the lips to plump them or into the upper contour to enhance the Cupid's bow. Top-ups are usually needed every couple of months.

**FROWNLINE PREVENTION:** Injections of botulism toxin paralyse the frowning muscles.

## ARTECOLL

Collagen is mixed with microscopic spheres of methyl methacrylate. Within three months of injection, the skin produces natural collagen fibres that hold the plastic spheres in place. You may still need a top up, but the effects can last up to three years. On lips the collagen/plastic sphere mix may give a fullness that remains for two years.

## HYLAFORM GEL

A relatively new treatment. The gel contains hyaluronidase, a natural component of skin which plumps and cushions the connective tissue between cells. Because it is non-immunogenic, the body accepts injections of it without reaction. The skin swells, reddens and bruises after injection, but this is relatively mild and subsides in a couple of days. Top ups are recommended every five to 12 months.

## GORE-TEX

A synthetic textile widely used in surgery to reconstruct tissue. In cosmetic surgery, it is implanted in the skin to pad out nose-to-mouth lines and augment thin lips. A viable alternative to collagen, it is non-allergenic and permanent, although it can also be removed. The line-filling is an out-patient procedure done under local anaesthetic. Afterward, pain and swelling is inevitable and takes about a week to subside. As a cosmetic treatment for lips, Gore-Tex is approved in the UK, but not in the USA where it is used to plump up lines only.

## BOTOX

Botulism toxin is becoming increasingly popular as an antidote to a furrowed brow. Small amounts injected directly into the muscle causes temporary paralysis – you literally can't frown, or raise your brows for that matter. Crow's feet can also be treated: lines are less noticeable five days afterward. However, there are risks: if the wrong muscles are paralysed, eyebrows can droop until the Botox wears off – usually in three to six months.

## DERMABRASION, CHEMICAL AND AHA PEELS

Dermabrasion is the traditional resurfacing treatment for pitted, acne-scarred skin, superficial lines and brown freckles. This mechanical scouring is carried out by a rotating wire brush or diamond "emery" wheel under local or general anaesthetic. It planes off the skin's surface layers and stimulates the production of collagen and smooth, new skin. Skin

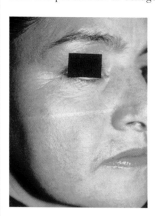 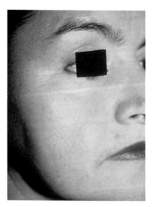

**CHEMICAL PEEL:** These pictures above show the difference between before (left) and after successful treatment.

## LASERS AND THEIR USES

| | LASERS USED | WHAT HAPPENS | RISKS |
|---|---|---|---|
| **Lines, wrinkles and acne scars** | Carbon dioxide | The laser travels to and fro across the skin, burning off the surface layer to encourage the formation of new smooth skin to take its place. Resurfacing works best on paler skins which absorb laser light more readily than darker skins on which a bleaching cream must be used before and after treatment to prevent uneven pigmentation. Lines around lips can be treated and occasionally hands. After successful resurfacing, skin looks smoother and firmer. Those who suffer fungal infections of the nail must take additional drugs to prevent cross-infection. Loose, turkey necks don't respond well to laser treatment: the neck scars easily and lasers don't tighten slack skin. | You have weepy, crusty skin for up to five days after a resurfacing treatment, then itching for two to three weeks. Perhaps the biggest blow is that skin stays bright red and shiny – rather like a bad dose of sunburn – for six to eight weeks. If you're really unlucky, this redness can persist for four months or so if the laser has seered the skin too deeply. Also, if the surgeon holds the laser in one area for too long, the concentrated burn penetrates the deepest tissue layers and results in a lumpy, bumpy scar. During the critical red phase, sunblock must be worn constantly to protect the vulnerable new skin, which can blister on exposure to ultraviolet light. |
| **Broken "spider" veins on face and legs** | Pulse dye and copper bromide | Pulse dye lasers cauterize by exploding blood cells in the capillary. Bruising lasts for two weeks. Copper bromide lasers burn off cells in the vein lining, so that it withers and dies. Crusting on the skin surface is minimal. Lasers treat small leg veins only as they cannot reach deeper, larger veins with thicker walls. But they can be used to treat surface "spiders" in conjunction with sclerotherapy, which treats deeper veins. | Results are permanent on the veins treated. But lasers can't stop you developing further broken veins. Treatment is most successful if veins are caught early. |
| **Age spots, brown birthmarks and tattoos** | Q Switch Nd-YAG, ruby or alexandrite | Lasers are chosen according to the colour of the blemish. They work by "selective photothermolysys" – pigmented areas absorb the laser heat more than surrounding skin. The laser breaks up pigment into micro-particles which are metabolized by the body. | After two or three sessions, results are permanent, but work better on brown spots than tattoos, which have only a 20 per cent success rate. Elaborate tattoos may take up to 15 sessions to treat and patients are often left with a faded "ghost". Suntanned skin is difficult to treat as the pigments act as a filter. |
| **Red birthmarks and port wine stains** | Pulsed Dye, Nd-YAG | Some birthmarks are notoriously stubborn so a patch test must be done to determine which laser will work best and how the area will respond. Pulse dye lasers are used in 80 per cent of cases. | As for broken veins. Several sessions may be needed to fade the birthmark permanently. |

is agonisingly painful, bleeds, swells then scabs. Once the scab falls off (seven to 10 days later) tender, red skin is revealed. The angriness subsides over three months.

Chemical peeling involves burning off the top layers of skin with an acid. Deepest acting is phenol, a toxic substance that corrodes and may scar if it penetrates too deeply. Patients are sedated and must wear a pressurized bandage for 48 hours after treatment. When the bandage comes off, it rips the outer skin layer with it, which is horrifically painful. More widely used and predictable is trichloroacetic acid (TCA), which requires only an anaesthetic cream before it is painted on the skin. This is less painful with marginally less scabbing, but redness still lasts a good three months.

Most popular these days are light or "mini" peels carried out with mild TCA or alpha-hydroxy (fruit) acids. One of the newest clinical treatments involves glycolic acid at a concentration of up to 90 per cent. It can encourage surface desquamation without long-term scabbing or redness. No anaesthetic is needed and the peel can be done in a lunch hour.

## LASERS

Lasers are fast replacing both scalpels and chemical peels in cosmetic surgery treatments. These computer-linked, high-energy light beams can be concentrated to precision-cut or used at a lower diffusion to ablate, or peel, the skin surface during "resurfacing" treatments. Lasers enable surgeons to carry out treatments with more control and accuracy. During "cutting", for example, the laser seals blood vessels as slices, so reducing bleeding and tissue damage. Because there is also less bruising and swelling, wounds heal faster – within two rather than the conventional four weeks after surgery.

During resurfacing, the surgeon can accurately control the depth to which the laser ablates the skin. Older skins heal just as quickly as young skins after resurfacing treatments. Lasers also work faster, so patients are under anaesthetic for a shorter time and sometimes only a local anaesthetic is needed. They also allow two procedures to be carried out in a single operation – a lift plus resurfacing – without having to leave a two- or three-month gap in between.

# Skin care glossary

## ACTIVE INGREDIENTS EXPLAINED

**Carnosine.** An antioxidant, said to inhibit free radicals formed by cigarette smoke. There are an estimated 100 billion free radicals in every drag on a cigarette.

**Bisabolol.** An anti-inflammatory agent, derived from chamomile.

**Ceramides.** Found naturally in sebum, these lipids form a water-tight bond between the cells of the stratum corneum. Creams containing ceramides claim to repair breaches in the skin's barrier mechanism and to encourage smoother cell arrangement in the epidermis. Ceramides can also be converted into hollow liposomes to be filled with other skin-care ingredients.

**Chitin.** Extracted from crab and mollusc shells, chitin retains moisture and bonds with the skin's keratin protein to form a flexible, protective film. It is also an ingredient of many hair-strengthening products.

**Collagen.** In the dermis, collagen gives skin its plumpness and strength. In creams, this protein, usually of bovine origin, was once thought to reinforce ageing skin's dwindling collagen supplies. It is now conceded that collagen molecules are too fat to penetrate the skin deeply. They make good surface emollients, however.

**Deoxyribonucleic acid (DNA).** Housed in the cell nucleus, DNA carries genetic information and controls cell mechanisms. DNA in cosmetics comes from plant, cow and sheep cells or fish roe. It cannot replace human DNA, but it can moisturize the skin.

**Elastin.** A spiral-shaped molecule responsible for skin elasticity, cosmetic elastin is of bovine origin. Used in "firming" creams to improve the suppleness of the epidermis.

**Essential fatty acids (EFAs).** Linolenic and gamma-linolenic acids are found in vegetable oils, such as borage, evening primrose, grape pips, musk rose and corn. EFAs are essential to the body, which cannot make them, even though they are an integral component of cell membranes. In skin-care formulas EFAs strengthen the barrier function of the stratum corneum by reinforcing the lipids there.

**Gatuline R.** Extracted from baby beech tree shoots, gatuline R is said to boost the skin's oxygen consumption.

**Gingko biloba.** Derived from a tree that has survived since the Jurassic period, it's easy to understand gingko's link with anti-ageing. An antioxidant, gingko is said to have energizing properties.

**Glycerol.** Derived from oils and fats, glycerol is a moisture-attracting emollient that helps prevent surface dehydration.

**Gluconic acid.** A gentle exfoliant, gluconic acid is said to be less irritating to the skin than AHAs and is used in products formulated for sensitive skins.

**Hyaluronic acid.** Found in the dermis, hyaluronic acid binds moisture in tissues and is vital to the skin's Natural Moisture Factor (NMF). Biochemists synthsize it from bacteria for cosmetic use. Because of its high molecular weight, it cannot penetrate the skin deeply, but is an excellent smoothing, plumping surface emollient.

**Milk peptides.** These help boost collagen and elastin support.

**Nayad.** The trade name for beta-glucan, derived from the cell walls of yeast, Nayad is said to stimulate the skin's immune cells, promoting repair and healing.

**Panthenol.** Also called pro-vitamin B5, panthenol helps soothe and strengthen the skin.

**Petrolatum.** An occlusive agent, petrolatum holds moisture in the skin's upper layers.

**Phospholipids.** These are the components of the cell membrane that keep it resistant and watertight. Ageing cells with fewer phospholipids dehydrate faster than young cells. In creams, phospholipids make good moisturizers.

**Salycilic acid.** Derived from witch hazel, salicylic acid is a beta-hydroxy acid (BHA) with an exfoliating effect. Often used in acne products and combined with AHAs in anti-ageing creams.

**Silicones.** These boost the "slip factor" of moisturizers, helping them to glide on evenly. Cyclomethicone is a popular ingredient in firming gels, providing them with a satin, rather than greasy glide-on.

**Soft coral.** This is a new-generation antioxidant.

**Squalene.** Derived from shark liver oil, squalene retains moisture in the skin's upper layers and has a temporary tightening effect.

**Titanium dioxide.** Also referred to as titanium micropigments, these inorganic particles deflect UV light and infra-red heat and form efficient, non-irritating alternatives to chemical sunscreens. In foundations, they give a luminous finish. Other light-reflective mineral pigments, such as zirconium, ferric oxide and zinc oxide are also used in high-protection sun products.

**Urea.** Containing a powerful amino acid that attracts and holds moisture in the skin's upper layers.

# Index

# **A**cknowledgements

The Publishers would like to thank the following sources for their kind permission to reproduce the pictures in this book:

**Steve Bartholomew**: /You Magazine 96, **Corbis UK Ltd**: /WolfgangKaehler 110 /David Lees 30/ Phil Schermeister 116, **Robert Harding**: 8*br*, 8*c*, 16, 68 /IPC magazines, Richard Waite 120*c*, 120*tr*, 120*br* /Richard Lohr 48 /Picture Works, M. Hacker 41*tr* /P.Rouchon 8 *tr* /Catherine Worman 118, **Images Colour Library**: 9*bl*, 9*c*, 31, 40, 41*br*, 85, 104, 106, 108*cr*, 108*t*, 117*c*, **Janssen-Cilag**: 17, **Medi-cell, Futureshape Int. Ltd**.: 64, 65, **MD Forté, Allergan**: 124*cbr*, *br*, **Pictor International**: 9*tl*, 60, **Retna pictures Ltd**: Jenny Acheson 11, **Rex Features**: /Florence Durrand 125 /Denny Lorrentzen 124*cla*, **Schwarzkopf**: 82, 89, **Science Photo Library**: / Dr. Jeremy Burgess 84 /CC Studio 67*tl* / Mark De Fraeye 117*tl* /G. Hadjo, Cnri 113 /Dr.P. Marazzi 29*tc* /St. Bartholomew's hospital 29*ca* /Dr. H.C. Robinson 49 /Nick Wall 67*bl*.

The Publishers and the Author would like to thank the following for their generosity in supplying products to photograph during the preparation of this book:
Jane McCorriston at Elizabeth Arden; Babyliss; Bobbi Brown Essentials; Julie Robertson at Colourings (Body Shop); Nicky Lyon-Maris at Clarins; Emma Bonnar at Clinique; Sophie Peter at Christian Dior (UK) Ltd; Jonathan King at Denman; Daniel Field; John Frieda Haircare; Gatineau; Sarah Griffiths at Estée Lauder Cosmetics Ltd; Cassandra Duncan at Lancôme; Gwyn Davies at Helena Rubinstein; Linsey Wooldridge at Revlon Press Office; Schwarzkopf Ltd; Angela Wray at Wella; Charles Worthington.

Every effort has been made to acknowledge correctly and contact the source and/copyright holder of each picture, and Carlton Books Limited apologises for any unintentional errors or omissions which will be corrected in future editions of this book.